THE TRUTH IS

1. Leveling up your craft to write a story that lives long after you've left the planet is what some might call a ridiculous goal.

2. You know that you will not tell that story after reading just one how-to-write book.

3. You know that you will not tell that story as the result of taking one seminar.

4. You know that creating a timeless work of art will require the dedication of a world-class athlete. You will be training your mind with as much ferocity and single-minded purpose as an Olympic gold medal hopeful. That kind of cognitive regimen excites you, but you just haven't found a convincing storytelling dojo to do that work.

5. The path to leveling up your creative craft is a dark and treacherous course. You've been at it a long time, and it often feels like you're wearing three-dimensional horse blinders. More times than you'd wish to admit, you're not sure if you are moving north or south or east or west. And the worst part? You can't see anyone else, anywhere going through what you're going through. You're all alone.

WELCOME TO THE STORY GRID UNIVERSE. HERE'S HOW WE CONTEND WITH THOSE TRUTHS:

1. We believe we find meaning in the pursuit of creations that last longer than we do. This is *not* ridiculous. Seizing opportunities and overcoming obstacles as we stretch ourselves to reach for seemingly unreachable creations is transformational. We believe this pursuit is the most valuable and honorable way to spend our time here. Even if—especially if—we never reach our lofty creative goals.

2. Writing just one story isn't going to take us to the top. We're moving from point A to Point A^{5000}. We've got lots of mountains to climb, lots of rivers and oceans to cross, and many deep dark forests to traverse along the way. We need topographic guides, and if they're not available, we'll have to figure out how to write them ourselves.

3. We're drawn to seminars to consume the imparted wisdom of an icon in the arena, but we leave with something far more valuable than the curriculum. We get to meet the universe's other pilgrims and compare notes on the terrain.

4. The Story Grid Universe has a virtual Dojo, a university in which to work out and get stronger—a place to stumble, correct mistakes, and

stumble again, until the moves become automatic and mesmerizing to outside observers.

5. The Story Grid Universe has a performance space, a publishing house dedicated to leveling up the craft with clear boundaries of progress, and the ancillary reference resources to pack for each project mission. There is an infinite number of paths to where you want to be, with a story that works. Seeing how others have made it down their own yellow-brick roads to release their creations into the timeless creative cosmos will help keep you on the straight and narrow path.

All are welcome—the more, the merrier. But please abide by the golden rule:

Put the work above all else, and trust the process.

FRANKENSTEIN; OR THE MODERN PROMETHEUS BY MARY SHELLEY

A STORY GRID MASTERWORKS ANALYSIS GUIDE

MAYA RUSHING WALKER

STORY GRID

STORY GRID

Story Grid Publishing LLC
223 Egremont Plain Road
PMB 191
Egremont, MA 01230

Cover Design by Magnus Rex
Edited by Shawn Coyne and Leslie Watts

First Story Grid Publishing Paperback Edition October 2020

For Information About Special Discounts for Bulk Purchases,

Please visit www.storygridpublishing.com

ISBN: 978-1-64501-033-3
Ebook: 978-1-64501-034-0

For

All Past, Present, and Future Story Nerds

HOW TO READ THIS EDITION OF FRANKENSTEIN BY MARY SHELLEY

When was the last time you read *Frankenstein*? In high school? College? Possibly for an English class?

And did you actually read it—the entire book—or did you read an excerpt? Maybe you resorted to a story guide or cheat sheet? Or perhaps you watched the classic movie, released in 1931, with Boris Karloff? (Or did you watch a modern version, such as the 1994 or 2014 films?)

And what was your reaction? Were you frightened? Or amused? Or bored?

Not many books continue to sell copies for hundreds of years. *Frankenstein*'s language can be fussy and the grammatical constructions can be elliptical. So as modern readers, we have to work a little harder to stay focused when we read these classic books.

Maybe that's why many of us don't really know why this book has been so popular for so long. Perhaps the challenges of reading a book published in 1818 can be partly to blame for the commonplace perception of *Frankenstein* as a quaint, moralizing tale about why we shouldn't try to emulate the Creator. Perhaps too many generations of high school students have yawned their way through poorly chosen excerpts, and perhaps too many viewers have watched the movie versions, none of which are faithful to the book.

I promise there is much more to this book, especially for writers, than you might realize.

Mary Shelley was a mere teenage girl when she wrote this novel, and yet she was able to describe acute torment of the soul. Why? And how? She didn't have any way to research the subject, except to look into herself and into the lives of the people around her. Shelley managed not only to fill an entire novel with existential suffering, but she created a metaphor in *Frankenstein*'s terrifying monster that would haunt us for generations to come.

Whatever the case may be, I believe if you want to write the kind of horror tale that goes right to the gut of the reader and strikes fear in his or her heart, you need to both read and study *Frankenstein*. In fact, while there are many innovative ways in which to write a horror novel, using *Frankenstein* as your guide will help you create a tale that is disturbing in a way that is true-to-life, with a genuine sense of horror that isn't a caricature. What gives *Frankenstein* its ability to deliver such a powerful sucker punch is that the emotional horror that Mary Shelley was trying to describe was something real, not supernatural. It's the kind of horror that any one of us might experience in the course of real life, when we make a serious mistake or see our best-laid plans go awry. It's very human, despite the fact that (as far as we know!) modern civilization does not have a practice of animating corpses at the present time.

The copy you hold in your hands is designed to help the writer craft a horror story with all of the characteristics described above. I will take you, scene by carefully drafted scene, through Mary Shelley's entire narrative, and you will be able to see the artistry (and angst) that went into her craft, despite her youth and inexperience. I've highlighted in bold type the passages that help to grab you, shake you and propel you into the next scene as well as any phrases or sentences I felt were placed there deliberately to evoke emotion.

Note that I chose to use Mary Shelley's original 1818 edition. She made changes in the second edition that altered some of the backstory as well as gave Victor Frankenstein more motivation for his actions, so I made a conscious choice to use the 1818 edition because as writers, it is instructive for us to see the earliest, most "original" decisions the author made. The fact that she was eighteen or nineteen years old when she wrote that version is inspiring. I imagine that in later years she was smarter, more worldly, and perhaps a tad bit more careful about what she said in public. I would rather see her reckless prose than her careful prose, and I hope you agree because writers often wonder how far they can or should go in the effort to trigger emotion.

When examining a complex novel like *Frankenstein*, it can be daunting to look at the book as a whole. And since actual writing occurs in small pieces, it is instructive to break a book into individual scenes in order to figure out exactly how the author wrote them. Shelley, for example, uses a technique called the "frame" story. It's a handy tool, particularly for a book written in the first-person point of view, because it allows you to present more than one perspective. Frankenstein's first-person storytelling is sandwiched between two sets of letters from another character, Walton, to his sister in England. The letters describe Walton's adventures in the Arctic, including meeting Frankenstein and hearing his story, which presumably is technically written in a letter from Walton to his sister although we only hear Frankenstein's voice. In the middle of Frankenstein's tale is the creature's first-person tale, so what we also have is Walton writing the creature's story as told to him by Frankenstein.

The Story Grid's Shawn Coyne suggests using a three-act format when looking at the overall story arc: Beginning Hook, Middle Build (split into Middle Build I and II), and Ending Payoff. Most novels follow this structure with a roughly 25 percent–50 percent–25 percent split. When we divide Frankenstein this way, we have:

- **Beginning Hook:** Frankenstein becomes obsessed with science at university and creates a sentient being in an effort to do something important with his life. He abandons it and it runs away.
- **Middle Build:** Frankenstein's little brother William is murdered by the creature. Frankenstein meets the creature, who demands that he build him a female, or he will continue to cause harm. Frankenstein agrees, but then

reneges on the deal, and the creature threatens to attack on his wedding night.
- **Ending Payoff:** Frankenstein's best friend is then murdered. Frankenstein's bride Elizabeth is murdered. Frankenstein at first tries to get the law on his side, but this fails, and he commits himself to following the creature for the rest of his life.

Notice that when evaluating the overall story, I have left out all the intricacies of scene-writing and narration. *The Story Grid* addresses both these requirements with its use of the spreadsheet for micro-level analysis and planning, and the Foolscap for overall macro-level analysis and planning. In the scene-by-scene analysis that follows, I will focus on the micro elements. For macro-level story analysis, use the conventions and obligatory moments to help navigate the story landscape. Take a look at the Foolscap, which I have included as an extra on the Story Grid website, and the Story Grid itself, which represents the scene-level adrenaline as a large-scale experience. You can create your own documents and tinker with your story directly in the Grid, but don't forget that at the micro level, the scenes need to work before they will do what you want on the macro level.

To that end, each chapter has been split into its component scenes and then each of them analyzed in its own separate section so you can see how each scene turns and on what value. I've also included my own parenthetical notes. Some are italicized within the text while others are mentioned at the end of the scene. The elements noted in the analyses will show you how to find the *Story Event* and the *Value Shift*, two key pieces of the Story Grid Spreadsheet. Creating a Story Grid Spreadsheet is possibly the most valuable way to study a fine work of literature and to understand where one's own effort must be focused in order to write a successful book in that genre.

I've also broken down each scene into its Five Commandments of Storytelling: *Inciting Incident*, *Turning Point Progressive Complication*, *Crisis*, *Climax*, and *Resolution*. It's fantastic to be reminded that no one taught Mary Shelley how to write a scene, and yet all of these parts are there. It's also comforting to those of us who work hard to write effective scenes because it's proof that our effort isn't wasted. Great writers all have scenes that work. These component parts are described in detail in the book, *The Story Grid: What Good Editors Know*, and much of the book is available on the website at www.storygrid.com. As well, I've made available my own Story Grid Spreadsheet, Foolscap Global Story Grid, and the Story Grid itself for *Frankenstein*. You'll find them at www.storygrid.com/masterwork/frankenstein.

INTRODUCTION

Are you a fan of spine-tingling, heart-pumping, adrenaline-filled moments in your stories? If so, you may want to write a horror novel.

But how? How do we craft horror stories that are so compelling, so deeply and profoundly emotional, and in fact perhaps even "familiar" in a terrifying way to our psyches, that our readers find themselves obsessively turning pages in our books late into the night?

The answer to this lies in a deep examination of what Shawn Coyne, the author of *The Story Grid,* calls "masterworks" of the genre. These are classic works (some old, some recent—in this instance "classic" does not necessarily mean "old," but rather "exemplary") that by virtue of their brilliant construction serve as examples of their genre to the writer community. Take them apart, scene by scene, and you will expose their structural underpinnings in a way that will help you put together your own genius work. Will it be filled with beautiful words? Well, that's up to you. The fact is, you don't have to have pretty words in order to tell a great story, but you do need to understand and obey your boss—the reader. The reader knows what she or he wants, and the reader will absolutely get it, or your writerly career will not even last the length of your book. How do we do that? We study the masters.

Frankenstein is a true masterwork. Two hundred years later we're still reading it! Also, because we know so much about Mary Shelley, we can plumb the depths of how she came to write this story. We can both learn about her life and also see her emotional experience right there in the pages of the book, and yes, the horrific journey encompasses a full range of human experience.

With a horror novel, the reader can "safely" journey to the edge of reason and back, to experience danger and perhaps even damnation, without leaving the comforts of home. When readers pick up a horror novel, that's what they want. But also, no matter what kind of novel you want to read, you are expecting some kind of emotional journey. As such, I believe *Frankenstein* is a great study tool for any writer, even if you don't write horror. Mary Shelley will teach you a lot about what it means to play with fire (not electricity, despite what you may have seen in the movie versions), which is a good thing for anyone who wants to write stories that have the enduring impact of *Frankenstein*.

But first, let's look at the horror genre itself.

WHAT IS THE HORROR GENRE?

So what, exactly, is *horror*? I mean this both for purposes of the experience and in terms of the literary genre.

Let's start with the definition of Horror as a literary genre. In *The Four Core Framework*, Shawn Coyne writes: "The Horror genre answers the primal question, 'How do we secure and maintain the safety of our lives, our homes, and our beliefs when we are victimized by the manifestation of our greatest fears?'"

Story Grid's Four Core Framework is a tool to help us understand the experience readers of the twelve content genres expect to have. Each genre explores a problem related to our core needs, which are the basic human requirements we have to survive and thrive in the world. These correspond to psychologist Abraham Maslow's hierarchy of needs, and for Horror, this is *safety*. From the need for safety, we can describe the protagonist's state or condition at any given point in the story along a spectrum of universal human value. The core value in a Horror story spans *damnation,* or a fate worse than death, on the far negative side and *life* on the far positive end, with *death*, *unconsciousness*, and many other gradations of human experience in between.

We'll unpack this—gingerly—as we go along. Horror as a genre represents for us (as readers and as humans) the most terrifying possibilities in this world of ours. It's the most basic response to our nervous questioning of the Universe. "What if this could happen?" we ask. The response of the Horror genre is always, "It can, and much worse."

These stories evoke the core emotion of *fear* in us, particularly in a special moment in the story called the core event. In the Horror genre, we call this the *victim at the mercy of the monster* scene, and the reader is expecting this climactic moment from the time they begin reading. We seek out Horror stories for this feeling, for more than just thrills and chills. We need to learn how to face our own fears, and in seeing a protagonist do this, we may feel a little braver.

This framework sets up an exceedingly wide range of possibilities for the genre. Anything you could possibly imagine, from the end of the world after an asteroid's impact to a psychopath with a machine gun (or a light saber, or a syringe of anthrax bacteria), can and will be introduced to our gentle planet (or beyond) in a Horror novel. The reader gains the opportunity to participate in the most complete spectrum of emotions available to the human experience. If it can destroy you, it's fair game for Horror. But it's not only death that we fear.

Here's Shawn Coyne again from the *Four Core Framework*, refining the genre's characteristics:

> Horror Story is Action Story intensified exponentially because the negative life value reaches into the darkest realms of the human psyche. In our ordinary lives we don't face ghouls or vampires, but we do face external and internal forces that threaten us with a fate worse than death. For example, damnation in our real lives would be causing the death of someone we love and living with that truth for decades.

What this means is it isn't enough for the emotional temperature to be "terrifying." We need a monster that represents the worst fears of the protagonist. Because the goal is *life*, we need to face a force that wants to destroy us. Does it have to be a real creature? No. But it has to be at least a metaphorical monster. And yes, you can have the monster within yourself, too. Victor Frankenstein is all too familiar with this situation.

This leads us to a somewhat more complex question. What is the nature of horror? When do we declare that something is "horrific" versus merely "scary" or "disturbing"?

This is an important consideration for the writer of not only Horror novels, but any writer who wants to explore the extreme edges of human experience—because every story, no matter its global genre, can take us to the far negative state we call the negation of the negation.

Here's an example to help illuminate what we mean by *horror*. Let's say that your villain is dangling you by one foot from the Golden Gate Bridge, high over San Francisco Bay. You are terrified. You're so terrified, you are ready to throw up. In fact, you do throw up. The villain taunts you. You are losing control of your reason.

Suppose we change the scene a bit. Now you're the one dangling someone over San Francisco Bay. Maybe it's your little sister. Your mother stands at the other end of the bridge, screaming and crying. You know that if you let go, you'll never forgive yourself. In fact, *you'd rather die* than live with the knowledge that you killed your little sister and tormented your mother. But wait, someone's holding a gun to your head. That's why you're doing this. Phew, there's a villain, so it's not your fault. But wait—it *is* your fault because the villain is your best friend, Rudolph. He's mad because you wouldn't lend him your umbrella and he had to walk home in the rain last week. So this entire situation was set into motion by your decision. He taunts you with this fact. It's *your* fault, he hisses. *You* could have easily prevented this, but you didn't. So actually—*you're* the monster in this scenario.

It's true that you let him walk home in the rain, and it's also true that you shrugged and didn't feel bad about it then. Oh, boy, you feel bad about it now. And it doesn't matter that Rudolph's position is unreasonable. By definition, the monster in a Horror story can't be reasoned with. Their goal is destruction by any means. At this point, you'd like to just die so you don't have to deal with any of this.

That's the difference between fear and horror. Being dangled over San Francisco Bay involves fear. Anyone would be afraid of dying in such a violent, terrifying way. But horror is something more. Horror involves fear, but it also involves reaching the point in your innermost being where you decide that death would be a mercy, either because you don't want to live in a world with monsters who would make you dangle your sister over San Francisco Bay or because you fear that you, yourself, are really the monster, and you don't want to find out this is true. Victor Frankenstein experiences both forms of damnation (more on that in a later section).

Horror is the experience you bring to life in these stories, what you put your protagonist through. *Fear* is the less intense emotion you evoke in the reader while they sit in the safety of their living room.

Surprisingly, the experience of horror in the "real" sense can be quite mundane because our worst fears are specific and personal. It could be a dream demon wielding gloves with knives attached. But Horror might also be a paycheck that's a little too small—so a family is evicted and spends a frigid winter night huddled in their car, after which they are chased by thugs with baseball bats who kill Mom and Dad, leaving three children under the age of twelve alone to wander the streets, dodging drug dealers and gangs. Who would want to live in that world? No one. But if you read the papers, you know that we *do* live in that world, and it's quite unremarkable. We don't wake up every day aghast at the state of things, at least most of the time.

I use extreme examples because we don't read Horror novels to experience the everyday world or emotions or circumstances. We read Horror stories because we know that crazy situations sometimes happen, and we wonder how we would deal with them, and indeed if we could summon the courage to survive them at all. Sometimes we are curious. Sometimes we want to practice our mental readiness—just in case. And sometimes we don't feel entertained unless our heart is pumping and our adrenaline has kicked in.

The sensation of the protagonist's horror has to be accessible to the reader as fear. Perhaps the reader hasn't met a vampire lately, but the fear that goes beyond mere fright must be an emotional possibility that makes sense and is familiar to the reader. It's got to be intense enough that most people can feel it, or it will not feel like a novel but perhaps more like a cartoon. This is true for any story, no matter the genre or the core emotion you want to evoke in the reader.

HORROR'S THREE SUBGENRES

The three subgenres of Horror are distinguished by the nature of the primary force of antagonism or the monster. But where does it come from? The monster arises from a setting capable of giving life to the protagonist's worst fears, but I'll say more about that later. What you need to understand is that the writer's job is to explore the full range of the Horror novel's core emotion, which is fear. It really doesn't matter what kind of monster you use for that purpose, except that it must be personal to the protagonist, and therefore the setting too must be specific.

Uncanny

In the Uncanny category, the monster is a creature that can be understood by the protagonist. This includes human monsters (psychopaths or criminals) or a creature with any rational origin. By this standard, Martians are Uncanny, and so are cyborgs, robots, and killer dogs. Uncanny stories include Jordan Peele's film *Get Out* or Stephen King's *Misery*.

Supernatural

The second subgenre is currently extremely popular—supernatural. The supernatural never really goes out of style, and if one wanted to invest in a reliable source of monsters with many examples available for mining, this would be it. Supernatural evil cannot be explained with logic and includes monsters like vampires, zombies, demons, and other creatures from the spirit world. They may have some basis in mythology or religion, or they can be off-the-wall. The long-running hit television show *Supernatural*, created by Eric Kripke, features a character referred to as "God's sister," for example (and yes, she's villainous). Gothic Horror author Anne Rice's stories feature vampires and occasionally werewolves; *The Omen*'s Damien is supposedly the spawn of the devil in a screenplay written by David Seltzer.

Ambiguous

And last, we have the Ambiguous subgenre. An ambiguous monster is a creature with an unexplained source of evil. The film based on Stephen King's novel, *The Shining*, features a monster that is difficult to identify. Is it the house? Is it the main character, Jack? Another example is *Annihilation* by Jeff VanderMeer, whose monster is a strange force attacking people who attempt to investigate the mysterious Area X. And in James Dickey's *Deliverance*, we aren't sure who or what the source of evil is, but at the end of the story, the protagonist is left with a terrible collection of secrets to protect for the rest of his life.

Mary Shelley focused on the human experience, so *Frankenstein* resides squarely within the Uncanny subgenre. You might find it difficult to tell in *Frankenstein* whether the creature or Victor Frankenstein himself (or both) is the monster. But both are explainable and human, even if the monster is a human created by the hands of Frankenstein. Both allow their emotions to get the better of them and are directly or indirectly responsible for the deaths of others. When Mary Shelley came up with the idea for the novel, she was a single mom living in Europe with her lover, broke and in disgrace. It's no wonder she felt that the "monster" in her story was a human monster. In addition, the suffering described by her characters centers on loneliness, a notion with which she was surely familiar.

THE CONTROLLING IDEA

So far, we've talked about what makes a horror story "horrific," and we've thought about the different kinds of monsters we could feature. After doing all this reading and research, you now know what kind of experience the reader wants from your novel and have considered the different setups you could use.

But this is the point at which many writers feel overwhelmed with information.

"I've done all the reading and I've got a ton of notes *about* the horror genre. But how do I *write* one? What do I *do*?"

Perhaps the example of the Golden Gate Bridge made you a bit uncomfortable. After all, we don't want to have to do any real-life research in order to write a horror novel. And if your novel features vampires or zombies, research might be difficult to do.

Rest assured, you don't have to actually experience a zombie apocalypse in order to write a great zombie apocalypse novel. But you do have to convince your reader that you know how facing a zombie apocalypse would *feel*. And in order to do that, you have to reach into the depths of your own experience as a member of the human race. Not your experience of an identical event, but your experience of something that would be a convincing emotional stand-in.

In order to figure out how to do this, we need to know what your story is *really* about.

The Controlling Idea in any story is the primary takeaway or lesson the reader is left with at the end of the story. We boil the events of the story and their results down to a single statement that explains what happened and why. If the end is on balance positive, we have a prescriptive tale and takeaway. If the balance tips into the negative, the resulting lesson is cautionary.

In a typical prescriptive tale with a positive ending, *life is preserved when the ordinary person overpowers or outwits a monster, facing the limits of human courage.*

In a typical cautionary tale with a negative ending, *death or damnation results when the ordinary person cannot confront their greatest fears to outwit or overpower the monster.*

These are pretty straightforward and reflect a lot of Horror stories you can read or watch. But phrases like "the limits of human courage" and "confronting their greatest fears" may seem grandiose. How do we actually portray these huge emotions so the reader experiences the emotional stakes faced by the protagonist?

This is where a close study of *Frankenstein* proves to be particularly helpful. Writers of Horror novels must access their own worst fears if they want to evoke this in the reader. How did Mary Shelley accomplish this? At the time she wrote this, she was nineteen years old and without much formal education. Young women of her social and economic background normally lived quite sheltered lives. What could she know of real horror?

The way we answer this question is to consider what she really wanted to talk about in her novel. Victor Frankenstein, in an act of vanity, constructs a huge creature out of body parts stolen from crypts and graveyards. He animates it, and when he sees that it is huge and ugly, he runs away from it. Frankenstein spends most of the novel running away from his responsibility for the creature; however, when the creature has murdered nearly everyone he loves in an effort to punish him for this abandonment, Frankenstein cracks. He resolves to chase the creature down in order to kill it. The creature leads Frankenstein on a wild chase through the frozen north before his creator finally dies of illness and exhaustion. Devastated to lose his only tie to humanity, the creature announces that he will die also.

Is this a book merely about the animation of a gruesome monster? Far from it. And to learn more about where Mary Shelley found the emotional depth sufficient to write such a book as a teenager, all we have to do is take a look at the dramatic circumstances of her life.

For Mary Shelley, "real" horror began with the mundane, when her mother died as a result of complications from her birth. Mary Wollstonecraft was a famous intellectual and early feminist who claimed that marriage was an outdated institution (she wrote the well-known tract, *A Vindication of the Rights of Woman*, available through Project Gutenberg). In fact, she had borne a child out of wedlock with another man before meeting Mary's father, William Godwin, and did not marry Godwin until she was quite pregnant with Mary. This may be ho-hum in the twenty-first century, but in the eighteenth century, it was shocking behavior on a scale that is hard for us to fathom.

Godwin continued to idolize Wollstonecraft after her death, and Mary was raised to venerate her mother. However, Wollstonecraft's novel interpretation of marriage and her free-thinking ways were not accepted by wider society. When Mary, following in her mother's footsteps, pursued a relationship with a married man, she was opening the door to forces greater than herself that she did not fully understand. She was, after all, a child, and she would have had no idea that ignoring the strictures of society would have dire consequences. And despite her unconventional upbringing, when she did exactly as her mother did, her father and stepmother were furious at her.

Mary and her lover, the poet Percy Bysshe Shelley (who was still married), fled together to Europe when she was sixteen but couldn't make ends meet and returned to London a few months later. By this time, Mary was pregnant, and so was Percy's wife, whom he had abandoned. During the course of Mary's pregnancy, Percy also took up with her stepsister and housemate, Claire Clairmont.

Mary's baby was born the following February. That child died, and Mary conceived again soon afterward, giving birth to a son in January 1816. Mary began writing *Frankenstein* in June 1816 during a stay in Switzerland with Percy, Claire, and Claire's lover, George Gordon (Lord

Byron). She was still not married to Percy, but when his wife committed suicide in December of that year, they married. Mary wrote the bulk of *Frankenstein* over the course of 1817. Her third child, Clara, was born that year.

Whatever interpretation one might put upon these facts from Mary Shelley's personal life,[1] taking up with a married man and becoming pregnant, at the very least, was toying with forces that were beyond her control—a theme that runs strongly throughout *Frankenstein.* For her child to have died (and indeed she lost two more children very quickly after that) makes this story even more poignant.

Mary Shelley's personal experience with horror was that of a young girl who believes what she has been taught by her parents, who discovers that her parents lied to her about the impact of social consequences on one's life, and who finds that the forces of nature that she tried to fence with were larger than she was and beyond her control. When she chose love in order to stand up for her values, she was deprived of the one thing that was hers alone—the love of a child, taken away through death. Again, she was powerless in the face of nature. And the love of Percy was also uncertain, given the presence of Claire in their household.

It was my teenaged daughter who pointed out to me that Frankenstein was a terrible "parent" to his "child." When she read this book at the age of fourteen, she immediately understood Mary Shelley's story as a cautionary morality tale about teen sexuality and the definition of a "good" parent. She didn't find the monster frightening so much as pathetic. She found Victor Frankenstein irresponsible and arrogant. This story, she told me, complements Mary Shelley's life as a pregnant teen whose parents would not help her when she needed it. Shelley was both the Frankenstein who played with fire, and the creature who was abandoned. My daughter understood "horror" from the point of view of a modern girl because Shelley expressed a range of emotional depth that is relatable even for a middle-class teenager. Even today, in our liberal climate of hook-ups and swiping left-and-right, for a bright, ambitious young woman, a pregnancy with no support from society or family can mean personal tragedy. A scary clown might not have frightened my daughter nearly as much as the thought of an unexpected pregnancy, a boyfriend who won't leave his ex and can't seem to stop straying, and parents who decline to help when things go horribly wrong.

These themes appear repeatedly throughout *Frankenstein* and tug at one's heartstrings. We feel the horror and the emotion because the questions asked by the creature are so simple and so poignant. What is our responsibility to our children? Why do we love parents who fail us? What is justice? Who gets to say what is good or bad? And what is truth worth, if what we say doesn't match our actions?

So really, *Frankenstein* is more than a journey into the horrific. It's a little lacking to suggest that it's all about the failure of Frankenstein to kill the creature and about his own unhappy demise. That would be like a James Bond movie, where we watch the hero waltz through fight choreography for two hours. While Mary Shelley certainly scares the reader, the result of her labors is something much more powerful than a monster story.

That's because a second genre comes into play, with its own controlling idea. Psychologist Abraham Maslow proposed that human beings are motivated to fulfill needs based on a hierarchy, starting with the basic physical needs of survival. As needs are satisfied, we reach for higher levels of need—beyond sheer physiological survival, human beings need safety, love, esteem, self-transcendence and self-actualization.[2]

It helps to view genres as extensions of human need. You can correlate physiological needs with the Action genre, for example. Action stories involve survival. Horror stories, as I mentioned, are at the next level, and involve safety. But what's fascinating about *Frankenstein* is that while both Frankenstein and the monster *want* safety, they both *need* something else.

In essence, we have a second trajectory going on at the same time as Horror's life to damnation trajectory. That trajectory is what governs the protagonist's personal, internal journey. In the case of *Frankenstein*, that genre is the Morality genre. And the Morality genre belongs near the top of Maslow's Hierarchy of Needs. It involves self-transcendence.

It's no wonder there is so much dramatic tension in this story because what Frankenstein and his creature both need is to transcend or sacrifice themselves for the good of humanity. Frankenstein needs to think of someone besides himself, something besides his own personal glory. And the monster needs to stop focusing on his own pain if he is to become truly human. The areas in which their wants and needs not only do not coincide, but absolutely conflict, are the areas where we experience a powerful dramatic journey.

If you want to really nail your Horror story, tie in another genre and put your protagonist through some real soul-sucking pain—not just fear but existential agony.

Given Shelley's unhappy personal story, it's tempting to view this novel purely through the lens of her experience. That would be a mistake. After all, we don't want to suggest that a happy young woman can't write a convincing tale of a heartbroken elderly man, or that a professor from Poughkeepsie can't write a good story about a Medieval nun or an Egyptian child. That type of analysis is short-sighted and far too limiting to be of use to us as writers. You don't have to live your novel in order to write it.

However, the novel was still a relatively young literary form in 1818. Shelley didn't have any writing workshops or writing teachers, and she still managed to nail the emotional trajectory of the novel in a satisfying way.

Why does *Frankenstein* work? How did she do it?

I think it works because the story form that she used to support her tale of horror, the Morality story, was so familiar to her. And because that story form made sense to her, she was able to take genuine feelings and plop them into the context of Morality stories that she had been reading or hearing about since she was a child. What is "the Passion," for example, but a Horror story with a redemptive controlling idea underneath? Milton's *Paradise Lost* is also a Horror story—the monster in that one is unclear. Is it God? Is it Satan? We can't be sure, just as we can't be sure that Victor Frankenstein is the monster, or that the creature is the monster. Mary Shelley gave herself permission to leave the question of "who is the monster" open, just as it is open in *Paradise Lost*.

Frankenstein is peppered with reflections from all of the characters on the questions, what is good, what is evil, what is moral, and what is correct behavior? Frankenstein's creature reflects on these questions as he views humanity around him. Who gets to decide if a person is good or bad? What happens when justice is corrupt, as when Safie's father is unjustly imprisoned, Justine is wrongly executed, and the magistrate refuses to help Frankenstein chase after the creature?

The Morality story is not just about being good or evil, though. It is about behavior, sacrifice versus selfishness. A truly "good" person gives himself up for the good of humanity, whereas a "bad" person behaves selfishly. The very worst kind of person, in fact, is not only selfish but pretends to be noble while actively performing selfish actions. Therefore, *Frankenstein* also encompasses the range of values for the Morality story quite nicely. Frankenstein sacrifices his life and comfort in order to pursue the creature until the end; the creature sacrifices his life after the death of his only friend. Both characters got themselves into trouble to begin with by pretending they were doing the "right" thing when they were actually acting out of their own arrogance and selfish desires.

If we consider the Horror story combined with a Morality tale, we might rephrase the controlling idea this way. *An ordinary person can avoid a fate worse than death when they muster the courage to face the monster that resides within, in a sacrifice for the good of humanity.*

Notice that Mary Shelley did not have to leave the realm of her understanding or experience in order to write convincingly about any of this, including the controlling idea. She just had to bring her emotional depth to bear on issues that were very familiar to her while keeping in mind that sense of horror evoked by the image of the grotesque monster-murderer.

As a unique individual on this planet, consider what your special story "gift" might be. We probably all have some perspective that we keep returning to over and over again. It might be a Worldview type of story or perhaps the distress you feel every time you think of Catherine and Heathcliff in *Wuthering Heights*. You probably keep returning to a theme when you read. What gets you going? Are you preoccupied with themes of status? Social justice? Coming of age? Obsessive love gone tragically wrong?

We've all had our share of powerful life experiences that have shaped us into the people we are. Writers are trying to share their innermost thoughts with the world, into eternity. What are you trying to say? What feelings are you trying to provoke? What lessons have you learned that you think people should hear?

If you can find that controlling idea, whatever it is, and marry it to the Horror structure, you'll probably find that the storyline will play itself out quite naturally as you write. Remember that you need to keep the core emotion in the fear department but allow your characters to develop and change with the help of the secondary genre. And after you are done, go back through your manuscript to check for the conventions and obligatory moments of both genres. In fact, we'll discuss those now.

CONVENTIONS

When we talk about Story Grid content genres, including Horror, we really mean a collection of characteristics that meet reader expectations for a particular type of story. As I mentioned earlier, within the Story Grid Methodology, those characteristics come from the Four Core Framework of the core need (safety), core value (damnation–life), core emotion (fear), and core event (victim at the mercy of the monster).

Genre conventions are the way we create the conditions for and set up a pattern of events that meet reader expectations for the genre. The Horror genre has specific conventions, just as every genre category has conventions. If you're missing any of these conventions, your readers will know. They may not know exactly what's wrong, but something will feel "off" about the story.

Conventions include *selective constraints* and *enabling constraints.* The Horror genre's selective constraints consist of a particular setting (which we also call an arena) and certain qualities that give rise to a monster that is the protagonist's worst nightmare. Enabling constraints include character roles (e.g., the protagonist, other victims, and the monster) as well as catalysts or circumstances that increase conflict (e.g., the power divide between the monster and the protagonist). This pressure forces the protagonist to face their fears directly and, in Victor

Frankenstein's case, make a sacrifice or suffer a fate worse than death. These constraints create the type of monster that corresponds to the subgenres (uncanny, supernatural, or ambiguous) but also offer the means to defeat it.

In the Horror genre, the core emotion is Fear. The reader is looking for a "safe" way to experience a life-and-death situation and its accompanying rollercoaster of emotion. The conventions, therefore, "help" the reader through that rollercoaster by providing the atmosphere the reader expects. The progression through the conventions is both familiar and reassuring because it provides a framework for the intense emotional experience the reader craves. But the best use of conventions is to make them as current and original as you can. In other words, deliver what the reader expects in a way they aren't expecting. If you find yourself using conventions that seem a trifle worn, do your best to flip them and create some new versions, even "metaphorically" new versions of the same conventions.

Here are the conventions of the Horror genre and how Mary Shelley satisfies them in *Frankenstein*.

Setting or Arena

Horror stories are set in **mundane and conventional settings and situations** where things aren't quite right and within which fantastical elements appear. This could be a public-school classroom (*Carrie* by Stephen King) or boarding school (*Every Heart a Doorway* by Seanan McGuire), a long-haul tug in deep space (*Alien* written by Dan O'Bannon and Ronald Shusett, directed by Ridley Scott) or a riverboat (*Heart of Darkness* by Joseph Conrad), an urban apartment (*Rosemary's Baby* by Ira Levin) or a place in the country (*The Haunting of Hill House*). Familiar environments orient the reader, which allows them to notice elements that are uncomfortable or alien. The contrast deepens the uncertain mood, and it also keeps your reader focused instead of distractedly trying to figure out the story world.

Though conventional, the setting should evoke the sense of a **labyrinth**. This doesn't need to be a literal labyrinth—like the hedge maze in *The Shining*. It can be figurative or metaphorical like the confusion we experience when trying to understand the natural world or even human nature.

Interior locations within a dwelling or other building often include tight corridors that resemble a maze, as in *The Haunting of Hill House*, *Every Heart a Doorway*, and *Carrie*. But the great outdoors can serve as a labyrinth too, for example the winding river surrounded by jungle in *Heart of Darkness* or an abandoned coastal area in the Southern US in *Annihilation*. The setting and circumstances mean the protagonist can't see everything that is going on and either chases or is chased through a maze-like environment. This type of setting creates the conditions for many of Horror's catalysts, which increase the conflict in the story.

Mary Shelley has crafted an apt context for *Frankenstein* with realistic descriptions of real locations she would have been very familiar with, even while suggesting that Frankenstein is able to steal body parts from crypts and tombs. The mountains of Switzerland are the perfect hiding place for a monster that doesn't mind cold temperatures and apparently runs like the wind (scene 22). Walton's ship, a confined space in its own right, navigates icebergs in the far north while the monster lurks about somewhere out on the ice (scene 51).

Finally, the protagonist cannot escape either because they are isolated or because of their specific situation. In *The Haunting of Hill House*, the inhabitants are warned that they should not leave the house and that no one will be able to help them.

Victor Frankenstein and the creature must continue to engage and cannot escape each other because each is the source of the other's fate worse than death. Victor knows the creature will keep killing, which will be a constant source of damnation, so he must pursue. The creature faces being alone and scorned by all humans unless he convinces Victor to provide a companion or become one.

Character Roles and Catalysts

Like an Action Story, the stakes in a Horror Story are life and death, so we have a **hero** (now called the luminary agent) and **victim(s)** (now called the agency-deprived), but because we take those stakes to the negation of the negation, or a fate worse than death, the force of antagonism or shadow agent is represented as a **monster.**

The **protagonist-hero** is an **everyday person** who must face their worst fears to defeat the monster. *Carrie*'s protagonist is a high school student, *Alien*'s Ripley is a blue-collar worker on the spacecraft, and in *Annihilation*, we read the field notes of the exploration team's biologist. There are several victims of the monster's initial attacks, and the protagonist-hero becomes the final victim unless they can change in time.

Victor Frankenstein inhabits all three roles at different times in the story. In the beginning, he arguably is the monster playing God with forces he can't understand to make a creature he then abandons (scene 13). Victor is also a victim of the creature's killing spree, which causes a fate worse than death as Victor realizes he is indirectly responsible for those deaths (scene 21). In the end, he is the hero who refuses to give in to the creature's demand to have a mate (scene 39) and pursues the creature until his own death.

The creature is the victim brought to life and immediately abandoned, without guidance, who is deprived of the connection we need as humans (scene 23). The creature becomes the monster attacking other humans to act out his rage and gain Victor's attention (scenes 33-34). In the end, the creature sacrifices his life, rather than continue to harm others, once he knows Victor is dead (scene 55).

The **power divide** between the hero-protagonist and the monster is massive. When Victor plays the role of creator-monster, he holds the power of life and death over the creature. But once the creature is loose and at the mercy of his own emotions, Victor cannot hold him. Whichever character inhabits the role of monster, the other is at their mercy.

What other characteristics of the monster must we take into account?

The monster is a force of antagonism that **cannot be reasoned with. It is possessed by the spirit of Evil and is present to devour and annihilate.** The monster represents the protagonist's worst fears. Your bad guy needs to be bad "enough" or you won't trigger the full range of fear. Don't forget your readers and why they chose this genre. If it's labeled "Horror," you are promising a horrific reading journey. In *Alien*, Ripley and the rest of the crew are attacked so the monster can fulfill its own need for survival and reproduction at the expense of other individuals. In *Every Heart a Doorway*, the human monster collects body parts to create the perfect girl to appease her master.

In *Frankenstein*, we aren't sure who the monster is, in part because both Frankenstein and his creature appear to be impervious to reason. While Victor can speak with the monster, he cannot make the creature see the problem with creating a mate (scene 35). Likewise, when Victor is under the spell of creation, nothing can bring him to his senses (scene 12).

The **monster's power is masked at first, and greater levels of power are progressively revealed** through the story. This catalyst increases the protagonist's (and reader's) stress level by leaving them wondering if the monster has more capabilities than previously indicated. Fulfill your promise to the reader by gradually making it plain that the monster is much more powerful than they appeared at first. In *Heart of Darkness*, Marlow's impression of Kurtz begins with an uneasy feeling that progresses to a concern that Kurtz is insane, and eventually Marlow sees that Kurtz is a monster.

A great example of this progression in *Frankenstein* happens when the monster's threat about Victor Frankenstein's wedding night is repeated several times as Victor convinces himself he will be the target of a violent and bloody attack (first in scene 39). In fact, the monster's superpower does not lie in weaponry or violence but in his speed, strength, and understanding of human nature. It becomes clear that no one can outrun him and no one can hide from him, no matter where they go or what they do.

The **Monster attacks randomly**, which leaves the protagonist (and the reader) in a perpetual state of discomfort. There are moments of calm before the monster strikes, but we don't feel safe until the end of the story. The monster may attack only at night, as in *The Haunting of Hill House*, or may attack when no one is paying attention, as in the monster in *The Ocean at the End of the Lane* by Neil Gaiman.

Not only does Shelley's monster attack randomly, but the method of attack varies. In the case of Justine, he doesn't kill her directly but instead frames her so she is accused by the law of killing little William (scene 34). In fact, the setup is successful primarily because her friends will not come to her defense. It's disturbing to think the monster might have been able to predict the direction of the law, based on the human interactions he had experienced as well as the lessons he'd learned from books. In any case, Shelley has set up the monster's victims so you can't be sure of when the crimes will occur. In fact, Frankenstein's best friend, Clerval, is killed right after Frankenstein receives a letter from him.

The **Monster remains offscreen as long as possible.** By keeping the Monster offscreen, all we have in front of us is the evidence of evil. Similarly, the **victims experience horrific attacks at a remove.** In *Every Heart a Doorway*, we don't know for sure who the monster is until the final twenty pages of the story. The reader, along with the characters, see the evidence of the vicious attacks but not who or what is perpetrating them. How can we defeat forces of antagonism we cannot see?

Frankenstein himself does not ever see the monster do his dastardly deeds, and as a result of the narrative device, the reader doesn't experience them either, only their results.

A sadomasochistic flip-flop lets the reader experience the power of the monster while empathizing with the victims. The Horror genre presents a unique perspective for the reader because they have the opportunity to relate to the force of antagonism and the victim-protagonist. This is especially true in a story like *Carrie* when some of the victims may have brought on the attack by their own selfish or cruel actions.

Even when victims are blameless, we can appreciate the agency and power of the monster to enact its will without remorse. In *Alien* the science officer expresses this feeling when he says, "The perfect organism. Its structural perfection is matched only by its hostility. ... I admire its purity. A survivor ... unclouded by conscience, remorse, or delusions of morality."

Shelley's victims are described in heartbreaking detail. William is a sweet little boy. Justine is an innocent girl with a tragic life story. Clerval is Frankenstein's lifelong best friend. And Elizabeth is the love of his life. Given that we've had a look into the monster's mind in the section where he describes his life since leaving Frankenstein, we wonder how on earth someone who doesn't seem to be so evil can do such evil things? It makes us despise him all the more, and in fact, to despise Frankenstein for creating this situation out of his vanity and arrogance. Even so, we empathize with the creature, and we even empathize with Frankenstein when all of his loved ones are dead.

Frankenstein's Secondary Genre: The Morality Tale

The Morality story also has conventions. They aren't as critical since the reader isn't picking up this book in order to read a Morality story. Rather, the utility of the Morality story here is in the character's internal journey. It gives a sense of authenticity and depth, so if you look for them, they should be there.

Here are the conventions of the Morality story that Shelley set up as fuel for internal change within the Horror story.

Despicable protagonist begins at his/her worst. Frankenstein isn't quite despicable, but by the time you begin to wrestle with what he did, he's pretty unlikeable.

Spiritual mentor/sidekick. Frankenstein has several spiritual mentors who show him "goodness" and the moral high road. These include his mother, Elizabeth, and his father. There are also family stories, like that of his parents' marriage or bringing Justine into the family, that emphasize moral choices.

Seemingly impossible external conflict. The external conflict here (that Frankenstein has created life he can't control) has no answer; how does he take responsibility for what he has done? How does he own up to his folly? Any option that includes telling people about his activities seems impossible. He must face the creature himself.

Ghosts from the protagonist's past torment him. Frankenstein tells Walton several times that he holds conversations with the dead, although he denies that they are ghosts, claiming instead that they are real.

Aid from unexpected sources. The most unexpected source of aid is the creature himself, who leaves food, clothing, and directions for him when he is chasing him through the Arctic (scene 49). But also, by telling his story, the creature informs Frankenstein of his moral duty (scenes 23–35).

Some would argue that Mary Shelley chose to write a Morality story about the dangers of messing with "science," rather than a Horror story. That may be true, despite what she herself claimed to be the case. All of the conventions and obligatory moments for a Morality tale are there, and certainly she was well-schooled in those stories. I have chosen to view the Global genre of *Frankenstein* as Horror, but you may see it differently. My goal for you as a writer is to be able to take apart your own writing and look for the elements that will bring it to life and keep it on stage for many years to come.

OBLIGATORY MOMENTS

All stories focus on a global change, and the Horror genre is no exception. Every scene that works should change the protagonist's situation along the spectrum of universal human value related to the global genre. In Horror, as I mentioned above, the universal value spectrum is *damnation* to *life*. But in key moments, these small changes build to bigger changes that create change within larger units of story. We call these key points of change obligatory moments, and they consist of unexpected events, revelations, and actions or decisions.

Depending on the lens through which you view a story, you could identify five, eight, fifteen or twenty specific moments from beginning to end. In the Foolscap, you'll find twenty obligatory moments, that is, the Five Commandments of Storytelling for the Beginning Hook, Middle Build parts one and two, and the Ending Payoff. Here I'll focus on five specific moments of change required in a Horror story.

An Inciting Attack by a Monster. This first obligatory moment may seem obvious, but it's a requirement for a reason. You can't have a "theoretical" monster. It needs to be an actual monster that harms a victim. That isn't the same thing as saying that the monster needs to be visible, as I mentioned in the conventions. Often, an invisible monster is the most frightening kind of monster there is. However, the monster needs to actually attack. It can't merely threaten a victim.

This is the global inciting incident of the story, the one that establishes the protagonist's main problem.

Whether you believe Frankenstein or the creature is the monster, the story establishes an inciting attack for both. If you feel that Frankenstein is the monster, the inciting attack happens when he abandons his creature—this is the manifestation of his arrogance (scene 13). While this isn't a conventional attack, he does harm the creature. There needs to be harm, not merely the threat of harm. In essence Frankenstein took one look at his hideous newborn and decides he'd changed his mind about becoming a parent. I think most people would say this was a "monstrous" act of callousness.

The creature's attack is a more conventional attack. He murders Frankenstein's little brother William—this comes at the beginning of the Middle Build (scene 34).

A Speech in Praise of the Monster. A Horror novel needs a speech that explains the monster's special powers or plans and why they are going to win. We need to understand what the protagonist is up against. It should terrify us. And most of the time, it leads us into some big story event, or a sequence of events.

When Frankenstein has destroyed the female form he promised to make, the enraged creature responds (scene 39):

> "Slave, I before reasoned with you, but you have proved yourself unworthy of my condescension. Remember that I have power; you believe yourself miserable, but I can make you so wretched that the light of day will be hateful to you. You are my creator, but I am your master; obey!"

And then subsequently:

> "Beware, for I am fearless and therefore powerful. I will watch with the wiliness of a snake, that I may sting with its venom. Man, you shall repent of the injuries you inflict."

There's also a case to be made that Frankenstein himself is the monster. Frankenstein's great crime in this story is that his arrogance and thirst for self-importance overpowers the knowledge of right and wrong, and he oversteps the boundaries between science and humanity. We see the moment when he decides to succumb to the monster within after listening to Professor Waldman's lecture (scene 10).

> Such were the professor's words—rather let me say such the words of the fate—enounced to destroy me. As he went on I felt as if my soul were grappling with a palpable enemy; one by one the various keys were touched which formed the mechanism of my being; chord after chord was sounded, and soon my mind was filled with one thought, one conception, one purpose. So much has been done, exclaimed the soul of Frankenstein—more, far more, will I achieve; treading in the steps already marked, I will pioneer a new way, explore unknown powers, and unfold to the world the deepest mysteries of creation.

At the end of this scene, Frankenstein says, "Thus ended a day memorable to me; it decided my future destiny."

The Protagonist becomes the final Victim after a series of "kill-off" scenes of the minor characters. Spoiler: Frankenstein dies at the end of the book. But the real spoiler here is that the monster doesn't actually kill Frankenstein with his own hands. The monster kills the rest of Frankenstein's family and friends (directly in the case of William and Elizabeth and indirectly in the case of Frankenstein's father). Frankenstein actually dies of illness after chasing the monster through the Arctic (scene 54). This might almost seem anticlimactic. We aren't treated to a scene where the creature puts his grotesque hands around Frankenstein's neck. Why not?

Consider that the death of the servant girl Justine is not by the creature's hand. She is executed because she is convicted falsely of killing William. Frankenstein's death is also a result of events triggered by the creature. This is a wonderful chain of logic because this questioning of the nature of "responsibility" is how we can flip-flop the role of monster from the creature to Frankenstein. Whose fault is all of this? Frankenstein's because he created the creature and then refused to "parent" him? Or the creature's because he has an ego just as big as Frankenstein's?

Great questions, all of these, but they arise only because Shelley makes sure there are three brutal, actual murders in the midst of all of this moralizing.

And if you feel that the real protagonist of the story is the creature, he too dies at the end of the story.

Victim at the Mercy of the Monster Scene (the Core Event). The Core Event of any Horror novel is the scene when the monster appears to have won. At that point, the protagonist needs to unleash the gift that will save him—or not.

Readers and movie viewers tend to think of the Core Event as the big moment of conflict. In *Frankenstein*, there are several shockers, but Elizabeth's death on their wedding night is possibly the most disturbing because of the symbolic value of the wedding night (scene 46). Frankenstein refuses to finish building a female companion for the monster, and the creature gets his revenge by destroying Frankenstein's female companion. These moments are powerful, both visually and psychologically.

And yet, while it is certainly the worst murder (and the final direct murder at the hands of the monster), is it the Core Event? It is indeed arguable; the creature has been warning us for some time that the wedding night was at risk. One might say that the murder of Elizabeth is the trigger for Frankenstein's path forward. Everything hinges on this one final crime.

However, one more event lies between Elizabeth's murder and Frankenstein's decision to hunt the creature down across the planet. That is Frankenstein's attempt to get the magistrate to help him hunt down and capture the creature. Until that moment, Frankenstein has not divulged his story to anyone. It is the first time he has ever admitted what he has done out loud, and he does this in order to assert responsibility and to acknowledge that this problem is not his problem alone. It is now a problem belonging to the community. Only after the magistrate refuses to help does Frankenstein realize he is truly alone, indeed he has no community at all, regardless of his willingness to take responsibility for his crime (scene 47).

For this reason, I believe the Core Event of the story is the incredibly cinematic moment where Frankenstein kneels in the graveyard in front of the tombs of his family. Shelley takes pains to describe the setting, as if she were designing a movie set (scene 48).

This decisive moment is the result of Frankenstein's realization that he is now absolutely alone. And guess what—the creature is also alone. That's why he wanted a female companion. That's been the problem all along. Frankenstein can't even turn to the law, because it refuses to back him up. He and the creature are now on even footing in the ring, unable to turn to the law or to family or friends. They are not alone if they have each other. **The creature's goal all along was to have a family, and this is how he managed to acquire Frankenstein as his lifelong companion.**

If you view the full trajectory of the story, the events of Frankenstein's back story are only the beginning. They are the reason behind his wild chase through the Arctic, and the moment where he made the decision to embark on the chase is right there in the graveyard scene.

So if you think creature is the monster, the Core Event is the graveyard scene (scene 47). Frankenstein has nothing left, so he unleashes his special gift, which is "obsession." Obsession is the reason he was able to create the monster in the first place. He swears revenge and says he will never quit until he has caught the monster. Shelley takes note of this trait of "obsession" at the end of the story, when Frankenstein lectures Walton and his men on never giving up, not even when surrounded by sea ice in the Arctic. Frankenstein tries to persuade Walton to continue his voyage. Walton wants to continue, but when his men beg him for mercy, he accedes to their request and heads home. In every way, Walton and Frankenstein are mirrors of each other in their yearnings and temperament, except that Walton isn't obsessed.

If you think Frankenstein is the monster, the Core Event is the moment when Frankenstein tears up the female creature he has built, right before the monster's very eyes (scene 39). This moment sets in motion the creature's determination to make sure that just as he will always be alone, Frankenstein will always be alone. All is lost for the monster, and he will use his special super-human size and strength to make sure Frankenstein doesn't have what the creature does not have.

False Ending. In a Horror story, **there must be two endings.** Just as you think the story is ending with Frankenstein's death and defeat (scene 54), the creature appears. It's hard to imagine feeling compassion for a creature who has strangled several people with seemingly no remorse, but his speech is touching (scene 55).

In essence, a false ending is an unexpected complication just when you think the global story problem has been resolved. Here, it is subtle. We thought we knew what was going on. We thought Frankenstein wanted to kill the creature, and the creature was trying to escape him. But after Frankenstein dies, seemingly resolving the global story problem, we discover that the creature did not want Frankenstein to die at all. He wasn't actually trying to "escape" at all. This last complication needs its own resolution—the creature's death, which is the true ending to the tale. It's not as obvious a false ending as you might find in a more modern horror tale, but it does work.

If you are truly digging deep into your own psyche for passion and depth, you will probably find most of the relevant scenes and conventions already in your manuscript. Pay particular attention to "weak" or unoriginal obligatory moments. It helps to isolate these scenes by looking through the Foolscap as you write, but if you haven't done this, definitely create a Foolscap Global Story Grid after the fact and go through the entire manuscript with your Foolscap in hand, identifying those scenes and evaluating them for power and punch. Ideally, your reader won't be able to get these scenes out of his or her mind, so try your very best to deliver.

WHY FRANKENSTEIN ENDURES

Let's return to the question we began with. Why does this story endure? And why should we read and study *Frankenstein* today? It's a Horror Story that works and meets the genre requirements, but it does so much more.

When I ask myself how this book has managed to endure despite all else that competes for our time, I believe the answer lies in Mary Shelley channeling the most primal fears of a teenager messing around with nature's greatest force, which is the creation of life. While the many science-focused conversations are critical (and definitely a part of Mary Shelley's world), the power-packed punch in this emotional story lies in who she was and her willingness to live "on the edge" at a time when it was difficult to be young, female, and smart.

We read Horror in order to experience the extremes of life, death, and the possibilities that make life not worth living, a continuum Mary Shelley understood well, even at the tender age of nineteen. As writers, we know how difficult it is to write a story that makes sense to the reader with believable character motivation. Even when we know the "plot" or the "theme" we are going for, we need the reader to buy into our view of the universe, our explanation of the character's value system and decision-making process. We've all had the experience of reading something that disappoints us because we got stuck somewhere near the beginning where the protagonist was making a choice we just couldn't imagine. And that's because a novel is a journey through powerful emotions and human experience, and when we don't understand why the characters do what they're doing, we lose interest.

Frankenstein is a wonderful example of a convincing emotional journey, even though the Horror plot elements are fantastical. The painful emotional trajectory of Mary Shelley's life is apparent. By the time she was engaged in writing *Frankenstein*, she had experienced pregnancy, the death of a child, the death of a sister by suicide, and the knowledge that her lover was not faithful. She had certainly contemplated the notion that life sometimes feels as if it's not worth living. She also had made difficult decisions about what was truly important. Marriage? Not important. Society's good opinion? Not important. Love? Perhaps. Commitment? Maybe...or maybe not.

All of these questions belong in the Morality genre. But too, they belong in the Horror genre, when the answers to the questions bring you to the notion of life that is or is not "worth" living. And this is why everyone should read *Frankenstein*. Because we all ask these questions, every day. And even if we don't think about Horror very much, as we have seen, Horror resides in the mundane and the everyday.

In a decades-long effort to avoid what I thought was a preachy story about monsters and electricity, I almost missed Mary Shelley's *Frankenstein*. But one might almost say that just as Frankenstein chased his monster down over the surface of the earth, as far as the ice-filled waters of the north, *Frankenstein* the novel chased me down, too. Despite the fact that I am not usually a fan of Horror, the journey was well worth it and taught me some important lessons about how to get my reader to join me on an emotional journey of a lifetime.

If you love the thrills and chills of the Horror genre, please enjoy this journey through *Frankenstein* while you admire a teenager's willingness to open herself up to scrutiny. Her bravery and honesty are impressive and can teach us a lot about how to dazzle our own readers through our writing, perhaps for centuries to come.

FRANKENSTEIN; OR THE MODERN PROMETHEUS BY MARY SHELLEY

LETTER 1 - SCENE 1

St. Petersburgh, Dec. 11th, 17—

To Mrs. Saville, England

You will rejoice to hear that no disaster has accompanied the commencement of an enterprise which you have regarded with such evil forebodings. I arrived here yesterday, and my first task is to **assure my dear sister of my welfare and increasing confidence in the success of my undertaking.** [*A somewhat cocky or defensive tone here?*]

I am already far north of London, and as I walk in the streets of Petersburgh, I feel a cold northern breeze play upon my cheeks, which braces my nerves and fills me with delight. Do you understand this feeling? This breeze, which has travelled from the regions towards which I am advancing, gives me a foretaste of those icy climes.

Inspirited by this wind of promise, my daydreams become more fervent and vivid. I try in vain to be persuaded that the pole is the seat of frost and desolation; **it ever presents itself to my imagination as the region of beauty and delight.** There, Margaret, the sun is forever visible, its broad disk just skirting the horizon and diffusing a perpetual splendour. There—for with your leave, my sister, I will put some trust in preceding navigators—**there snow and frost are banished; and, sailing over a calm sea, we may be wafted to a land surpassing in wonders and in beauty every region hitherto discovered on the habitable globe.** *[A rather bizarre and delusional belief!]* Its productions and features may be without example, as the phenomena of the heavenly bodies undoubtedly are in those undiscovered solitudes. **What may not be expected in a country of eternal light? I may there discover the wondrous power which attracts the needle and may regulate a thousand celestial observations that require only this voyage to render their seeming eccentricities consistent forever.** *[He has grand scientific goals.]* I shall satiate my ardent curiosity with the sight of a part of the world never before visited, and may tread a land never before imprinted by the foot of man. These are my enticements, and they are **sufficient to conquer all fear of danger or death** and to induce me to commence this laborious voyage with the joy a child feels when he embarks in a little boat, with his holiday mates, on an expedition of discovery up his native river. But supposing all these conjectures to be false, you cannot contest the **inestimable benefit which I shall confer on all mankind,** *[So he is both delusional and arrogant.]* to the last generation, by discovering a passage near the pole to those countries, to reach which at present so many months are requisite; or by ascertaining the secret of the magnet, which, if at all possible, can only be effected by an undertaking such as mine.

These reflections have dispelled the agitation with which I began my letter, and I feel my heart glow with an enthusiasm which elevates me to heaven, for nothing contributes so much to tranquillize the mind as a steady purpose—a point on which the soul may fix its intellectual eye. This expedition has been the favourite dream of my early years. I have read with ardour the accounts of the various voyages which have been made in the prospect of arriving at the North Pacific Ocean through the seas which surround the pole. **You may remember that a history of all the voyages made for purposes of discovery composed**

the whole of our good Uncle Thomas' library. My education was neglected, yet I was passionately fond of reading. *[He is self-taught—so was Shelley.]* These volumes were my study day and night, and my familiarity with them increased that regret which I had felt, as a child, on learning that **my father's dying injunction had forbidden my uncle to allow me to embark in a seafaring life.** *[A theme of parents forbidding "exploration."]*

These visions faded when I perused, for the first time, those poets whose effusions entranced my soul and lifted it to heaven. I also became a poet and for one year lived in a paradise of my own creation; I imagined that I also might obtain a niche in the temple where the names of Homer and Shakespeare are consecrated. **You are well acquainted with my failure and how heavily I bore the disappointment.** But just at that time I inherited the fortune of my cousin, and my thoughts were turned into the channel of their earlier bent.

Six years have passed since I resolved on my present undertaking. I can, even now, remember the hour from which I dedicated myself to this great enterprise. I commenced by inuring my body to hardship. I accompanied the whale-fishers on several expeditions to the North Sea; I voluntarily endured cold, famine, thirst, and want of sleep; I often worked harder than the common sailors during the day and devoted my nights to the study of mathematics, the theory of medicine, and those branches of physical science from which a naval adventurer might derive the greatest practical advantage. Twice I actually hired myself as an under-mate in a Greenland whaler, and acquitted myself to admiration. I must own I felt a little proud when my captain offered me the second dignity in the vessel and entreated me to remain with the greatest earnestness, so valuable did he consider my services. **And now, dear Margaret, do I not deserve to accomplish some great purpose? My life might have been passed in ease and luxury, but I preferred glory to every enticement that wealth placed in my path.** *[More interesting arrogance—he has no particular education but has worked* *hard and feels he "deserves" glory.]* Oh, that some encouraging voice would answer in the affirmative! **My courage and my resolution is firm; but my hopes fluctuate, and my spirits are often depressed.** I am about to proceed on a long and difficult voyage, the emergencies of which will demand all my fortitude: I am required not only to raise the spirits of others, but sometimes to sustain my own, when theirs are failing.

This is the most favourable period for travelling in Russia. They fly quickly over the snow in their sledges; the motion is pleasant, and, in my opinion, far more agreeable than that of an English stagecoach. The cold is not excessive, if you are wrapped in furs—a dress which I have already adopted, for there is a great difference between walking the deck and remaining seated motionless for hours, when no exercise prevents the blood from actually freezing in your veins. I have no ambition to lose my life on the post-road between St. Petersburgh and Archangel. I shall depart for the latter town in a fortnight or three weeks; and my intention is to hire a ship there, which can easily be done by paying the insurance for the owner, and to engage as many sailors as I think necessary among those who are accustomed to the whale-fishing. I do not intend to sail until the month of June; and when shall I return? Ah, dear sister, how can I answer this question? If I succeed, many, many months, perhaps years, will pass before you and I may meet. If I fail, you will see me again soon, or never. Farewell, my dear, excellent Margaret. Heaven shower down blessings on you, and save me, that I may again and again testify my gratitude for all your love and kindness.

Your affectionate brother,

R. Walton

• ANALYZING THE SCENE •
LETTER I – SCENE I

A Story Event is an active change of universal human value for one or more characters as a result of conflict (one character's desires clash with another's or an environmental shift changes the universal human value).

A Working Scene contains at least one Story Event. To determine a scene's Story Event, answer these four questions:

1. What are the characters literally doing—that is, what are their micro on-the-ground actions?

Robert Walton is describing his current situation in a letter to his sister in England. He is in St. Petersburg, preparing for a journey to the North Pole.

2. What is the essential tactic of the characters—that is, what macro behaviors are they employing that are linked to a universal human value?

Walton is justifying the decision he has made to go to the North Pole.

3. What universal human values have changed for one or more characters in the scene? Which one of those value changes is most important and should be included in the Story Grid Spreadsheet?

Walton was a failure as a poet, but when he inherited a fortune, he was able to defy his father's dying injunction to never adopt a seafaring life, which was Walton's fantasy since childhood. He has been working for six years toward this trip, and he is afraid he will fail but also hopeful he will witness the mysteries of "eternal daylight."

In a Horror story, the global value spectrum is Damnation to Life, and indeed Walton does address the possibility of death, but his journey to self-actualization seems to require this risk. He doesn't want to play it safe although there is some sense that he thinks science will keep him safe, and this belief in science is a recurring theme in the book. In the spreadsheet we will note Walton's progression from

Despair (at being prevented from exploring the seas) to Hope (at inheriting a fortune and being able to pursue his dream although ironically approaching death).

Despair to Hope

4. What is the Story Event that sums up the scene's on-the-ground actions, essential tactics, and value change? We will enter that event in the Story Grid Spreadsheet.

Robert Walton, after being prevented by his father from becoming an explorer, inherits money and can pursue his dream of traveling to the North Pole.

HOW THE SCENE ABIDES BY THE FIVE COMMANDMENTS OF STORYTELLING

Inciting Incident: Walton discovers books about exploration and discovery at his uncle's house.

Turning Point Progressive Complication: Walton inherits a fortune and can pursue his lifelong dream of exploration.

Crisis: Does he defy his father? Best bad choice.

Climax: He defies his father.

Resolution: Walton becomes an explorer and sets out to "train" for his ultimate goal, exploration of the North Pole.

NOTES

- Shelley has some severe limitations in terms of exposition, as she has chosen a first-person point of view for her novel. She needs to find ways to bring in other perspectives as well as parts of the past or events from other locales that the reader needs to know in order to make sense of the story.

- The novel begins with four letters from Robert Walton, an explorer who is attempting a sea voyage to the North Pole, to his sister in London. In the first letter, Walton tells her he is in St. Petersburg, Russia, preparing for the journey. The point of this is to recap the series of events that led to him wanting to become an explorer, the obstacles that were put in his way, and the lucky inheritance that enabled him to carry through with his dream. Shelley is able to give you some backstory by reminding his sister that this trip is something of a life's dream for him ("You may remember that ..." and "You are acquainted with ....") It's a handy technique but can feel a little bit clunky in a modern novel.
- This first letter sets up the protagonist of the novel nicely because there are parallels between Walton and the eventual creator of the monster, Victor Frankenstein. Later, Walton will meet Frankenstein and feel a deep connection with him. Both have an inexplicable yearning for adventure and a desire for explanations behind otherwise magical occurrences in life.
- Take note of Walton's reasons for wanting to reach the North Pole. He says that "snow and frost are banished" and that the seas are calm. "What may not be expected in a country of eternal light?" Where does he get these ideas? He further states that even if none of these reports are true, learning something about the magnetic nature of the pole will be of benefit to mankind, and he might find a passage through the pole to the North Pacific. What motivates him? What justifies his curiosity, given that he will risk his life for it? All of this justification has a false ring to it. Perhaps vanity drives someone to try to know more than they are meant to know.
- Walton later states that he trained his body and mind for six years in order to prepare for this journey. Why? Shelly poses this question right at the beginning of the book. Why does man do what he does? He says, "—do I not deserve to accomplish some great purpose? My life might have been

passed in ease and luxury, but I preferred glory to every enticement that wealth placed in my path." This seems to answer the question we posed above. Vanity, then, is why humans do what they do.

LETTER 2 – SCENE 2

Archangel, 28th March, 17—

To Mrs. Saville, England

How slowly the time passes here, encompassed as I am by frost and snow! Yet a second step is taken towards my enterprise. I have hired a vessel and am occupied in collecting my sailors; those whom I have already engaged appear to be men on whom I can depend and are certainly possessed of dauntless courage.

But I have one want which I have never yet been able to satisfy, and the absence of the object of which I now feel as a most severe evil, I have no friend, Margaret: when I am glowing with the enthusiasm of success, there will be none to participate my joy; if I am assailed by disappointment, no one will endeavour to sustain me in dejection. *[This theme of being alone and loneliness appears throughout the novel.]* I shall commit my thoughts to paper, it is true; but that is a poor medium for the communication of feeling. **I desire the company of a man who could sympathize with me, whose eyes would reply to mine.** You may deem me romantic, my dear sister, but I bitterly feel the want of a friend. **I have no one near me, gentle yet courageous, possessed of a**

cultivated as well as of a capacious mind, whose tastes are like my own, to approve or amend my plans. How would such a friend repair the faults of your poor brother! **I am too ardent in execution and too impatient of difficulties. But it is a still greater evil to me that I am self-educated: for the first fourteen years of my life I ran wild on a common and read nothing but our Uncle Thomas' books of voyages.** *[Once again, he laments that he is merely self-educated.]* At that age I became acquainted with the celebrated poets of our own country; but it was only when it had ceased to be in my power to derive its most important benefits from such a conviction that I perceived the necessity of becoming acquainted with more languages than that of my native country. **Now I am twenty-eight and am in reality more illiterate than many schoolboys of fifteen.** It is true that I have thought more and that my daydreams are more extended and magnificent, but they want (as the painters call it) KEEPING; and **I greatly need a friend who would have sense enough not to despise me as romantic, and affection enough for me to endeavour to regulate my mind. Well, these are useless complaints; I shall certainly find no friend on the wide ocean, nor even here in Archangel, among merchants and seamen.** Yet some feelings, unallied to the dross of human nature, beat even in these rugged bosoms. My lieutenant, for instance, is a man of wonderful courage and enterprise; he is madly desirous of glory, or rather, to word my phrase more characteristically, of advancement in his profession. He is an Englishman, and in the midst of national and professional prejudices, unsoftened by cultivation, retains some of the noblest endowments of humanity. I first became acquainted with him on board a whale vessel; finding that he was unemployed in this city, I easily engaged him to assist in my enterprise. The master is a person of an excellent disposition and is remarkable in the ship for his gentleness and the mildness of his discipline. This circumstance, added to his well-known integrity and dauntless courage, made me very desirous to engage him. **A youth passed in solitude, my best years spent under your gentle and feminine fosterage, has so refined the groundwork of my character that I cannot overcome an intense distaste to the usual brutality exercised on board ship:** I have never believed it to be necessary, and when I heard of a mariner equally noted for his kindliness of heart and the respect and obedience paid to him by his crew, I felt myself peculiarly fortunate in being able to secure his services. I heard of him first in rather a romantic manner, from a lady who owes to him the happiness of her life. This, briefly, is his story. **Some years ago he loved a young Russian lady of moderate fortune, and having amassed a considerable sum in prize-money, the father of the girl consented to the match. He saw his mistress once before the destined ceremony; but she was bathed in tears, and throwing herself at his feet, entreated him to spare her, confessing at the same time that she loved another, but that he was poor, and that her father would never consent to the union.** My generous friend reassured the suppliant, and on being informed of the name of her lover, instantly abandoned his pursuit. He had already bought a farm with his money, on which he had designed to pass the remainder of his life; but he bestowed the whole on his rival, together with the remains of his prize-money to purchase stock, and then himself solicited the young woman's father to consent to her marriage with her lover. But the old man decidedly refused, thinking himself bound in honour to my friend, who, when he found the father inexorable, quitted his country, nor returned until he heard that his former mistress was married according to her inclinations. *[This is the first of many morality stories in the novel.]* **"What a noble fellow!" you will exclaim. He is so; but then he is wholly uneducated: he is as silent as a Turk, and a kind of ignorant carelessness attends him, which, while it renders his conduct the more astonishing, detracts from the interest and sympathy which otherwise he would command.** *[Once again, a comment on "uneducated" people.]*

Yet do not suppose, because I complain a little or because I can conceive a consolation for my toils which I may never know, that I am wavering in my resolutions. Those are as fixed as fate, and my voyage is only now delayed until the weather shall permit my embarkation. The winter has been dreadfully severe, but the spring promises well, and it is considered as a remarkably early season, so that perhaps I may sail sooner than I expected. **I shall do nothing rashly: you know me sufficiently to confide in my prudence and considerateness**

whenever the safety of others is committed to my care. *[Remember this detail, it is important at the very end of the story—he does not risk the lives of others.]*

I cannot describe to you my sensations on the near prospect of my undertaking. It is impossible to communicate to you a conception of the trembling sensation, half pleasurable and half fearful, with which I am preparing to depart. **I am going to unexplored regions, to "the land of mist and snow," but I shall kill no albatross; therefore do not be alarmed for my safety or if I should come back to you as worn and woeful as the "Ancient Mariner."** You will smile at my allusion, but I will disclose a secret. **I have often attributed my attachment to, my passionate enthusiasm for, the dangerous mysteries of ocean to that production of the most imaginative of modern poets. There is something at work in my soul which I do not understand. I am practically industrious—painstaking, a workman to execute with perseverance and labour—but besides this there is a love for the marvellous, a belief in the marvellous, intertwined in all my projects, which hurries me out of the common pathways of men, even to the wild sea and unvisited regions I am about to explore.** *[He admits to a belief in something beyond work.]* But to return to dearer considerations. Shall I meet you again, after having traversed immense seas, and returned by the most southern cape of Africa or America? I dare not expect such success, yet I cannot bear to look on the reverse of the picture. Continue for the present to write to me by every opportunity: I may receive your letters on some occasions when I need them most to support my spirits. I love you very tenderly. Remember me with affection, should you never hear from me again.

Your affectionate brother,

Robert Walton

LETTER 2 – SCENE 2

A Story Event is an active change of universal human value for one or more characters as a result of conflict (one character's desires clash with another's or an environmental shift changes the universal human value).

A Working Scene contains at least one Story Event. To determine a scene's Story Event, answer these four questions:

1. What are the characters literally doing—that is, what are their micro on-the-ground actions?

Robert Walton is now in Archangel, a Russian port city on the White Sea, from which he plans to set sail on his expedition to the North Pole. He writes to his sister in England, updating her on his activities.

2. What is the essential tactic of the characters—that is, what macro behaviors are they employing that are linked to a universal human value?

Walton is setting up his ship and contemplating his suitability for this adventure; he is reflecting on the fact that emotionally, he is unhappy without an understanding friend or partner in his life. Yet he is headed toward an adventure where he will certainly be alone.

3. What universal human values have changed for one or more characters in the scene? Which one of those value changes is most important and should be included in the Story Grid Spreadsheet?

At the beginning of the letter, Walton complains of loneliness and says he wishes he had a sympathetic friend with him on this journey. He speaks of his "faults," blames his lack of formal education, and says that a friend would help "repair" those faults. By the end of the letter he notes the exemplary character of the men he has hired, his commitment to leading them responsibly, and says he will definitely follow through on his plans; he also jokes that he will "kill no albatross" and assures his sister that she need not fear that he will not return or will end up crazed like the "ancient mariner" of the Coleridge poem. He also admits that he is in the power of some flavor of wanderlust, and he cannot resist its call.

In this scene we will note Walton's progression from Uncertainty (that he is both lonely and not educated enough to succeed at this mission) to Resignation (because he is a responsible leader and because he cannot resist his "love for the marvelous"). This progression is tied to the global value in that he is only happy if he is doing something that brings him close to death.

Uncertainty to Resignation

4. What is the Story Event that sums up the scene's on-the-ground actions, essential tactics, and value change? We will enter that event in the Story Grid Spreadsheet.

Walton travels from St. Petersburg to Archangel to prepare for his trip; he is lonely and is traveling to an empty part of the world, where he will certainly not meet anyone or make any friends.

HOW THE SCENE ABIDES BY THE FIVE COMMANDMENTS OF STORYTELLING

Inciting Incident: Walton is in Archangel, where he has to organize the ship that will take him to the North Pole.

Turning Point Progressive Complication: He is alone; he doesn't have any educated friends who can compensate for his "faults." Yet he is headed into an adventure where he will certainly not find any friends.

Crisis: Does he give up his expedition? This is the last moment where he can pull out. Best bad choice.

Climax: Walton resolves to go forward with his plans.

Resolution: He hires the men he needs, reminds himself that he is a responsible leader, and admits that his "love of the marvelous" drives him forward.

NOTES

- This writing is characteristic for this era, where the action doesn't seem to "turn." Shelley has boxed herself into a bit of a corner with the first-person point of view, but the revelatory nature of this letter gives us quite a bit of useful information. The "climax" of this letter is almost invisible but critical, as we want to know (and be convinced of) why he is actually going through with a scheme that seems harebrained and reckless.
- Walton dwells on the fact that he feels ill-educated and wishes for a friend "who would have sense enough not to despise me as romantic, and affection enough for me to endeavour to regulate my mind." This sets up another parallel to Frankenstein, who is similarly self-educated and similarly fascinated by the world beyond the practical. It is so tidily done, we wonder whether Shelley wrote this series of letters after she had completed the book as a way to properly "bookend" the narrative. The novel begins with Walton pining for a friend and ends with Walton pining for his friend, Frankenstein.
- Though Walton despairs of finding the friend who will both sympathize with him and instruct him, he praises the character of the ordinary working sailors he hires in Archangel.
- The story of the ship's master, who declined to marry the young woman whose father would not allow her to marry her penniless lover, is presented as an example of virtue. The sailor hands all of his wealth and assets over to the young couple in order to convince the girl's father to permit the marriage. This seems a little strange and indeed overdramatic, but there was a prevailing attitude among

Shelley's set that this kind of act of generosity was worthy of praise. In fact, her husband, Percy Shelley, was known to have been the benefactor of Shelley's father, William Godwin. Since we know that the internal genre of *Frankenstein* is a Morality story, be on the lookout for examples of "right living" and putting the needs of others above one's own wants throughout the book.

- "The Rime of the Ancient Mariner" was a celebrated poem of the era, which most certainly any reader of popular fiction would have recognized. What is notable is that the poem features several themes that would have served as foreshadowing here: the concept of the "albatross" around the neck after taking an irreversible step (the mariner of the poem shoots an albatross, and all kinds of bad things then happen to his ship), the notion of living "life as death," and the mariner's fate, which was to tell his personal tale to everyone he met throughout his journey in life (a parallel of Frankenstein, who in the very next chapters will tell Walton his life story). Walton tells his sister not to worry because he doesn't plan to shoot an albatross! One wonders again whether Shelley wrote these letters as a sort of "prequel" to Frankenstein's sad story in order to properly "bookend" the Horror plot. It's stylistically beautifully done and another tool in the toolbox for the writer. It may be worth a glance at the text of "Ancient Mariner" to see what Shelley was referring to, as the notion of the albatross comes up a couple of times in the book. (You can find the poem on the Gutenberg site: *http://www.gutenberg.org/files/151/151-h/151-h.htm).*

LETTER 3 – SCENE 3

July 7th, 17—

To Mrs. Saville, England

My dear Sister,

I write a few lines in haste to say that I am safe—and well advanced on my voyage. This letter will reach England by a merchantman now on its homeward voyage from Archangel; more fortunate than I, who may not see my native land, perhaps, for many years. I am, however, **in good spirits: my men are bold and apparently firm of purpose, nor do the floating sheets of ice that continually pass us, indicating the dangers of the region towards which we are advancing, appear to dismay them.** We have already reached a very high latitude; but it is the height of summer, and although not so warm as in England, the southern gales, which blow us speedily towards those shores which I so ardently desire to attain, breathe a degree of renovating warmth which I had not expected.

No incidents have hitherto befallen us that would make a figure in a letter. One or two stiff gales and the springing of a leak are accidents which experienced navigators scarcely remember to record, and I shall be well content if nothing worse happen to us during our voyage. Adieu, my dear Margaret. Be assured that for my own sake, as well as yours, **I will not rashly encounter danger. I will be cool, persevering, and prudent.**

But success SHALL crown my endeavours. Wherefore not? Thus far I have gone, tracing a secure way over the pathless seas, the very stars themselves being witnesses and testimonies of my triumph. **Why not still proceed over the untamed yet obedient element? What can stop the determined heart and resolved will of man?** *[This sounds ominous! What indeed? There is an answer to this question by the end of the book.]*

My swelling heart involuntarily pours itself out thus. But I must finish. Heaven bless my beloved sister!

R.W.

• ANALYZING THE SCENE •
LETTER 3 – SCENE 3

A Story Event is an active change of universal human value for one or more characters as a result of conflict (one character's desires clash with another's or an environmental shift changes the universal human value).

A Working Scene contains at least one Story Event. To determine a scene's Story Event, answer these four questions:

1. What are the characters literally doing—that is, what are their micro on-the-ground actions?

The last letter was written in March; this letter is dated July. Walton says he is "well advanced" on his voyage.

2. What is the essential tactic of the characters—that is, what macro behaviors are they employing that are linked to a universal human value?

Walton contemplates his own success, which he shares with his sister: "But success SHALL crown my endeavours. Wherefore not? Thus far I have gone, tracing a secure way over the pathless seas, the very stars themselves being witnesses and testimonies of my triumph. Why not still proceed over the untamed yet obedient element? What can stop the determined heart and resolved will of man?"

3. What universal human values have changed for one or more characters in the scene? Which one of those value changes is most important and should be included in the Story Grid Spreadsheet?

In a Horror story, the global value spectrum is Damnation to Death to Life; this scene anchors what will surely be a trajectory in a negative direction. If anything, you might regard this scene as part of the following scene rather than a stand-alone scene. This scene is positive, and you can expect what follows will be negative.

No change.

4. What is the Story Event that sums up the scene's on-the-ground actions, essential tactics, and value change? We will enter that event in the Story Grid Spreadsheet.

Walton is having a good voyage; nothing untoward has happened. He asks a rhetorical question about whether it is worth going on and answers his own question in the affirmative. Things are good!

HOW THE SCENE ABIDES BY THE FIVE COMMANDMENTS OF STORYTELLING

Inciting Incident: Walton is on his way to the North Pole.

Turning Point Progressive Complication: A few minor incidents have occurred, such as stiff gales and leaks. There isn't much in the way of "progression" here, and the turning point is faint.

Crisis: Walton asks the questions, "Why not still proceed over the untamed yet obedient element? What can stop the determined heart and resolved will of man?" Should he go on? Best bad choice.

Climax: Walton resolves to go forward with his plans.

Resolution: Walton answers his own question by saying, "success SHALL crown my endeavors." This very short chapter sets up the next event and the rest of the novel, where he will learn "what can stop the determined heart and resolved will of man." In short, success is not a guarantee, no matter how "resolved" the will of man might be.

NOTES

- Literature of the 1800s can seem wordy and stagnant. It helps to ask why the writer might have wanted to insert the scene and what purpose it serves over the larger arc of the story.
- This letter is short and might be viewed as not really having its own story event. Instead, perhaps, view this letter as a setup of the important events to follow. The tone of the letter is quite positive; therefore, tension is increasing. We know bad things are going to happen, and we are nervous as we wait for the other shoe to drop.
- Still, Shelley did follow the Five Commandments of Storytelling at a minimal level. She sets up the scene (Walton is sailing toward the North Pole), throws in some minor happenings (it's windy, there are leaks), posits a question (is there any reason to give up?), answers it (no!), then resolves the tension by moving toward the next scene with the Big Question that confronts Walton (and Frankenstein) over the course of the entire novel: "**What can**

stop the determined heart and resolved will of man?" We should be a bit concerned about Walton's arrogance and his assumption that he can overcome anything that might develop.

LETTER 4 – SCENE 4

August 5th, 17—

To Mrs. Saville, England

So strange an accident has happened to us that I cannot forbear recording it, although it is very probable that you will see me before these papers can come into your possession.
Last Monday (July 31st) we were **nearly surrounded by ice**, which closed in the ship on all sides, scarcely leaving her the sea-room in which she floated. *[We could have attached the previous scene to this one in order to track movement.]* Our situation was somewhat dangerous, especially as we were compassed round by a **very thick fog**. We accordingly lay to, hoping that some change would take place in the atmosphere and weather.

About two o'clock **the mist cleared away, and we beheld, stretched out in every direction, vast and irregular plains of ice, which seemed to have no end.** Some of my comrades groaned, and my own mind began to grow watchful with anxious thoughts, when a strange sight suddenly attracted our attention and diverted our solicitude from our own situation. **We perceived a low carriage, fixed on a sledge and**

drawn by dogs, pass on towards the north, at the distance of half a mile; a being which had the shape of a man, but apparently of gigantic stature, sat in the sledge and guided the dogs. We watched the rapid progress of the traveller with our telescopes until he was lost among the distant inequalities of the ice. *[What a cinematic description!]* This appearance excited our unqualified wonder. We were, as we believed, many hundred miles from any land; but this apparition seemed to denote that it was not, in reality, so distant as we had supposed. Shut in, however, by ice, it was impossible to follow his track, which we had observed with the greatest attention. About two hours after this occurrence we heard the ground sea, and before night the ice broke and freed our ship. We, however, lay to until the morning, fearing to encounter in the dark those large loose masses which float about after the breaking up of the ice. I profited of this time to rest for a few hours.

In the morning, however, as soon as it was light, I went upon deck and found all the sailors busy on one side of the vessel, apparently talking to someone in the sea. **It was, in fact, a sledge, like that we had seen before, which had drifted towards us in the night on a large fragment of ice. Only one dog remained alive; but there was a human being within it whom the sailors were persuading to enter the vessel. He was not, as the other traveller seemed to be, a savage inhabitant of some undiscovered island, but a European.** When I appeared on deck the master said, "Here is our captain, and he will not allow you to perish on the open sea." *[Another example of goodness/morality.]*

On perceiving me, the stranger addressed me in English, although with a foreign accent. **"Before I come on board your vessel," said he, "will you have the kindness to inform me whither you are bound?" You may conceive my astonishment on hearing such a question addressed to me from a man on the brink of destruction and to whom I should have supposed that my vessel would have been a resource which he would not have exchanged for the most precious wealth the earth can afford.** *[How strange, he isn't eager to be rescued?]* I replied, however, that we were on a voyage of discovery towards the northern pole.

Upon hearing this he appeared satisfied and consented to come on board. Good God! Margaret, if you had seen the man who thus capitulated for his safety, your surprise would have been boundless. His limbs were nearly frozen, and his body dreadfully emaciated by fatigue and suffering. I never saw a man in so wretched a condition. We attempted to carry him into the cabin, but as soon as he had quitted the fresh air he fainted. We accordingly brought him back to the deck and restored him to animation by rubbing him with brandy and forcing him to swallow a small quantity. As soon as he showed signs of life we wrapped him up in blankets and placed him near the chimney of the kitchen stove. By slow degrees he recovered and ate a little soup, which restored him wonderfully.

Two days passed in this manner before he was able to speak, and I often feared that his sufferings had deprived him of understanding. When he had in some measure recovered, I removed him to my own cabin and attended on him as much as my duty would permit. I never saw a more interesting creature: his eyes have generally an expression of wildness, and even madness, but there are moments when, if anyone performs an act of kindness towards him or does him any the most trifling service, his whole countenance is lighted up, as it were, with a beam of benevolence and sweetness that I never saw equalled. But **he is generally melancholy and despairing, and sometimes he gnashes his teeth, as if impatient of the weight of woes that oppresses him.**

When my guest was a little recovered I had great trouble to keep off the men, who wished to ask him a thousand questions; but I would not allow him to be tormented by their idle curiosity, in a state of body and mind whose restoration evidently depended upon entire repose. Once, however, **the lieutenant asked why he had come so far upon the ice in so strange a vehicle.**

His countenance instantly assumed an aspect of the deepest gloom, and he replied, "To seek one who fled from me."

"And did the man whom you pursued travel in the same fashion?"

"Yes."

"Then I fancy we have seen him, for the day before we picked you up we saw some dogs drawing a sledge, with a man in it, across the ice."

This aroused the stranger's attention, and he asked a multitude of questions concerning the route which the demon, as he called him, had pursued. Soon after, when he was alone with me, he said, "I have, doubtless, excited your curiosity, as well as that of these good people; but you are too considerate to make inquiries."

"Certainly; it would indeed be very impertinent and inhuman in me to trouble you with any inquisitiveness of mine."

"And yet you rescued me from a strange and perilous situation; you have benevolently restored me to life."

Soon after this he inquired if I thought that the breaking up of the ice had destroyed the other sledge. I replied that I could not answer with any degree of certainty, for the ice had not broken until near midnight, and the traveller might have arrived at a place of safety before that time; but of this I could not judge. From this time a new spirit of life animated the decaying frame of the stranger. *[He is happy that the creature lives.]* He manifested the greatest eagerness to be upon deck to watch for the sledge which had before appeared; but I have persuaded him to remain in the cabin, for he is far too weak to sustain the rawness of the atmosphere. I have promised that someone should watch for him and give him instant notice if any new object should appear in sight.

Such is my journal of what relates to this strange occurrence up to the present day. The stranger has gradually improved in health but is very silent and appears uneasy when anyone except myself enters his cabin. Yet his manners are so conciliating and gentle that the sailors are all interested in him, although they have had very little communication with him. For my own part, **I begin to love him as a brother, and his constant and deep grief fills me with sympathy and compassion. He must have been a noble creature in his better days, being even now in wreck so attractive and amiable. I said in one of my letters, my dear Margaret, that I should find no friend on the wide ocean; yet I have found a man who, before his spirit had been broken by misery, I should have been happy to have possessed as the brother of my heart.**

I shall continue my journal concerning the stranger at intervals, should I have any fresh incidents to record.

• ANALYZING THE SCENE •
LETTER 4 – SCENE 4

A Story Event is an active change of universal human value for one or more characters as a result of conflict (one character's desires clash with another's or an environmental shift changes the universal human value).

A Working Scene contains at least one Story Event. To determine a scene's Story Event, answer these four questions:

1. What are the characters literally doing—that is, what are their micro on-the-ground actions?

The last letter was written in July. This one was written on August 5 and reports an incident that happened on July 31. Walton and the crew are stuck in sea ice and in the midst of a thick fog when they see a grotesque man in the distance driving a sledge. He disappears, and eventually the ship manages to get free of the ice. The following day they find another stranger stuck on the ice and take him aboard.

2. What is the essential tactic of the characters—that is, what macro behaviors are they employing that are linked to a universal human value?

Walton and the crew are desperately trying to stay alive; ironically, the second stranger who is stuck on the ice isn't sure he wants to be rescued. There is a contrast here between Walton's desire for life and the stranger's apparent hesitation over staying alive.

3. What universal human values have changed for one or more characters in the scene? Which one of those value changes is most important and should be included in the Story Grid Spreadsheet?

Walton moves from alone to finding camaraderie. The stranger moves from despair to hope.

In this scene we should highlight the change in mood for the stranger. When he is rescued, he is lackluster and melancholy. When he realizes that his quarry may still be out there, alive, and that Walton and his crew may have even seen him nearby, he becomes animated and excited. The stranger only appears midway through the scene, but Walton's emotional journey mirrors the stranger's by starting out with fear and panic because of the ice and ending up with joy at finding the friend that he has longed for.

Despair to Hope

4. What is the Story Event that sums up the scene's on-the-ground actions, essential tactics, and value change? We will enter that event in the Story Grid Spreadsheet.

Walton and his crew are surrounded by ice and mist; when it clears, they see a huge man in the distance, riding a sledge guided by dogs. After the ice breaks up, they encounter another man on a sledge; he is starving and cold. He has apparently been chasing the giant man on the first sledge. He regains his strength when he realizes that his quarry may still be alive. Walton grows fond of this stranger.

HOW THE SCENE ABIDES BY THE FIVE COMMANDMENTS OF STORYTELLING

Inciting Incident: Walton's ship is stuck in the ice.

Turning Point Progressive Complication: Walton and his crew see first one man on the ice, and then after the ship manages to float free of the ice, they see another.

Crisis: There is a dual crisis. Should Walton rescue this man from certain death? Should this man rescue himself from certain death? It's a best bad choice for the victim, who is in a bad way but appears to not want to give up his journey.

Climax: Walton and his crew insist on taking the man aboard; the man, however, only agrees to be rescued when he hears that the ship is still on a voyage of exploration (i.e., not returning home).

Resolution: Walton is overjoyed to have found a friend; the stranger is excited when he realizes that the mysterious giant seen by the rest of the crew may still be alive somewhere out on the ice.

NOTES

- In this scene, the Five Commandments are not immediately apparent because we're tracking two trajectories. Is the inciting incident the sighting of the giant? The rescue of the stranger? What's the turning point —being surrounded by ice and mist? The appearance of a half-dead European on the ice? Any of these could be taken as part of the structure of the scene. We need to consider which journey we're trying to follow. This is a great opportunity for a writer to learn how to structure a scene where the POV character is not experiencing the entire trajectory himself or herself.

- Overall, we have a Horror story, and we know we have to track a disturbing emotional journey as we read. We suspect Walton isn't the protagonist although we aren't really sure if the real protagonist is the pursuer or the pursued. But we can put the giant aside for a moment and concentrate on just Walton and the stranger. This is where thinking about the essential tactic of the scene is helpful. What is really going on here? What did Shelley want you to take away from this scene?
- Now let's back up from the scene a bit and consider Shelley's overall story goal. Readers want life-and-death situations in a Horror novel with the risk of a fate worse than death. They don't necessarily want to agonize over someone's lonely life (the main Walton emotional shift from beginning to end of the scene). But the stranger appears midway through the scene, so the stranger's activities can't be the only elements that we're supposed to trace. And although Walton does face a life-and-death situation with the ice, it is resolved by an act of God as the ice moves aside and sets the ship free in the middle of the scene, so that set of conditions can't be the one that Shelley wants us to focus on, either.
- What are the main emotional changes in this scene? Walton starts out lonely and ends up with a friend. This is a positive change. The stranger starts out despondent and without a will to live but regains his will to live when he realizes his quarry may still be alive, somewhere out on the ice. This is also a positive change. Overall, we should focus on the stranger's change because while Walton's loneliness and desire for company is an important theme in the book, if we are writing a Horror novel, we aren't "merely" looking for company as we amble through life. Something bigger, more disturbing must be at stake. The core emotion for a Horror novel is fear, so it needs to provoke an internal sense of danger in the reader compared to the Action genre, where

the danger is more external. Shelley has combined the life-and-death trajectory of both Walton and the stranger so there is almost a “false ending” as Walton’s ice problem is resolved, just as he meets the stranger. The stranger’s emotional journey starts just as Walton’s ends, but at the same time, Walton’s larger overall emotional arc is soaring over the actual life-and-death events of the scene. It’s a wonderfully natural way to keep Walton’s POV and emotions at center stage while continuing the life-death arc smoothly, switching from Walton to the stranger in the middle.

- So, let’s boil the scene down to the essentials of both perspectives. This makes it fairly simple to evaluate. Walton and the crew are stuck in the ice (inciting incident); they see two strangers out on the ice, one of whom they try to rescue, and this stranger is going to die if he refuses to accept Walton’s help (complication); should he board the ship (crisis)? He boards the ship and eventually learns that his quarry has been sighted (climax); he becomes newly obsessed with the chase (resolution).
- When writing from a first-person POV, remember that you don’t have to restrict yourself to the emotions of the POV character in order to construct a scene. You can use all of the information at hand. Keep your mind focused on the core emotion of the novel and the purpose of your scene. If you are trying to convey information that extends beyond the knowledge of your POV character, start with the turning point (the unexpected event that gives rise to the crisis). In this case, the turning point is the moment where the stranger realizes his rescue may mean the permanent loss of his quarry. This should help you to construct a scene that moves, even without leaving your POV character’s perspective, and taking full advantage of all of the events of your scene.

LETTER 4 – SCENE 5

August 13th, 17—

My affection for my guest increases every day. He excites at once my admiration and my pity to an astonishing degree. How can I see so noble a creature destroyed by misery without feeling the most poignant grief? He is so gentle, yet so wise; his mind is so cultivated, and when he speaks, although his words are culled with the choicest art, yet they flow with rapidity and unparalleled eloquence. **He is now much recovered from his illness and is continually on the deck, apparently watching for the sledge that preceded his own.** Yet, although unhappy, he is not so utterly occupied by his own misery but that he interests himself deeply in the projects of others. He has frequently conversed with me on mine, which I have communicated to him without disguise. He entered attentively into all my arguments in favour of my eventual success and into every minute detail of the measures I had taken to secure it. **I was easily led by the sympathy which he evinced to use the language of my heart, to give utterance to the burning ardour of my soul and to say, with all the fervour that warmed me, how gladly I would sacrifice my fortune, my existence, my every hope, to the furtherance of my enterprise. One man's life or death were but a small price to pay for the acquirement of the**

knowledge which I sought, for the dominion I should acquire and transmit over the elemental foes of our race. *[This view led Frankenstein to his terrible state!]* **As I spoke, a dark gloom spread over my listener's countenance.** At first I perceived that he tried to suppress his emotion; he placed his hands before his eyes, and my voice quivered and failed me as I beheld tears trickle fast from between his fingers; a groan burst from his heaving breast. I paused; at length he spoke, in broken accents: **"Unhappy man! Do you share my madness? Have you drunk also of the intoxicating draught? Hear me; let me reveal my tale, and you will dash the cup from your lips!"**

Such words, you may imagine, strongly excited my curiosity; but the paroxysm of grief that had seized the stranger overcame his weakened powers, and many hours of repose and tranquil conversation were necessary to restore his composure. **Having conquered the violence of his feelings, he appeared to despise himself for being the slave of passion**; and quelling the dark tyranny of despair, he led me again to converse concerning myself personally. He asked me the history of my earlier years. The tale was quickly told, but it awakened various trains of reflection. I spoke of my desire of finding a friend, of my thirst for a more intimate sympathy with a fellow mind than had ever fallen to my lot, and expressed my conviction that a man could boast of little happiness who did not enjoy this blessing. "I agree with you," replied the stranger; "**we are unfashioned creatures, but half made up, if one wiser, better, dearer than ourselves—such a friend ought to be—do not lend his aid to perfectionate our weak and faulty natures.** I once had a friend, the most noble of human creatures, and am entitled, therefore, to judge respecting friendship. *[Obviously, we will hear more eventually about this friend.]* You have hope, and the world before you, and have no cause for despair. **But I—I have lost everything and cannot begin life anew.**"

As he said this his countenance became expressive of a calm, settled grief that touched me to the heart. But he was silent and presently retired to his cabin.

Even broken in spirit as he is, no one can feel more deeply than he does the beauties of nature. The starry sky, the sea, and every sight afforded by these wonderful regions seem still to have the power of elevating his soul from earth. Such a man has a double existence: he may suffer misery and be overwhelmed by disappointments, yet when he has retired into himself, he will be like a celestial spirit that has a halo around him, within whose circle no grief or folly ventures.

Will you smile at the enthusiasm I express concerning this divine wanderer? You would not if you saw him. You have been tutored and refined by books and retirement from the world, and you are therefore somewhat fastidious; but this only renders you the more fit to appreciate the extraordinary merits of this wonderful man. Sometimes I have endeavoured to discover what quality it is which he possesses that elevates him so immeasurably above any other person I ever knew. I believe it to be an intuitive discernment, a quick but never-failing power of judgment, a penetration into the causes of things, unequalled for clearness and precision; add to this a facility of expression and a voice whose varied intonations are soul-subduing music.

• ANALYZING THE SCENE •
LETTER 4 – SCENE 5

A Story Event is an active change of universal human value for one or more characters as a result of conflict (one character's desires clash with another's or an environmental shift changes the universal human value).

A Working Scene contains at least one Story Event. To determine a scene's Story Event, answer these four questions:

1. What are the characters literally doing—that is, what are their micro on-the-ground actions?

It is now August 13, eight days since Walton has last written. Walton and the stranger are spending time together, and Walton tells the stranger he would sacrifice anything in the world in order to achieve his goal of reaching the North Pole. The stranger has a violent reaction.

2. What is the essential tactic of the characters—that is, what macro behaviors are they employing that are linked to a universal human value?

Walton and his guest are in complete disagreement over whether one should sacrifice everything in the name of knowledge. The stranger has had some terrible life experience that has led him to disagree violently with Walton.

3. What universal human values have changed for one or more characters in the scene? Which one of those value changes is most important and should be included in the Story Grid Spreadsheet?

The stranger is not exactly happy, but he seems at peace until Walton tells him of his conviction that knowledge is worth the most extreme sacrifice. The range of emotion is from Calm to Agitated.

Walton seems to have no particular change in his emotional state. Since in this scene the stranger's experiences an emotional shift, we'll add that to the spreadsheet.

Calm to Agitated

4. What is the Story Event that sums up the scene's on-the-ground actions, essential tactics, and value change? We will enter that event in the Story Grid Spreadsheet.

Walton and the stranger are becoming friends. Walton confides his belief that knowledge and mastery are worth any price, and the stranger objects violently.

HOW THE SCENE ABIDES BY THE FIVE COMMANDMENTS OF STORYTELLING

Inciting Incident: The stranger, having recovered from his illness, has become friendly and is very curious about Walton's adventure.

Turning Point Progressive Complication: Walton is led by the stranger's friendliness to confide his deepest belief: "One man's life or death were but a small price to pay for the acquirement of the knowledge which I sought, for the dominion I should acquire and transmit over the elemental foes of our race."

Crisis: Should the stranger react and tell his bizarre tale that may prejudice Walton against him? Best bad choice.

Climax: He attempts to refrain, but eventually the stranger bursts into tears and says he has a tale to share that will lead Walton to change his views.

Resolution: He eventually calms down and begins to ask Walton more questions about himself.

NOTES

- The two men start out the scene in a calm state of mind. It seems they are going to be good friends when suddenly the stranger has a violent reaction to something Walton says. What does Walton say? He is confiding his deepest belief, the whole reason why he is embarking on this dangerous journey, namely that he will make any sacrifice in order to obtain the knowledge he seeks. The stranger's reaction is so violent the reader knows instantly that he disagrees vehemently. Not only does the stranger disagree, but he says to Walton, "Do you share my madness?"
- Curiously, Walton does not seem as disturbed by the stranger's outburst as the stranger was by Walton's words. He doesn't comment any further, even when the stranger says he has "lost everything and cannot begin life anew." Walton is not a very perceptive narrator! Perhaps this explains his

fascination with the stranger, about whom he says, "no one can feel more deeply than he does the beauties of nature." Perhaps Shelley is trying to point out that our narrator is a little dense, by thus describing the exquisitely sensitive stranger. Since we are subject to the observations of our POV character, if he is a relatively unemotional storyteller, we're almost getting an omniscient viewpoint, which is a useful storytelling technique.

LETTER 4 – SCENE 6

August 19, 17—

Yesterday the stranger said to me, "You may easily perceive, Captain Walton, that I have suffered great and unparalleled misfortunes. I had determined at one time that the memory of these evils should die with me, but you have won me to alter my determination. **You seek for knowledge and wisdom, as I once did; and I ardently hope that the gratification of your wishes may not be a serpent to sting you, as mine has been.** I do not know that the relation of my disasters will be useful to you; yet, when I reflect that you are pursuing the same course, exposing yourself to the same dangers which have rendered me what I am, I imagine that you may deduce an apt moral from my tale, one that may direct you if you succeed in your undertaking and console you in case of failure. Prepare to hear of occurrences which are usually deemed marvellous. **Were we among the tamer scenes of nature I might fear to encounter your unbelief, perhaps your ridicule; but many things will appear possible in these wild and mysterious regions which would provoke the laughter of those unacquainted with the ever-varied powers of nature;** nor can I doubt but that my tale conveys in its series internal evidence of the truth of the events of which it is composed."

You may easily imagine that I was much gratified by the offered communication, yet I could not endure that he should renew his grief by a recital of his misfortunes. I felt the greatest eagerness to hear the promised narrative, partly from curiosity and partly from a strong desire to ameliorate his fate if it were in my power. I expressed these feelings in my answer.

"I thank you," he replied, "for your sympathy, but it is useless; **my fate is nearly fulfilled. I wait but for one event, and then I shall repose in peace.** I understand your feeling," continued he, perceiving that I wished to interrupt him; "but you are mistaken, my friend, if thus you will allow me to name you; nothing can alter my destiny; listen to my history, and you will perceive how irrevocably it is determined."

He then told me that he would commence his narrative the next day when I should be at leisure. This promise drew from me the warmest thanks. I have resolved every night, when I am not imperatively occupied by my duties, to record, as nearly as possible in his own words, what he has related during the day. If I should be engaged, I will at least make notes. This manuscript will doubtless afford you the greatest pleasure; but to me, who know him, and who hear it from his own lips—with what interest and sympathy shall I read it in some future day! Even now, as I commence my task, his full-toned voice swells in my ears; his lustrous eyes dwell on me with all their melancholy sweetness; I see his thin hand raised in animation, while the lineaments of his face are irradiated by the soul within.

Strange and harrowing must be his story, frightful the storm which embraced the gallant vessel on its course and wrecked it—thus!

• ANALYZING THE SCENE •
LETTER 4 – SCENE 6

A Story Event is an active change of universal human value for one or more characters as a result of conflict (one character's desires clash with another's or an environmental shift changes the universal human value).

A Working Scene contains at least one Story Event. To determine a scene's Story Event, answer these four questions:

1. What are the characters literally doing—that is, what are their micro on-the-ground actions?

Walton and the stranger are talking. It is August 19, six days since the previous letter.

2. What is the essential tactic of the characters—that is, what macro behaviors are they employing that are linked to a universal human value?

The stranger decides to tell Walton his life story as a cautionary tale.

3. What universal human values have changed for one or more characters in the scene? Which one of those value changes is most important and should be included in the Story Grid Spreadsheet?

In this scene, the stranger's universal human value does not change. He starts out with the resolute intention to tell Walton his story and ends the scene with the same determination. Walton experiences a change; he starts the scene hesitant and concerned because he does not want the stranger to become upset, but he is overcome with curiosity.

Hesitation to Curiosity

4. What is the Story Event that sums up the scene's on-the-ground actions, essential tactics, and value change? We will enter that event in the Story Grid Spreadsheet.

The stranger tells Walton he has decided to tell him the story of his life, which he had thought he would never share with anyone; he thinks it will serve as a cautionary tale for Walton.

HOW THE SCENE ABIDES BY THE FIVE COMMANDMENTS OF STORYTELLING

Inciting Incident: The stranger offers to tell Walton his life story.

Turning Point Progressive Complication: The stranger warns that this is a tale of disasters, and he was once on the same course as Walton. He is curious, but the stranger is distraught.

Crisis: Every time the stranger talks about his past, he becomes agitated. Should Walton allow him to talk about his misfortunes and potentially become distraught? Best bad choice.

Climax: Walton wants to hear the tale; he offers to help the stranger solve whatever problems he faces.

Resolution: The stranger assures him that his destiny has already been determined.

NOTES

- This is another one of those scenes that almost seems too quiet to be a scene on its own. However, there is a very specific structural reason for this scene to exist.
- The first four "letters" of Shelley's book serve as an introduction to the stranger's tale of woe. After this letter she switches into the first-person POV from the stranger's point of view as he relates his story to Walton. One may look at the four letters as a mini-act. As such, it needs to have its own inciting incident, progressive complications, crisis, climax, and resolution.
- Therefore, the tone of this last letter before the stranger commences to tell his tale is a bit quiet, but this is

appropriate given that it serves as the resolution of this first part of the book. The stranger announces his intention to tell his story; Walton protests faintly; the stranger insists; Walton acquiesces. One might characterize the four letters as a lonely man goes on a voyage (inciting incident); he runs into a grotesque giant and rescues a stranger (progressive complications); he is delighted with the stranger and confides his innermost hopes and dreams (crisis); the stranger has a powerful reaction and tries to control his reaction but fails (climax); the stranger decides to tell him his personal story in order to help him.

CHAPTER 1 – SCENE 7

I am by birth a Genevese, and my family is one of the most distinguished of that republic. My ancestors had been for many years counsellors and syndics, and my father had filled several public situations with honour and reputation. **He was respected by all who knew him for his integrity and indefatigable attention to public business.** *[A definition of a "good" man.]* He passed his younger days perpetually occupied by the affairs of his country; a variety of circumstances had prevented his marrying early, nor was it until the decline of life that he became a husband and the father of a family.

As the circumstances of his marriage illustrate his character, I cannot refrain from relating them. One of his most intimate friends was a merchant who, from a flourishing state, fell, through numerous mischances, into poverty. This man, whose name was Beaufort, was of a proud and unbending disposition and could not bear to live in poverty and oblivion in the same country where he had formerly been distinguished for his rank and magnificence. Having paid his debts, therefore, in the most honourable manner, he retreated with his daughter to the town of Lucerne, where he lived unknown and in wretchedness. **My father loved Beaufort with the truest friendship and was deeply grieved by his retreat in these unfortunate**

circumstances. He bitterly deplored the false pride which led his friend to a conduct so little worthy of the affection that united them. He lost no time in endeavouring to seek him out, with the hope of persuading him to begin the world again through his credit and assistance. *[Another example of a good choice versus a bad choice; Frankenstein's father deplores "false pride."]*

Beaufort had taken effectual measures to conceal himself, and it was ten months before my father discovered his abode. Overjoyed at this discovery, he hastened to the house, which was situated in a mean street near the Reuss. But when he entered, misery and despair alone welcomed him. Beaufort had saved but a very small sum of money from the wreck of his fortunes, but it was sufficient to provide him with sustenance for some months, and in the meantime he hoped to procure some respectable employment in a merchant's house. **The interval was, consequently, spent in inaction; his grief only became more deep and rankling when he had leisure for reflection, and at length it took so fast hold of his mind that at the end of three months he lay on a bed of sickness, incapable of any exertion.**

His daughter attended him with the greatest tenderness, but she saw with despair that their little fund was rapidly decreasing and that there was no other prospect of support. But **Caroline Beaufort possessed a mind of an uncommon mould, and her courage rose to support her in her adversity.** She procured plain work; she plaited straw and by various means contrived to earn a pittance scarcely sufficient to support life. *[A gentlewoman who is not too proud to work to support her ill father—another example of moral living.]*

Several months passed in this manner. Her father grew worse; her time was more entirely occupied in attending him; her means of subsistence decreased; and in the tenth month her father died in her arms, leaving her an orphan and a beggar. This last blow overcame her, and she knelt by Beaufort's coffin weeping bitterly, when my father entered the chamber. **He came like a protecting spirit to the poor girl, who committed herself to his care;** and after the interment of his friend he conducted her to Geneva and placed her under the protection of a relation. Two years after this event Caroline became his wife. *[More moral choices—protecting the daughter of his friend and then marrying her.]*

There was a considerable difference between the ages of my parents, but this circumstance seemed to unite them only closer in bonds of devoted affection. **There was a sense of justice in my father's upright mind which rendered it necessary that he should approve highly to love strongly. Perhaps during former years he had suffered from the late-discovered unworthiness of one beloved and so was disposed to set a greater value on tried worth.** *[Even Frankenstein thinks his father's life choices are unusual.]* There was a show of gratitude and worship in his attachment to my mother, differing wholly from the doting fondness of age, for it was inspired by reverence for her virtues and a desire to be the means of, in some degree, recompensing her for the sorrows she had endured, but which gave inexpressible grace to his behaviour to her. Everything was made to yield to her wishes and her convenience. He strove to shelter her, as a fair exotic is sheltered by the gardener, from every rougher wind and to surround her with all that could tend to excite pleasurable emotion in her soft and benevolent mind. Her health, and even the tranquillity of her hitherto constant spirit, had been shaken by what she had gone through. During the two years that had elapsed previous to their marriage my father had gradually relinquished all his public functions; and immediately after their union they sought the pleasant climate of Italy, and the change of scene and interest attendant on a tour through that land of wonders, as a restorative for her weakened frame. *[She has given her life for her values.]*

From Italy they visited Germany and France. I, their eldest child, was born at Naples, and as an infant accompanied them in their rambles. I remained for several years their only child. **Much as they were attached to each other, they seemed to draw inexhaustible stores of affection from a very mine of love to bestow them upon me.** My mother's tender caresses and my father's smile of benevolent pleasure while regarding me are my first recollections. **I was their plaything and their idol, and something better—their child, the innocent and helpless creature bestowed on them by heaven, whom to bring up to good, and whose future lot it was in their hands to direct to happiness or misery, according as they fulfilled their duties towards me.** *[Here it is—the correct way to raise a child.]* **With this deep**

consciousness of what they owed towards the being to which they had given life, added to the active spirit of tenderness that animated both, it may be imagined that while during every hour of my infant life I received a lesson of patience, of charity, and of self-control, I was so guided by a silken cord that all seemed but one train of enjoyment to me. For a long time I was their only care. My mother had much desired to have a daughter, but I continued their single offspring. When I was about five years old, while making an excursion beyond the frontiers of Italy, they passed a week on the shores of the Lake of Como. Their benevolent disposition often made them enter the cottages of the poor. **This, to my mother, was more than a duty; it was a necessity, a passion—remembering what she had suffered, and how she had been relieved—for her to act in her turn the guardian angel to the afflicted.** *[More moral behavior—Frankenstein's mother is a saint!]* During one of their walks a poor cot in the foldings of a vale attracted their notice as being singularly disconsolate, while the number of half clothed children gathered about it spoke of penury in its worst shape. One day, when my father had gone by himself to Milan, my mother, accompanied by me, visited this abode. **She found a peasant and his wife, hard working, bent down by care and labour, distributing a scanty meal to five hungry babes. Among these there was one which attracted my mother far above all the rest.** She appeared of a different stock. The four others were dark-eyed, hardy little vagrants; this child was thin and very fair. Her hair was the brightest living gold, and despite the poverty of her clothing, seemed to set a crown of distinction on her head. Her brow was clear and ample, her blue eyes cloudless, and her lips and the moulding of her face so expressive of sensibility and sweetness that none could behold her without looking on her as of a distinct species, a being heaven-sent, and bearing a celestial stamp in all her features. The peasant woman, perceiving that my mother fixed eyes of wonder and admiration on this lovely girl, eagerly communicated her history. She was not her child, but the daughter of a Milanese nobleman. Her mother was a German and had died on giving her birth. The infant had been placed with these good people to nurse: they were better off then. They had not been long married, and their eldest child was but just born. The father of their charge was one of those Italians nursed in the memory of the antique glory of Italy—one among the schiavi ognor frementi, who exerted himself to obtain the liberty of his country. He became the victim of its weakness. Whether he had died or still lingered in the dungeons of Austria was not known. His property was confiscated; his child became an orphan and a beggar. She continued with her foster parents and bloomed in their rude abode, fairer than a garden rose among dark-leaved brambles. When my father returned from Milan, he found playing with me in the hall of our villa a child fairer than pictured cherub—a creature who seemed to shed radiance from her looks and whose form and motions were lighter than the chamois of the hills. The apparition was soon explained. With his permission my mother prevailed on her rustic guardians to yield their charge to her. They were fond of the sweet orphan. Her presence had seemed a blessing to them, but it would be unfair to her to keep her in poverty and want when Providence afforded her such powerful protection. They consulted their village priest, and the result was that Elizabeth Lavenza became the inmate of my parents' house—**my more than sister—the beautiful and adored companion of all my occupations and my pleasures.** *[Not only does Frankenstein's mother devote herself to her own child, she even adopts a poor, unfortunate child.]*

Everyone loved Elizabeth. The passionate and almost reverential attachment with which all regarded her became, while I shared it, my pride and my delight. On the evening previous to her being brought to my home, my mother had said playfully, "I have a pretty present for my Victor—tomorrow he shall have it." And when, on the morrow, she presented Elizabeth to me as her promised gift, I, with childish seriousness, interpreted her words literally and looked upon Elizabeth as mine—mine to protect, love, and cherish. All praises bestowed on her I received as made to a possession of my own. We called each other familiarly by the name of cousin. No word, no expression could body forth the kind of relation in which she stood to me—my more than sister, since till death she was to be mine only. *[What foreshadowing! Victor has unexpectedly been given a lifelong gift of a human life to love and treasure.]*

• ANALYZING THE SCENE •
CHAPTER 1 – SCENE 7

A Story Event is an active change of universal human value for one or more characters as a result of conflict (one character's desires clash with another's or an environmental shift changes the universal human value).

A Working Scene contains at least one Story Event. To determine a scene's Story Event, answer these four questions:

1. What are the characters literally doing—that is, what are their micro on-the-ground actions?

Victor Frankenstein is describing his family and childhood with broad brushstrokes. His father was a public servant who late in life married the daughter of a close friend who had fallen upon hard times.

2. What is the essential tactic of the characters—that is, what macro behaviors are they employing that are linked to a universal human value?

Victor's parents are always involved in kind, generous gestures; they are moral people, and they reap the reward of being moral with their happy marriage and blissful family life.

3. What universal human values have changed for one or more characters in the scene? Which one of those value changes is most important and should be included in the Story Grid Spreadsheet?

Two people experience a change in this scene. Victor's father rescues his dear friend's daughter from poverty and marries her; his mother rescues Elizabeth from poverty and adopts her. A small corollary to this is an increase in joy and happiness in Victor's life. He is the beloved only child of two loving parents, who then adopt Elizabeth and "give" him a treasured companion and playmate.

The best values to track here are those of Victor's mother and Victor's "cousin" Elizabeth, who were both rescued from poverty.

Poor to Wealthy

4. What is the Story Event that sums up the scene's on-the-ground actions, essential tactics, and value change? We will enter that event in the Story Grid Spreadsheet.

Victor Frankenstein describes his start in life; his father marries his friend's poverty-stricken daughter, his mother adopts a baby girl who has been abandoned, and that baby is raised with Victor as his future bride.

HOW THE SCENE ABIDES BY THE FIVE COMMANDMENTS OF STORYTELLING

Inciting Incident: Victor's father rescues Caroline from a tragic situation and marries her.

Turning Point Progressive Complication: Caroline discovers Elizabeth, an orphan.

Crisis: She has always wanted a daughter; Elizabeth is being cared for by a poor foster family. Should she adopt Elizabeth? Irreconcilable goods.

Climax: She adopts Elizabeth.

Resolution: Elizabeth becomes a member of the household and Victor's companion. Victor's mother presents Elizabeth as his "possession."

NOTES

- This chapter is a quick summary of Victor's sunny early

childhood and an explanation of how Elizabeth Lavenza came to live in his home.

- At first glance, the chapter doesn't seem to "move" very much. There are trite, almost melodramatic details (the story of Victor's father's friend Beaufort, the love story between Victor's parents, the degree to which they doted on him). Everyone seems much too happy! But as we know, a "happy" chapter only exists in order to set up the stressful chapters that are sure to follow! These are wonderful, loving people, in a wonderful, loving family. If you need to show something really horrible, remember to create some contrast. Horrible isn't truly horrible until you've been yanked out of the truly wonderful first.
- Note the preoccupation with "honor and reputation," and consider the core emotion of the genre (fear), as well as what we know about the story thus far. First of all, we may have a tendency to associate fear with something that threatens us in a bodily way, but loss of "honor and reputation" may well also cause fear. Then, consider the manner in which Shelley portrays the ideal relationships described in this chapter. We start with the stranger's father, a man of integrity, deeply respected, and in a visible, public occupation. The stranger describes his father's friend in a manner that suggests that while his father wanted to extend every assistance possible during a time of trial, he also judged him harshly for his "proud and unbending disposition." There is a strong sense of "he got what he deserved" suggested in the telling of this Morality story.
- Note that the friend was living in hiding, incapable of action, and eventually became ill. This set of dire circumstances will come up again later in the book; Shelley sets up "hiding" as the course of action one must take after serious moral lapses in judgment.
- The stranger's father ends up marrying his friend's poverty-stricken daughter. This is rather like a cautionary fairy tale. Everyone is making moral choices that seemingly have little

to do with personal happiness—the stranger's father tries to help his friend, and the daughter tries to help her father—but the eventual result of these moral choices is the conjugal happiness of the married couple. Remember this lesson because it appears repeatedly throughout the novel—if you do right according to the higher law, you will reap the rewards.

- "There was a sense of justice in my father's upright mind which rendered it necessary that he should approve highly to love strongly. Perhaps during former years he had suffered from the late-discovered unworthiness of one beloved and so was disposed to set a greater value on tried worth." So the stranger explains to Walton that in his father's universe, love didn't happen unless you had somehow earned it. How terrifying! In the case of his mother, her virtue made it possible for her to be loved.
- When their son is born, they view him as an "innocent and helpless creature bestowed on them by heaven," and a being to whom they owed a duty as parents. So apparently, children are exempt from the requirement that love be "earned." The couple adopts a second child, Elizabeth, the daughter of a Milanese nobleman who is being fostered by a peasant family after political tragedy strikes her noble family. Again, Elizabeth is characterized as an innocent child in a tragic circumstance; therefore she is not under obligation to "earn" love.
- Elizabeth is characterized as a "gift" for the stranger, whom we now know is called Victor. He tells Walton he viewed Elizabeth as "mine to protect, love, and cherish."
- This scene, which begins with Victor's father lamenting the moral and practical failings of his beloved friend, ends with the rescue of Elizabeth from a life of poverty. Thus, the scene has emotional movement, from distress to triumph. It doesn't feel quite as active as a modern scene, perhaps, because these emotions are spread out over several characters. However, this is exactly what is instructive about

this part of the tale. The sad tale of Beaufort is the result of moral failure ("false pride"), and all of the subsequent happiness described by Victor to Walton is the result of correct behavior and correct choices. Shelley has a preoccupation with choices, morality, and whether consequences are deserved or undeserved.

CHAPTER 2 – SCENE 8

We were brought up together; there was not quite a year difference in our ages. I need not say that we were strangers to any species of disunion or dispute. Harmony was the soul of our companionship, and the diversity and contrast that subsisted in our characters drew us nearer together. Elizabeth was of a calmer and more concentrated disposition; but, **with all my ardour, I was capable of a more intense application and was more deeply smitten with the thirst for knowledge.** She busied herself with following the aerial creations of the poets; and in the majestic and wondrous scenes which surrounded our Swiss home—the sublime shapes of the mountains, the changes of the seasons, tempest and calm, the silence of winter, and the life and turbulence of our Alpine summers—she found ample scope for admiration and delight. While my companion contemplated with a serious and satisfied spirit the magnificent appearances of things, I delighted in investigating their causes. **The world was to me a secret which I desired to divine.** Curiosity, earnest research to learn the hidden laws of nature, gladness akin to rapture, as they were unfolded to me, are among the earliest sensations I can remember.

On the birth of a second son, my junior by seven years, my parents gave up entirely their wandering life and fixed themselves in their native country. We possessed a house in Geneva, and a campagne on

Belrive, the eastern shore of the lake, at the distance of rather more than a league from the city. We resided principally in the latter, and the lives of my parents were passed in considerable seclusion. It was my temper to avoid a crowd and to attach myself fervently to a few. I was indifferent, therefore, to my school-fellows in general; but **I united myself in the bonds of the closest friendship to one among them. Henry Clerval** was the son of a merchant of Geneva. He was a boy of singular talent and fancy. He loved enterprise, hardship, and even danger for its own sake. He was deeply read in books of chivalry and romance. He composed heroic songs and began to write many a tale of enchantment and knightly adventure. He tried to make us act plays and to enter into masquerades, in which the characters were drawn from the heroes of Roncesvalles, of the Round Table of King Arthur, and the chivalrous train who shed their blood to redeem the holy sepulchre from the hands of the infidels.

No human being could have passed a happier childhood than myself. My parents were possessed by the very spirit of kindness and indulgence. We felt that they were not the tyrants to rule our lot according to their caprice, but the agents and creators of all the many delights which we enjoyed. When I mingled with other families I distinctly discerned how peculiarly fortunate my lot was, and gratitude assisted the development of filial love.

My temper was sometimes violent, and my passions vehement; but by some law in my temperature they were turned not towards childish pursuits but to an eager desire to learn, and not to learn all things indiscriminately. I confess that neither the structure of languages, nor the code of governments, nor the politics of various states possessed attractions for me. **It was the secrets of heaven and earth that I desired to learn**; and whether it was the outward substance of things or the inner spirit of nature and the mysterious soul of man that occupied me, still my inquiries were directed to the metaphysical, or in its highest sense, the physical secrets of the world.

Meanwhile Clerval occupied himself, so to speak, with the moral relations of things. The busy stage of life, the virtues of heroes, and the actions of men were his theme; and his hope and his dream was to become one among those whose names are recorded in story as the gallant and adventurous benefactors of our species. **The saintly soul of Elizabeth shone like a shrine-dedicated lamp in our peaceful home.** Her sympathy was ours; her smile, her soft voice, the sweet glance of her celestial eyes, were ever there to bless and animate us. **She was the living spirit of love to soften and attract**; I might have become sullen in my study, rough through the ardour of my nature, but that she was there to subdue me to a semblance of her own gentleness. And Clerval —could aught ill entrench on the noble spirit of Clerval? Yet he might not have been so perfectly humane, so thoughtful in his generosity, so full of kindness and tenderness amidst his passion for adventurous exploit, had she not unfolded to him the real loveliness of beneficence and made the doing good the end and aim of his soaring ambition. *[Clerval and Elizabeth are the gentle influences on Frankenstein's obsessive temperament.]*

I feel exquisite pleasure in dwelling on the recollections of childhood, before misfortune had tainted my mind and changed its bright visions of extensive usefulness into gloomy and narrow reflections upon self. Besides, in drawing the picture of my early days, I also record those events which led, by insensible steps, to my after tale of misery, for when I would account to myself for the birth of that passion which afterwards ruled my destiny I find it arise, like a mountain river, from ignoble and almost forgotten sources; but, swelling as it proceeded, it became the torrent which, in its course, has swept away all my hopes and joys. **Natural philosophy is the genius that has regulated my fate**; I desire, therefore, in this narration, to state those facts which led to my predilection for that science. When I was thirteen years of age we all went on a party of pleasure to the baths near Thonon; the inclemency of the weather obliged us to remain a day confined to the inn. In this house I chanced to find a volume of the works of Cornelius Agrippa. I opened it with apathy; the theory which he attempts to demonstrate and the wonderful facts which he relates soon changed this feeling into enthusiasm. A new light seemed to dawn upon my mind, and bounding with joy, I communicated my discovery to my father. **My father looked carelessly at the title page of my book and said, "Ah! Cornelius Agrippa! My dear Victor, do not waste your time upon this; it is sad trash."**

If, instead of this remark, my father had taken the pains to explain to me that the principles of Agrippa had been entirely exploded and that a modern system of science had been introduced which possessed much greater powers than the ancient, because the powers of the latter were chimerical, while those of the former were real and practical, under such circumstances I should certainly have thrown Agrippa aside and have contented my imagination, warmed as it was, by returning with greater ardour to my former studies. It is even possible that the train of my ideas would never have received the fatal impulse that led to my ruin. But the cursory glance my father had taken of my volume by no means assured me that he was acquainted with its contents, and I continued to read with the greatest avidity. When I returned home my first care was to procure the whole works of this author, and afterwards of Paracelsus and Albertus Magnus. I read and studied the wild fancies of these writers with delight; they appeared to me treasures known to few besides myself. I have described myself as always having been imbued with a fervent longing to penetrate the secrets of nature. In spite of the intense labour and wonderful discoveries of modern philosophers, I always came from my studies discontented and unsatisfied. **Sir Isaac Newton** is said to have avowed that he felt like a child picking up shells beside the great and unexplored ocean of truth. Those of his successors in each branch of natural philosophy with whom I was acquainted appeared even to my boy's apprehensions as tyros engaged in the same pursuit.

The **untaught peasant** beheld the elements around him and was acquainted with their practical uses. The **most learned philosopher** knew little more. He had partially unveiled the face of Nature, but her immortal lineaments were still a wonder and a mystery. He might dissect, anatomize, and give names; but, not to speak of a final cause, causes in their secondary and tertiary grades were utterly unknown to him. **I had gazed upon the fortifications and impediments that seemed to keep human beings from entering the citadel of nature, and rashly and ignorantly I had repined.**

But here were books, and here were men who had penetrated deeper and knew more. I took their word for all that they averred, and I became their disciple. It may appear strange that such should arise in the eighteenth century; but while I followed the routine of education in the schools of Geneva, **I was, to a great degree, self-taught with regard to my favourite studies.** My father was not scientific, and I was left to struggle with a child's blindness, added to a student's thirst for knowledge. *[Here Frankenstein blames his taste for discredited magical ideas on being self-taught.]* **Under the guidance of my new preceptors I entered with the greatest diligence into the search of the philosopher's stone and the elixir of life; but the latter soon obtained my undivided attention.** Wealth was an inferior object, but what glory would attend the discovery if I could banish disease from the human frame and render man invulnerable to any but a violent death! *[Arrogance is at work—he wants "glory."]* Nor were these my only visions. **The raising of ghosts or devils was a promise liberally accorded by my favourite authors, the fulfilment of which I most eagerly sought; and if my incantations were always unsuccessful, I attributed the failure rather to my own inexperience and mistake than to a want of skill or fidelity in my instructors.** *[Frankenstein assumes that his spells don't work because he isn't doing them right.]* And thus for a time I was occupied by exploded systems, mingling, like an unadept, a thousand contradictory theories and floundering desperately in a very slough of multifarious knowledge, guided by an ardent imagination and childish reasoning, till an accident again changed the current of my ideas. When I was about fifteen years old we had retired to our house near Belrive, when **we witnessed a most violent and terrible thunderstorm.** It advanced from behind the mountains of Jura, and the thunder burst at once with frightful loudness from various quarters of the heavens. I remained, while the storm lasted, watching its progress with curiosity and delight. As I stood at the door, on a sudden I **beheld a stream of fire issue from an old and beautiful oak** which stood about twenty yards from our house; and so soon as the dazzling light vanished, the oak had disappeared, and nothing remained but a blasted stump. When we visited it the next morning, we found the tree shattered in a singular manner. It was not splintered by the shock, but entirely reduced to thin ribbons of wood. I never beheld anything so utterly destroyed.

Before this I was not unacquainted with the more obvious laws of electricity. **On this occasion a man of great research in natural philosophy was with us, and excited by this catastrophe, he entered on the explanation of a theory which he had formed on the subject of electricity and galvanism, which was at once new and astonishing to me.** All that he said threw greatly into the shade Cornelius Agrippa, Albertus Magnus, and Paracelsus, the lords of my imagination; but **by some fatality the overthrow of these men disinclined me to pursue my accustomed studies. It seemed to me as if nothing would or could ever be known.** All that had so long engaged my attention suddenly grew despicable. By one of those caprices of the mind which we are perhaps most subject to in early youth, I at once gave up my former occupations, set down natural history and all its progeny as a deformed and abortive creation, and entertained the greatest disdain for a would-be science which could never even step within the threshold of real knowledge. In this mood of mind I betook myself to the mathematics and the branches of study appertaining to that science as being built upon secure foundations, and so worthy of my consideration. *[He decides he only trusts math; he doesn't trust scientists anymore because he sees that their efforts can fail.]*

Thus strangely are our souls constructed, and by such slight ligaments are we bound to prosperity or ruin. When I look back, it seems to me as if **this almost miraculous change of inclination and will was the immediate suggestion of the guardian angel of my life—the last effort made by the spirit of preservation to avert the storm that was even then hanging in the stars and ready to envelop me. Her victory was announced by an unusual tranquillity and gladness of soul which followed the relinquishing of my ancient and latterly tormenting studies. It was thus that I was to be taught to associate evil with their prosecution, happiness with their disregard.**

It was a strong effort of the spirit of good, but it was ineffectual. **Destiny was too potent, and her immutable laws had decreed my utter and terrible destruction.**

CHAPTER 2 – SCENE 8

A Story Event is an active change of universal human value for one or more characters as a result of conflict (one character's desires clash with another's or an environmental shift changes the universal human value).

A Working Scene contains at least one Story Event. To determine a scene's Story Event, answer these four questions:

1. What are the characters literally doing—that is, what are their micro on-the-ground actions?

Victor Frankenstein is describing his happy childhood and the studies that absorbed him.

2. What is the essential tactic of the characters—that is, what macro behaviors are they employing that are linked to a universal human value?

Frankenstein is a boy of quick temper and strong will ("My temper was sometimes violent and my passions vehement …") who wants to discover the "secrets of heaven and earth." His foster sister and best friend are inclined to prioritize kindness and morality. He undertakes a personal study of medieval philosophers in order to discover the elixir of life, among other natural secrets.

3. What universal human values have changed for one or more characters in the scene? Which one of those value changes is most important and should be included in the Story Grid Spreadsheet?

Frankenstein changes from agitated or excited to apathetic or uninterested. He describes his obsession with medieval thinkers and "natural philosophy" at the beginning of the scene and how he gave up these ideas in favor of mathematics and the more "secure" branches of study.

There are actually two Victor Frankensteins in this scene:

Frankenstein the narrator on Walton's ship, who knows the eventual outcome of the story, and Frankenstein the youthful protagonist. Frankenstein the narrator ends the scene with a gloomy warning of tragedy to come. Let's track Excited to Apathetic because in terms of the global value of life to death, "excited" tracks with "life." He starts out with enthusiasm and eventually sinks into apathy, a type of mental numbing.

Excited to Apathetic

4. What is the Story Event that sums up the scene's on-the-ground actions, essential tactics, and value change? We will enter that event in the Story Grid Spreadsheet.

Frankenstein discovers medieval natural philosophers as a teenager, but when he learns about electricity and "real" science, he abandons the medieval texts.

HOW THE SCENE ABIDES BY THE FIVE COMMANDMENTS OF STORYTELLING

Inciting Incident: Young Frankenstein, of violent temper and with an eager desire to learn "the secrets of heaven and earth," discovers the writings of Cornelius Agrippa.

Turning Point Progressive Complication: Frankenstein observes the destruction of an old oak tree during a lightning storm; a learned man who is with him explains a theory of "electricity and galvanism," which was "new and astonishing" to Frankenstein.

Crisis: Should he continue with his former obsession even though he has now been introduced to "real" science? Best bad choice.

Climax: Frankenstein abandons the teachings of Agrippa, Magnus, and Paracelsus because, "It seemed to me as if nothing would or could ever be known."

Resolution: Frankenstein settles on the study of mathematics and its related disciplines, "built upon secure foundations."

NOTES

- Frankenstein is a storm in the middle of a calm oasis. He is intense, possesses a violent temper, and wants to divine the "secrets of heaven and earth." Meanwhile, his dearest friends are his foster sister Elizabeth and his schoolmate Henry Clerval, both of whom are counterweights to Frankenstein's fiery nature.
- Clerval and Elizabeth are set up as opposites to Frankenstein. Elizabeth is sweet and calm, which makes her his opposite in temperament. Frankenstein yearns to know things while Elizabeth is content to admire. Clerval at first seems more similar in nature to Frankenstein because he is active and busy, but he chooses to focus on "moral relations." He loves tales of chivalry and aspires to charge out into the world and do good while Frankenstein is uninterested in issues having to do with the affairs of men.
- In this context Frankenstein explains his obsession with "natural philosophy" and the writings of medieval thinkers who wrote about magic and the supernatural. His father tells him not to bother with "sad trash," but still Frankenstein persists.
- Frankenstein spends two years, between the ages of thirteen and fifteen, studying this "sad trash" on his own, outside of school. This theme of ignorance, of not being "learned," is echoed with Walton, who feels also that he was self-taught and therefore is not a truly learned man. Frankenstein says he had been frustrated with the contemporary studies in science ("natural philosophy") because he could not find the answers he wanted using those tools. When he found Agrippa, and later Paracelsus and Magnus, he was thrilled because these authors seemed to have found answers that were missing in his studies. It's interesting that Frankenstein

felt traditional study was somehow "preventing" him from acquiring true knowledge ("I had gazed upon the fortifications and impediments that seemed to keep human beings from entering the citadel of nature ...").

- The result of Frankenstein's obsession was an excursion into the world of searching for the "philosopher's stone" and the "elixir of life." What's more, Frankenstein attempted to raise "ghosts and devils," and he attributed his lack of success to his own ineptitude. Taking account of the period in which this was written, it's fascinating that this is all explained in such a casual manner. At this time in European history (when Shelley wrote Frankenstein, in the early 1800s) it should have been at least mildly awkward to talk about raising "ghosts and devils" as a scientific goal! Frankenstein blames his "ardent imagination and childish reasoning" as well as being self-taught in these subjects.
- However, the turning point of this scene occurs when Frankenstein observes the power of a lightning storm and listens to a lecture on electricity delivered by a companion who watches with him as lightning strikes and destroys a tree. Frankenstein suddenly realizes that his idols and their theories don't hold up compared to the modern hypotheses put forth by his companion. He is disgusted, feeling that his previous pursuits were impossible, and immediately gives up on his search for truth, turning to the study of mathematics as a tonic.
- This scene has an interesting "scene-within-a-scene" quality, with the older, wiser Frankenstein explaining the events of his youth to Walton. The action itself is embedded within the events that Frankenstein is relating to Walton, but Frankenstein also comments that he views this sequence of events as an attempt by "the guardian angel of my life" to stop him from going down a path that would lead to tragedy. So from his point of view, there was actually another protagonist at work—his guardian angel—fighting against a stronger force, whom he characterizes as "Destiny." This is a

wonderful heads up from the genius pen of Shelley, putting you, the reader, on notice that while you may think you are reading a boring story about a spoiled rich kid and his ego, these events are mere symptoms of a bigger cosmic battle, one which you will not win.

CHAPTER 3 – SCENE 9

When I had attained the age of seventeen my parents resolved that I should become a student at the university of Ingolstadt. I had hitherto attended the schools of Geneva, but my father thought it necessary for the completion of my education that I should be made acquainted with other customs than those of my native country. My departure was therefore fixed at an early date, but before the day resolved upon could arrive, **the first misfortune of my life occurred—an omen, as it were, of my future misery.** Elizabeth had caught the scarlet fever; her illness was severe, and she was in the greatest danger. During her illness many arguments had been urged to persuade my mother to refrain from attending upon her. She had at first yielded to our entreaties, but when she heard that the life of her favourite was menaced, she could no longer control her anxiety. She attended her sickbed; her watchful attentions triumphed over the malignity of the distemper—Elizabeth was saved, but the consequences of this imprudence were fatal to her preserver. *[A mother's love! What could be more morally correct?]* On the third day my mother sickened; her fever was accompanied by the most alarming symptoms, and the looks of her medical attendants prognosticated the worst event. On her deathbed the fortitude and benignity of this best of women did not desert her. She joined the hands of Elizabeth and myself. "My children," she said, "**my firmest**

hopes of future happiness were placed on the prospect of your union. This expectation will now be the consolation of your father. Elizabeth, my love, you must supply my place to my younger children. Alas! I regret that I am taken from you; and, happy and beloved as I have been, is it not hard to quit you all? But these are not thoughts befitting me; I will endeavour to resign myself cheerfully to death and will indulge a hope of meeting you in another world."

She died calmly, and her countenance expressed affection even in death. I need not describe the feelings of those whose dearest ties are rent by that most irreparable evil, the void that presents itself to the soul, and the despair that is exhibited on the countenance. It is so long before the mind can persuade itself that she whom we saw every day and whose very existence appeared a part of our own can have departed forever—that the brightness of a beloved eye can have been extinguished and the sound of a voice so familiar and dear to the ear can be hushed, never more to be heard. These are the reflections of the first days; but when the lapse of time proves the reality of the evil, then the actual bitterness of grief commences. Yet from whom has not that rude hand rent away some dear connection? And why should I describe a sorrow which all have felt, and must feel? The time at length arrives when grief is rather an indulgence than a necessity; and the smile that plays upon the lips, although it may be deemed a sacrilege, is not banished. My mother was dead, but we had still duties which we ought to perform; we must continue our course with the rest and learn to think ourselves fortunate whilst one remains whom the spoiler has not seized.

My departure for Ingolstadt, which had been deferred by these events, was now again determined upon. I obtained from my father a respite of some weeks. It appeared to me sacrilege so soon to leave the repose, akin to death, of the house of mourning and to rush into the thick of life. I was new to sorrow, but it did not the less alarm me. I was unwilling to quit the sight of those that remained to me, and above all, I desired to see my sweet Elizabeth in some degree consoled.

She indeed veiled her grief and strove to act the comforter to us all. She looked steadily on life and assumed its duties with courage and zeal. She devoted herself to those whom she had been taught to call her uncle and cousins. Never was she so enchanting as at this time, when she recalled the sunshine of her smiles and spent them upon us. She forgot even her own regret in her endeavours to make us forget.

The day of my departure at length arrived. Clerval spent the last evening with us. **He had endeavoured to persuade his father to permit him to accompany me and to become my fellow student, but in vain. His father was a narrow-minded trader and saw idleness and ruin in the aspirations and ambition of his son.** Henry deeply felt the misfortune of being debarred from a liberal education. He said little, but when he spoke **I read in his kindling eye and in his animated glance a restrained but firm resolve not to be chained to the miserable details of commerce.**

We sat late. We could not tear ourselves away from each other nor persuade ourselves to say the word "Farewell!" It was said, and we retired under the pretence of seeking repose, each fancying that the other was deceived; but when at morning's dawn I descended to the carriage which was to convey me away, they were all there—my father again to bless me, Clerval to press my hand once more, my Elizabeth to renew her entreaties that I would write often and to bestow the last feminine attentions on her playmate and friend.

I threw myself into the chaise that was to convey me away and indulged in the most melancholy reflections. **I, who had ever been surrounded by amiable companions, continually engaged in endeavouring to bestow mutual pleasure—I was now alone.** In the university whither I was going I must form my own friends and be my own protector. **My life had hitherto been remarkably secluded and domestic, and this had given me invincible repugnance to new countenances.** I loved my brothers, Elizabeth, and Clerval; these were "old familiar faces," but **I believed myself totally unfitted for the company of strangers.** Such were my reflections as I commenced my journey; but as I proceeded, my spirits and hopes rose. I ardently desired the acquisition of knowledge. I had often, when at home, thought it hard to remain during my youth cooped up in one place and had longed to enter the world and take my station among other human beings. Now my desires were complied with, and it would, indeed, have been folly to repent.

• ANALYZING THE SCENE •
CHAPTER 3 – SCENE 9

A Story Event is an active change of universal human value for one or more characters as a result of conflict (one character's desires clash with another's or an environmental shift changes the universal human value).

A Working Scene contains at least one Story Event. To determine a scene's Story Event, answer these four questions:

1. What are the characters literally doing—that is, what are their micro on-the-ground actions?

Victor Frankenstein and his family are together, mourning the death of his mother from scarlet fever.

2. What is the essential tactic of the characters—that is, what macro behaviors are they employing that are linked to a universal human value?

Frankenstein is leaving his home and his family to go to university to pursue knowledge, but he is also symbolically embarking on a new life where he must rely on himself and not on the comfort of his family.

3. What universal human values have changed for one or more characters in the scene? Which one of those value changes is most important and should be included in the Story Grid Spreadsheet?

Frankenstein's value changes from With Loved Ones to Alone.

In a Horror story, the global value at stake is Damnation to Death to Life. There is certainly death in this scene, where Frankenstein's beloved mother contracts scarlet fever and dies, but the essential nature of the scene is somewhat more metaphorical. Victor begins the scene in the bosom of his family and ends the scene reluctantly taking his leave in order to go to university after the death of the most important moral example in his family. We will highlight Victor's emotional journey, as he ends the scene driving away from his loved ones.

With Loved Ones to Alone

4. What is the Story Event that sums up the scene's on-the-ground actions, essential tactics, and value change? We will enter that event in the Story Grid Spreadsheet.

Victor's mother dies of scarlet fever, and he delays his departure for university.

HOW THE SCENE ABIDES BY THE FIVE COMMANDMENTS OF STORYTELLING

Inciting Incident: Frankenstein's beloved mother insists on nursing his foster sister Elizabeth during a bout of scarlet fever, just as he is about to leave for university for the first time.

Turning Point Progressive Complication: Frankenstein's mother dies.

Crisis: Bereft, Frankenstein delays his departure for university; his mother has made clear her wish that he and Elizabeth marry, and his best friend Clerval is not allowed to go with him to university. If he leaves, he will be alone. The best bad choice is to be alone or not?

Climax: Frankenstein ultimately decides that he desires knowledge more than anything else. He forces himself to leave.

Resolution: The more distance he puts between himself and his family, the happier he becomes. He has always wanted to "enter the world."

NOTES

- Once again, Shelley uses morality as the measuring stick

against which all of her characters will be assessed. Frankenstein's mother sacrifices herself in order to nurse her beloved adopted daughter Elizabeth and dies from scarlet fever. When she tells Frankenstein that he and Elizabeth must marry in order to make his father happy, it's difficult to imagine any other path for them. They can't possibly refuse.

- Frankenstein's mother is at the top of a "moral hierarchy" in their family. She was the original self-sacrificing daughter for her father's sins, rescued by Frankenstein's father. She in turn rescued Elizabeth from poverty and an uncertain future, and now she has rescued Elizabeth from illness and death. On her death bed she instructs Elizabeth to replace her. This is a powerful way in which to have a character give the ultimate sacrifice but continue to live on after death. If Frankenstein does not end up marrying Elizabeth or if he somehow harms her, the reader will not forgive him!
- Shelley opens this chapter with an announcement that Victor must go to university in Ingolstadt (today's Germany; Victor lives in Geneva) because his parents want him to be more broadly educated. We already know that Victor is introverted and doesn't have many friends, so university will be an uncomfortable change in his life. Right after this announcement, Elizabeth is taken ill and nearly dies, and then his mother dies. Victor experiences, possibly for the first time in his life, the sense of being left alone. He then has to leave his family and journey—alone—to university in another country.
- His best friend, Clerval, who has come to stay with them during this difficult time, cannot persuade his father to let him go with Victor. Shelley returns to a theme that pops up in the novel from time to time, the idea that a "liberal education" is somehow a debauched and idle occupation from the point of view of the ordinary citizen, but then she refers to Clerval's father as "a narrow-minded trader" and his occupation as "the miserable details of commerce." This is an interesting, if curious, theme. Frankenstein's father was

a diplomat and statesman; Clerval comes from a merchant family. Neither Frankenstein nor Walton consider themselves to be well-educated. What does it mean to be educated?

- At the end of the scene, as the chaise pulls away, Frankenstein reflects on his "invincible repugnance to new countenances." Basically, he only likes his family members and Clerval, and no one else. Why did Shelley create a character who is such a loner and so very anti-social? Was she trying to suggest that there was something not normal about him, or perhaps he was merely tragic? He is surrounded by people who love him, yet he seems to have no interest in extending his relationships outside of his family. He doesn't seem inclined to share his affection or knowledge. He just doesn't sound like a very good person, yet he is obsessed with moral goodness, which he sees reflected in the people around him. Are we presented with a deliberately distorted view of Victor Frankenstein because he is the one narrating the story, many years later?

CHAPTER 3 – SCENE 10

I had sufficient leisure for these and many other reflections during my journey to Ingolstadt, which was long and fatiguing. At length the high white steeple of the town met my eyes. I alighted and was conducted to my solitary apartment to spend the evening as I pleased.

The next morning I delivered my letters of introduction and paid a visit to some of the principal professors. **Chance—or rather the evil influence, the Angel of Destruction, which asserted omnipotent sway over me from the moment I turned my reluctant steps from my father's door—led me first to M. Krempe, professor of natural philosophy.** He was an uncouth man, but deeply imbued in the secrets of his science. He asked me several questions concerning my progress in the different branches of science appertaining to natural philosophy. **I replied carelessly, and partly in contempt, mentioned the names of my alchemists as the principal authors I had studied.** *[Frankenstein seems to know the reaction he will get and doesn't care—more arrogance.]* **The professor stared. "Have you," he said, "really spent your time in studying such nonsense?"**

I replied in the affirmative. "Every minute," continued M. Krempe with warmth, "every instant that you have wasted on those books is utterly and entirely lost. You have burdened your memory with exploded systems and useless names. Good God! In what desert land have you lived, where no one was kind enough to inform you that these fancies which you have so greedily imbibed are a thousand years old and as musty as they are ancient? I little expected, in this enlightened and scientific age, to find a disciple of Albertus Magnus and Paracelsus. My dear sir, you must begin your studies entirely anew."

So saying, he stepped aside and wrote down a list of several books treating of natural philosophy which he desired me to procure, and dismissed me after mentioning that in the beginning of the following week he intended to commence a course of lectures upon natural philosophy in its general relations, and that M. Waldman, a fellow professor, would lecture upon chemistry the alternate days that he omitted.

I returned home not disappointed, for I have said that I had long considered those authors useless whom the professor reprobated; but I returned not at all the more inclined to recur to these studies in any shape. M. Krempe was a little squat man with a gruff voice and a repulsive countenance; the teacher, therefore, did not prepossess me in favour of his pursuits. In rather a too philosophical and connected a strain, perhaps, I have given an account of the conclusions I had come to concerning them in my early years. As a child I had not been content with the results promised by the modern professors of natural science. With a confusion of ideas only to be accounted for by my extreme youth and my want of a guide on such matters, I had retrod the steps of knowledge along the paths of time and exchanged the discoveries of recent inquirers for the dreams of forgotten alchemists. Besides, I had a contempt for the uses of modern natural philosophy. It was very different when the masters of the science sought immortality and power; such views, although futile, were grand; but now the scene was changed. **The ambition of the inquirer seemed to limit itself to the annihilation of those visions on which my interest in science was chiefly founded. I was required to exchange chimeras of boundless grandeur for realities of little worth.** *[He isn't interested in science anymore because it isn't "grand" enough.]*

Such were my reflections during the first two or three days of my residence at Ingolstadt, which were chiefly spent in becoming acquainted with the localities and the principal residents in my new abode. But as the ensuing week commenced, I thought of the information which M. Krempe had given me concerning the lectures. And although I could not consent to go and hear that little conceited fellow deliver sentences out of a pulpit, I recollected what he had said of M. Waldman, whom I had never seen, as he had hitherto been out of town.

Partly from curiosity and partly from idleness, I went into the lecturing room, which M. Waldman entered shortly after. This professor was very unlike his colleague. He appeared about fifty years of age, but with an aspect expressive of the greatest benevolence; a few grey hairs covered his temples, but those at the back of his head were nearly black. His person was short but remarkably erect and his voice the sweetest I had ever heard. He began his lecture by a recapitulation of the history of chemistry and the various improvements made by different men of learning, pronouncing with fervour the names of the most distinguished discoverers. He then took a cursory view of the present state of the science and explained many of its elementary terms. After having made a few preparatory experiments, he concluded with a panegyric upon modern chemistry, the terms of which I shall never forget: "The ancient teachers of this science," said he, "promised impossibilities and performed nothing. The modern masters promise very little; they know that metals cannot be transmuted and that the elixir of life is a chimera but these philosophers, whose hands seem only made to dabble in dirt, and their eyes to pore over the microscope or crucible, have indeed performed miracles. **They penetrate into the recesses of nature and show how she works in her hiding-places.** They ascend into the heavens; they have discovered how the blood circulates, and the nature of the air we breathe. **They have acquired new and almost unlimited powers; they can command the thunders of heaven, mimic the earthquake, and even mock the invisible world with its own shadows."**

Such were the professor's words—rather let me say such the words of the fate—enounced to destroy me. As he went on I felt as if my soul were grappling with a palpable enemy; one by one the various keys were touched which formed the mechanism of my being; chord after chord was sounded, and soon my mind was filled

with one thought, one conception, one purpose. *[Another cinematic moment!]* So much has been done, exclaimed the soul of Frankenstein —more, far more, will I achieve; treading in the steps already marked, **I will pioneer a new way, explore unknown powers, and unfold to the world the deepest mysteries of creation.** *[Frankenstein's arrogance is back.]*

I closed not my eyes that night. My internal being was in a state of insurrection and turmoil; I felt that order would thence arise, but I had no power to produce it. By degrees, after the morning's dawn, sleep came. I awoke, and my yesternight's thoughts were as a dream. **There only remained a resolution to return to my ancient studies and to devote myself to a science for which I believed myself to possess a natural talent.** On the same day I paid M. Waldman a visit. His manners in private were even more mild and attractive than in public, for there was a certain dignity in his mien during his lecture which in his own house was replaced by the greatest affability and kindness. I gave him pretty nearly the same account of my former pursuits as I had given to his fellow professor. He heard with attention the little narration concerning my studies and smiled at the names of Cornelius Agrippa and Paracelsus, but without the contempt that M. Krempe had exhibited. He said that "These were men to whose indefatigable zeal modern philosophers were indebted for most of the foundations of their knowledge. They had left to us, as an easier task, to give new names and arrange in connected classifications the facts which they in a great degree had been the instruments of bringing to light. **The labours of men of genius, however erroneously directed, scarcely ever fail in ultimately turning to the solid advantage of mankind.**" I listened to his statement, which was delivered without any presumption or affectation, and then added that his lecture had removed my prejudices against modern chemists; I expressed myself in measured terms, with the modesty and deference due from a youth to his instructor, without letting escape (inexperience in life would have made me ashamed) any of the enthusiasm which stimulated my intended labours. I requested his advice concerning the books I ought to procure.

"I am happy," said M. Waldman, "to have gained a disciple; and if your application equals your ability, I have no doubt of your success. Chemistry is that branch of natural philosophy in which the greatest improvements have been and may be made; it is on that account that I have made it my peculiar study; but at the same time, I have not neglected the other branches of science. A man would make but a very sorry chemist if he attended to that department of human knowledge alone. If your wish is to become really a man of science and not merely a petty experimentalist, I should advise you to apply to every branch of natural philosophy, including mathematics." He then took me into his laboratory and explained to me the uses of his various machines, instructing me as to what I ought to procure and promising me the use of his own when I should have advanced far enough in the science not to derange their mechanism. He also gave me the list of books which I had requested, and I took my leave.

Thus ended a day memorable to me; it decided my future destiny.

• ANALYZING THE SCENE •
CHAPTER 3 – SCENE 10

A Story Event is an active change of universal human value for one or more characters as a result of conflict (one character's desires clash with another's or an environmental shift changes the universal human value).

A Working Scene contains at least one Story Event. To determine a scene's Story Event, answer these four questions:

1. What are the characters literally doing—that is, what are their micro on-the-ground actions?

Victor has arrived at university and has met the two principal science professors, Krempe and Waldman.

2. What is the essential tactic of the characters—that is, what macro

behaviors are they employing that are linked to a universal human value?

Frankenstein finds his purpose in life; or, as he looks back on this time with anguish and regret, his soul was "grappling with a palpable enemy."

3. What universal human values have changed for one or more characters in the scene? Which one of those value changes is most important and should be included in the Story Grid Spreadsheet?

The two Frankensteins (the narrator and the youthful protagonist) are particularly evident in this scene. The narrator characterizes the pivotal moment as a struggle with an internal enemy that wants to destroy him, whereas the younger man in the scene is thrilled and excited to discover his purpose in life. If we use the Frankenstein character who is living the scene in real time, the value starts with disinterested and ends at interested; if we want to be clearer, he is beyond interested, perhaps in the "obsessive" range.

Disinterested to Obsessively Interested

4. What is the Story Event that sums up the scene's on-the-ground actions, essential tactics, and value change? We will enter that event in the Story Grid Spreadsheet.

Victor arrives at university in Ingolstadt, and he is ridiculed by one science professor and taken under the wing of another; he discovers chemistry and becomes a disciple.

HOW THE SCENE ABIDES BY THE FIVE COMMANDMENTS OF STORYTELLING

Inciting Incident: Frankenstein arrives at university and visits Professor Krempe, who teaches natural philosophy (science).

Turning Point Progressive Complication: Frankenstein attends a lecture by Professor Waldman, a teacher of chemistry recommended by Krempe; he is staggered at the pronouncements of Waldman about the possibilities of modern science.

Crisis: Frankenstein, who had been bored and disgusted by Krempe's "repulsive countenance" and massive ego, had not expected to be enthralled by modern science. Should he go back to his old field of obsession? Best bad choice.

Climax: After Waldman's lecture, he resolves to return to his "ancient studies" as part of a determination to discover the mysteries of creation, even if it means putting up with Krempe.

Resolution: Frankenstein visits Waldman and asks to become his disciple.

NOTES

- This is an epic scene indeed! One can almost hear the Hans Zimmer (of *Batman* and *Pirates of the Caribbean* fame) soundtrack swelling in the background. Once again, Shelley is the master of dramatic tension. She begins the scene with a humiliating moment between Frankenstein and Professor Krempe, a science ("natural philosophy") professor. Recall that Frankenstein is already feeling low; his mother has died, his best friend isn't allowed to go to university with him, and his foster sister and fiancée is far away. Now he meets an arrogant professor who is making fun of his academic background. It's hard to imagine anything worse. He responds with his own arrogance and lack of respect.
- Frankenstein claims that he did not take the insult personally, as he had already abandoned those ancient philosophers, but he also wasn't very inclined to pursue the study of science with Kempe. He makes it clear that science as a method of analysis bored him: "The ambition of the inquirer seemed to limit itself to the annihilation of those

visions on which my interest in science was chiefly founded." He is only interested in what you can do with science, not with mere observation, and this is all that modern science seemed to be doing. But everything changes when he attends the lecture of the chemistry professor, Waldman. Shelley takes advantage of the most basic storytelling tool by making Krempe ugly and Waldman handsome, with "his voice the sweetest I had ever heard." If you want to make sure your point gets across, remember that Cinderella was beautiful and the stepsisters were ugly —it's a blunt instrument but it works.

- The moment for the epic soundtrack occurs in the middle of Waldman's lecture. Shelley writes: "As he went on I felt as if my soul were grappling with a palpable enemy; one by one the various keys were touched which formed the mechanism of my being; chord after chord was sounded, and soon my mind was filled with one thought, one conception, one purpose." It is as if some kind of evil spirit has filled the lecture room and made directly for Frankenstein; Shelley portrays this as a battle for his soul. He loses the battle: "soon my mind was filled with one thought, one conception, one purpose." This purpose, the search for the "deepest mysteries of creation," is posed as the source of evil in the novel. Waldman's lecture is actually Frankenstein's "Speech in Praise of the Monster" although Frankenstein himself is not the one speaking.
- One question here is whether Frankenstein is "possessed" by some kind of evil. If so, is he is culpable? Is he responsible for the tragic sequence of events that is about to transpire? Or was he the recipient of an unlucky fate? The day following Frankenstein's earth-shattering battle for his soul, he resolves to return to the studies he had abandoned and to "devote myself to a science for which I believed myself to possess a natural talent." Is this simple vanity? Or something worse?

CHAPTER 4 – SCENE 11

From this day natural philosophy, and particularly chemistry, in the most comprehensive sense of the term, became nearly my sole occupation. I read with ardour those works, so full of genius and discrimination, which modern inquirers have written on these subjects. I attended the lectures and cultivated the acquaintance of the men of science of the university, and I found even in M. Krempe a great deal of sound sense and real information, combined, it is true, with a repulsive physiognomy and manners, but not on that account the less valuable. In M. Waldman I found a true friend. His gentleness was never tinged by dogmatism, and his instructions were given with an air of frankness and good nature that banished every idea of pedantry. In a thousand ways he smoothed for me the path of knowledge and made the most abstruse inquiries clear and facile to my apprehension. My application was at first fluctuating and uncertain; it gained strength as I proceeded and soon became so ardent and eager that the stars often disappeared in the light of morning whilst I was yet engaged in my laboratory. *[Obsession]*

As I applied so closely, it may be easily conceived that my progress was rapid. My ardour was indeed the astonishment of the students, and my proficiency that of the masters. Professor Krempe often asked me, with a sly smile, how Cornelius Agrippa went on, whilst M. Waldman expressed the most heartfelt exultation in my progress. **Two years passed in this manner, during which I paid no visit to Geneva, but was engaged, heart and soul, in the pursuit of some discoveries which I hoped to make.** *[More obsession]* None but those who have experienced them can conceive of the enticements of science. In other studies you go as far as others have gone before you, and there is nothing more to know; but in a scientific pursuit there is continual food for discovery and wonder.

A mind of moderate capacity which closely pursues one study must infallibly arrive at great proficiency in that study; and I, who continually sought the attainment of one object of pursuit and was solely wrapped up in this, improved so rapidly that at the end of two years I made some discoveries in the improvement of some chemical instruments, which procured me great esteem and admiration at the university. When I had arrived at this point and had become as well acquainted with the theory and practice of natural philosophy as depended on the lessons of any of the professors at Ingolstadt, my residence there being no longer conducive to my improvements, **I thought of returning to my friends and my native town, when an incident happened that protracted my stay.**

One of the phenomena which had peculiarly attracted my attention was the structure of the human frame, and, indeed, any animal endued with life. **Whence, I often asked myself, did the principle of life proceed?** It was a bold question, and one which has ever been considered as a mystery; yet with how many things are we upon the brink of becoming acquainted, if cowardice or carelessness did not restrain our inquiries. I revolved these circumstances in my mind and determined thenceforth to apply myself more particularly to those branches of natural philosophy which relate to physiology. **Unless I had been animated by an almost supernatural enthusiasm, my application to this study would have been irksome and almost intolerable.** To examine the causes of life, we must first have recourse to death. I became acquainted with the science of anatomy, but this was not sufficient; I must also observe the natural decay and corruption of the human body.

In my education my father had taken the greatest precautions

that my mind should be impressed with no supernatural horrors. I do not ever remember to have trembled at a tale of superstition or to have feared the apparition of a spirit. Darkness had no effect upon my fancy, and a churchyard was to me merely the receptacle of bodies deprived of life, which, from being the seat of beauty and strength, had become food for the worm. Now I was led to examine the cause and progress of this decay and forced to spend days and nights in vaults and charnel-houses. **My attention was fixed upon every object the most insupportable to the delicacy of the human feelings.** I saw how the fine form of man was degraded and wasted; I beheld the corruption of death succeed to the blooming cheek of life; I saw how the worm inherited the wonders of the eye and brain. I paused, examining and analysing all the minutiae of causation, as exemplified in the change from life to death, and death to life, until from the midst of this darkness a sudden light broke in upon me—a light so brilliant and wondrous, yet so simple, that while I became dizzy with the immensity of the prospect which it illustrated, I was surprised that among so many men of genius who had directed their inquiries towards the same science, that I alone should be reserved to discover so astonishing a secret. *[Obsession, arrogance, and vanity]*

Remember, I am not recording the vision of a madman. The sun does not more certainly shine in the heavens than that which I now affirm is true. Some miracle might have produced it, yet the stages of the discovery were distinct and probable. **After days and nights of incredible labour and fatigue, I succeeded in discovering the cause of generation and life; nay, more, I became myself capable of bestowing animation upon lifeless matter.**

The astonishment which I had at first experienced on this discovery soon gave place to delight and rapture. After so much time spent in painful labour, to arrive at once at the summit of my desires was the most gratifying consummation of my toils. But this discovery was so great and overwhelming that all the steps by which I had been progressively led to it were obliterated, and I beheld only the result. What had been the study and desire of the wisest men since the creation of the world was now within my grasp. Not that, like a magic scene, it all opened upon me at once: **the information I had obtained**

was of a nature rather to direct my endeavours so soon as I should point them towards the object of my search than to exhibit that object already accomplished. I was like the Arabian who had been buried with the dead and found a passage to life, aided only by one glimmering and seemingly ineffectual light.

I see by your eagerness and the wonder and hope which your eyes express, my friend, that you expect to be informed of the secret with which I am acquainted; that cannot be; listen patiently until the end of my story, and you will easily perceive why I am reserved upon that subject. I will not lead you on, unguarded and ardent as I then was, to your destruction and infallible misery. **Learn from me, if not by my precepts, at least by my example, how dangerous is the acquirement of knowledge and how much happier that man is who believes his native town to be the world, than he who aspires to become greater than his nature will allow.**

• ANALYZING THE SCENE •
CHAPTER 4 – SCENE 11

A Story Event is an active change of universal human value for one or more characters as a result of conflict (one character's desires clash with another's or an environmental shift changes the universal human value).

A Working Scene contains at least one Story Event. To determine a scene's Story Event, answer these four questions:

1. What are the characters literally doing—that is, what are their micro on-the-ground actions?

Victor throws himself into the study of chemistry; he then begins a study of anatomy and physiology by examining dead bodies.

2. What is the essential tactic of the characters—that is, what macro

behaviors are they employing that are linked to a universal human value?

Victor is acting out the manic demands of the spirit, which has now possessed him; for two years he does not return to Geneva or see his family but instead exhausts all the resources at hand and becomes proficient at chemistry before launching into a study of human anatomy that has him collecting bodies from graveyards and charnel houses.

3. What universal human values have changed for one or more characters in the scene? Which one of those value changes is most important and should be included in the Story Grid Spreadsheet?

Once more there are two Frankensteins in this scene. Young Victor journeys from gritty, driven focus (he doesn't see his family for two years) to ecstatic discovery and rapture. In sum, he journeys from "painful labor" to ecstasy. The older, wiser Victor who is telling the tale, has a different trajectory, taking his listener deeper into horror as he describes young Victor's obsession with chemistry. When that didn't please him, he studied anatomy and dead bodies. That particular value could be viewed as beginning with life and leading to death. The global value at stake is most closely mimicked by the emotional journey described by the older Victor.

Everyday Life to Death

4. What is the Story Event that sums up the scene's on-the-ground actions, essential tactics, and value change? We will enter that event in the Story Grid Spreadsheet.

Victor dives into a manic study of chemistry and human anatomy, and he succeeds at animating lifeless matter.

HOW THE SCENE ABIDES BY THE FIVE COMMANDMENTS OF STORYTELLING

Inciting Incident: Frankenstein applies himself obsessively to the study of chemistry.

Turning Point Progressive Complication: Frankenstein exhausts the university's resources in his scientific study and begins to research the origins of life.

Crisis: Frankenstein finds that he needs to study dead bodies in order to resolve his questions. Does he enter into this field of study even though it involves "every object the most insupportable to the delicacy of the human feelings?" Best bad choice.

Climax: Frankenstein plows ahead in his studies and succeeds in discovering the secret of animating lifeless matter.

Resolution: Frankenstein is in a state of "delight and rapture."

NOTES

- For such a critical scene, Shelley's narration here is not as dramatic as one might expect. However, it makes sense. An older, wiser, regretful Victor is telling Walton this story as a cautionary tale, so the last thing he would want is to describe the moment of discovery in a grand, hopeful way. Lesson to the writer: remember who the POV character is and ask yourself how that character would be telling the tale. In Horror, where it is important to bring the reader to his or her knees at some point, be careful how you distribute emotion in your text.
- In fact, this chapter is neither the climax of the beginning hook nor of the entire book. Chapter four of a seventy-five-thousand-word novel is clearly too early for a big reveal or a major emotional spike. When you are tempted to blow something out of the water, ask yourself where you are in the overall story arc. Does it make sense? Remember that if you do something shocking in chapter four, you'll have to

top that multiple times before reaching a climax that should be even more powerful if it is to sustain an entire book.

- Strangely, the dramatic tension in this passage is most sustained by the image of Victor as a grave robber, haunting the charnel houses and crypts for bodies, body parts, and other grotesque items that would help him to identify the change from life to death and death to life. He makes the point that this work would have been impossible if he had not been "animated by an almost supernatural enthusiasm." Thus once again, Victor asserts that something other-worldly (a demon? Satan?) is exercising control over him, and that he cannot imagine anyone doing the things he did without some nefarious source at work. Is this "supernatural enthusiasm" the real villain of the novel?

CHAPTER 4 – SCENE 12

When I found so astonishing a power placed within my hands, I hesitated a long time concerning the manner in which I should employ it. Although I possessed the capacity of bestowing animation, yet to prepare a frame for the reception of it, with all its intricacies of fibres, muscles, and veins, still remained a work of inconceivable difficulty and labour. I doubted at first whether I should attempt the creation of a being like myself, or one of simpler organization; but **my imagination was too much exalted by my first success to permit me to doubt of my ability to give life to an animal as complex and wonderful as man.** The materials at present within my command hardly appeared adequate to so arduous an undertaking, but I doubted not that I should ultimately succeed. I prepared myself for a multitude of reverses; my operations might be incessantly baffled, and at last my work be imperfect, yet when I considered the improvement which every day takes place in science and mechanics, I was encouraged to hope my present attempts would at least lay the foundations of future success. Nor could I consider the magnitude and complexity of my plan as any argument of its impracticability. It was with these feelings that I began the creation of a human being. **As the minuteness of the parts formed a great hindrance to my speed, I resolved, contrary to my first intention, to make the being of a gigantic stature, that is to say, about**

eight feet in height, and proportionably large. After having formed this determination and having spent some months in successfully collecting and arranging my materials, I began.

No one can conceive the variety of feelings which bore me onwards, like a hurricane, in the first enthusiasm of success. Life and death appeared to me ideal bounds, which I should first break through, and pour a torrent of light into our dark world. **A new species would bless me as its creator and source; many happy and excellent natures would owe their being to me. No father could claim the gratitude of his child so completely as I should deserve theirs.** *[An astonishing conclusion given his happy childhood and flawless moral examples at home.]* Pursuing these reflections, I thought that if I could bestow animation upon lifeless matter, I might in process of time (although I now found it impossible) renew life where death had apparently devoted the body to corruption.

These thoughts supported my spirits, while I pursued my undertaking with unremitting ardour. My cheek had grown pale with study, and my person had become emaciated with confinement. Sometimes, on the very brink of certainty, I failed; yet still I clung to the hope which the next day or the next hour might realize. One secret which I alone possessed was the hope to which I had dedicated myself; and the moon gazed on my midnight labours, while, with unrelaxed and breathless eagerness, I pursued nature to her hiding-places. **Who shall conceive the horrors of my secret toil as I dabbled among the unhallowed damps of the grave or tortured the living animal to animate the lifeless clay? My limbs now tremble, and my eyes swim with the remembrance; but then a resistless and almost frantic impulse urged me forward; I seemed to have lost all soul or sensation but for this one pursuit.** It was indeed but a passing trance, that only made me feel with renewed acuteness so soon as, the unnatural stimulus ceasing to operate, I had returned to my old habits. I collected bones from charnel-houses and disturbed, with profane fingers, the tremendous secrets of the human frame. In a solitary chamber, or rather cell, at the top of the house, and separated from all the other apartments by a gallery and staircase, I kept my workshop of filthy creation; my eyeballs were starting from their sockets in attending to the details of my employment. The dissecting room and the slaughter-house furnished many of my materials; and often did my human nature turn with loathing from my occupation, whilst, still urged on by an eagerness which perpetually increased, I brought my work near to a conclusion.

The summer months passed while I was thus engaged, heart and soul, in one pursuit. It was a most beautiful season; never did the fields bestow a more plentiful harvest or the vines yield a more luxuriant vintage, but my eyes were insensible to the charms of nature. And the same feelings which made me neglect the scenes around me caused me also to forget those friends who were so many miles absent, and whom I had not seen for so long a time. I knew my silence disquieted them, and I well remembered the words of my father: "I know that while you are pleased with yourself you will think of us with affection, and we shall hear regularly from you. You must pardon me if I regard any interruption in your correspondence as a proof that your other duties are equally neglected."

I knew well therefore what would be my father's feelings, but I could not tear my thoughts from my employment, loathsome in itself, but which had taken an irresistible hold of my imagination. I wished, as it were, to procrastinate all that related to my feelings of affection until the great object, which swallowed up every habit of my nature, should be completed.

I then thought that my father would be unjust if he ascribed my neglect to vice or faultiness on my part, but I am now convinced that he was justified in conceiving that I should not be altogether free from blame. A human being in perfection ought always to preserve a calm and peaceful mind and never to allow passion or a transitory desire to disturb his tranquillity. I do not think that the pursuit of knowledge is an exception to this rule. **If the study to which you apply yourself has a tendency to weaken your affections and to destroy your taste for those simple pleasures in which no alloy can possibly mix, then that study is certainly unlawful, that is to say, not befitting the human mind.** If this rule were always observed; if no man allowed any pursuit whatsoever to interfere with the tranquillity of his domestic affections, Greece had not been enslaved, Caesar would have spared his country,

America would have been discovered more gradually, and the empires of Mexico and Peru had not been destroyed.

But I forget that I am moralizing in the most interesting part of my tale, and your looks remind me to proceed. My father made no reproach in his letters and only took notice of my silence by inquiring into my occupations more particularly than before. Winter, spring, and summer passed away during my labours; but I did not watch the blossom or the expanding leaves—sights which before always yielded me supreme delight—so deeply was I engrossed in my occupation. The leaves of that year had withered before my work drew near to a close, and now every day showed me more plainly how well I had succeeded. But my enthusiasm was checked by my anxiety, and I appeared rather like one doomed by slavery to toil in the mines, or any other unwholesome trade than an artist occupied by his favourite employment. Every night I was oppressed by a slow fever, and I became nervous to a most painful degree; the fall of a leaf startled me, and I shunned my fellow creatures as if I had been guilty of a crime. Sometimes I grew alarmed at the wreck I perceived that I had become; the energy of my purpose alone sustained me: my labours would soon end, and I believed that exercise and amusement would then drive away incipient disease; and I promised myself both of these when my creation should be complete.

• ANALYZING THE SCENE •
CHAPTER 4 – SCENE 12

A Story Event is an active change of universal human value for one or more characters as a result of conflict (one character's desires clash with another's or an environmental shift changes the universal human value).

A Working Scene contains at least one Story Event. To determine a scene's Story Event, answer these four questions:

1. What are the characters literally doing—that is, what are their micro on-the-ground actions?

Victor Frankenstein has discovered the power of bestowing life upon flesh and sets about building a human being.

2. What is the essential tactic of the characters—that is, what macro behaviors are they employing that are linked to a universal human value?

Frankenstein is deep in an almost crazed frenzy; he has cut himself off from human contact, including that of his family, as he pursues his grotesque purpose.

3. What universal human values have changed for one or more characters in the scene? Which one of those value changes is most important and should be included in the Story Grid Spreadsheet?

Frankenstein moves from bad to worse—from obsessed to frenzied—and is in feverishly poor health.

In the previous scene, Frankenstein is obsessed with his goal of discovering the secret of life, even to the point of studying dead bodies and stealing body parts. He succeeds in discovering how to animate a body and ends the scene in delight. This scene starts with him pondering what to do with this knowledge, and his decision leads him into a crazed frenzy of obsession as he builds a human being. At the end of the scene, he is so obsessed, he is physically ill and has cut himself off from all human contact. While this isn't exactly a trajectory of life to death, it parallels it fairly well.

Health to Sickness

4. What is the Story Event that sums up the scene's on-the-ground actions, essential tactics, and value change? We will enter that event in the Story Grid Spreadsheet.

Victor sets about creating a human being out of the parts of dead bodies, and during this journey, he cuts himself off from his friends and family.

HOW THE SCENE ABIDES BY THE FIVE COMMANDMENTS OF STORYTELLING

Inciting Incident: Victor Frankenstein decides to build a human being.

Turning Point Progressive Complication: He is so obsessed, he neglects everything in his life but his work. Victor is aware that his father thinks something is wrong when he doesn't write home, yet he can't tear himself away from his work.

Crisis: Does he give in to his obsession or should he be more mindful of the extent to which he has neglected his correspondence? Best bad choice.

Climax: Victor eschews all human contact as his father persistently inquires after him.

Resolution: Victor is a mental and physical wreck.

NOTES

- The glimmer of vanity and human ego that we glimpsed in the previous scene rears its ugly head here! "No father could claim the gratitude of his child so completely as I should deserve theirs." This is a little strange, to be sure, for Victor himself seems to be a devoted member of his family. Why is Victor in search of such all-encompassing gratitude? Is this the grip of evil itself?
- Victor's obsession over the creation of this being causes him to build a colossal creature "of gigantic stature" because he thinks that working with small parts will cause him to slow down in his work. Once more, Victor seems to be in the grip of something bigger and more powerful than himself,

something that is pushing him to make unwise choices in the midst of his frenzy.

- Once again, Shelley stresses the horror of what Frankenstein needs to do in order to acquire the supplies needed to build the creature, as he "dabbled among the unhallowed damps of the grave or tortured the living animal to animate the lifeless clay."

CHAPTER 5 – SCENE 13

It was on a dreary night of November that I beheld the accomplishment of my toils. With an anxiety that almost amounted to agony, I collected the instruments of life around me, that I might infuse a spark of being into the lifeless thing that lay at my feet. It was already one in the morning; the rain pattered dismally against the panes, and my candle was nearly burnt out, when, by the glimmer of the half-extinguished light, I saw the dull yellow eye of the creature open; it breathed hard, and a convulsive motion agitated its limbs.

How can I describe my emotions at this catastrophe, or how delineate the wretch whom with such infinite pains and care I had endeavoured to form? His limbs were in proportion, and I had selected his features as beautiful. Beautiful! Great God! His yellow skin scarcely covered the work of muscles and arteries beneath; his hair was of a lustrous black, and flowing; his teeth of a pearly whiteness; but these luxuriances only formed a more horrid contrast with his watery eyes, that seemed almost of the same colour as the dun-white sockets in which they were set, his shrivelled complexion and straight black lips.

The different accidents of life are not so changeable as the feelings of human nature. I had worked hard for nearly two years, for the sole purpose of infusing life into an inanimate body. For this I had deprived myself of rest and health. **I had desired it with an ardour that far**

exceeded moderation; but now that I had finished, the beauty of the dream vanished, and breathless horror and disgust filled my heart. Unable to endure the aspect of the being I had created, I rushed out of the room and continued a long time traversing my bed-chamber, unable to compose my mind to sleep. At length lassitude succeeded to the tumult I had before endured, and I threw myself on the bed in my clothes, endeavouring to seek a few moments of forgetfulness. But it was in vain; I slept, indeed, but **I was disturbed by the wildest dreams.** I thought I saw Elizabeth, in the bloom of health, walking in the streets of Ingolstadt. Delighted and surprised, I embraced her, but as I imprinted the first kiss on her lips, they became livid with the hue of death; her features appeared to change, and I thought that I held the corpse of my dead mother in my arms; a shroud enveloped her form, and I saw the grave-worms crawling in the folds of the flannel. *[A terrible metaphor, the most virtuous examples in his life combined with death.]* I started from my sleep with horror; a cold dew covered my forehead, my teeth chattered, and every limb became convulsed; when, **by the dim and yellow light of the moon, as it forced its way through the window shutters, I beheld the wretch—the miserable monster whom I had created. He held up the curtain of the bed; and his eyes, if eyes they may be called, were fixed on me.** His jaws opened, and he muttered some inarticulate sounds, while a grin wrinkled his cheeks. He might have spoken, but I did not hear; one hand was stretched out, seemingly to detain me, but I escaped and rushed downstairs. I took refuge in the courtyard belonging to the house which I inhabited, where I remained during the rest of the night, walking up and down in the greatest agitation, listening attentively, catching and fearing each sound as if it were to announce the approach of **the demoniacal corpse to which I had so miserably given life.**

Oh! No mortal could support the horror of that countenance. A mummy again endued with animation could not be so hideous as that wretch. I had gazed on him while unfinished; he was ugly then, but when those muscles and joints were rendered capable of motion, it became a thing such as even Dante could not have conceived.

I passed the night wretchedly. Sometimes my pulse beat so quickly and hardly that I felt the palpitation of every artery; at others, I nearly sank to the ground through languor and extreme weakness. Mingled with this horror, I felt the bitterness of disappointment; dreams that had been my food and pleasant rest for so long a space were now become a hell to me; and the change was so rapid, the overthrow so complete!

• ANALYZING THE SCENE •
CHAPTER 5 – SCENE 13

A Story Event is an active change of universal human value for one or more characters as a result of conflict (one character's desires clash with another's or an environmental shift changes the universal human value).

A Working Scene contains at least one Story Event. To determine a scene's Story Event, answer these four questions:

1. What are the characters literally doing—that is, what are their micro on-the-ground actions?

Frankenstein brings his creation to life but is suddenly horrified at its ugliness. He then has nightmares and awakens to find the creature watching him as he sleeps.

2. What is the essential tactic of the characters—that is, what macro behaviors are they employing that are linked to a universal human value?

Frankenstein suddenly realizes that he has created a monster. He was able to deal with a theoretical creature, but when it actually begins to move, he suddenly realizes what he has done. His response is to sleep, to try to forget what he has done, and to pretend he hasn't created a monstrosity.

3. What universal human values have changed for one or more

characters in the scene? Which one of those value changes is most important and should be included in the Story Grid Spreadsheet?

At the start of this scene, Frankenstein brings his creation to life. He is feeling a certain amount of anxiety and eager expectation. He refers to the "infinite pains and care" he had taken to create this thing. By the end of the scene he has fled the creature, had dreadful nightmares, and woken up to find it staring at him. This is not only terror, it's a level beyond terror! Frankenstein experiences nervousness, then fear, and then terror.

Anxiety to Sheer Terror

4. What is the Story Event that sums up the scene's on-the-ground actions, essential tactics, and value change? We will enter that event in the Story Grid Spreadsheet.

Frankenstein animates the creature and suddenly realizes the horrific consequences of what he has done. The creature is no longer a science experiment; it is a monster. He runs away.

HOW THE SCENE ABIDES BY THE FIVE COMMANDMENTS OF STORYTELLING

Inciting Incident: Frankenstein brings his creature to life.

Turning Point Progressive Complication: He suddenly realizes the being is a monster.

Crisis: What should Victor do? How should he react? Should he confront the problem or run away? Best bad choice.

Climax: He runs away. Victor runs to his bedroom where he falls asleep and is tormented by nightmares. He awakens to find the creature staring at him.

Resolution: Victor runs away out of the building.

NOTES

- The monster, which is a necessary element of the Horror story, now exists. Until now, we may have wondered if the "true" monster was some kind of evil spirit, or perhaps Victor himself and his ego. But now we are assured that whatever the intellectual answer turns out to be, there is a genuine, hideous, flesh-and-blood creature of terrifying proportions out there, and Victor-the-Creator is frightened of what he has done. Great dramatic tension is the perfect way to remind us that yes, this is a Horror novel! This is the turning point of the Beginning Hook.
- Nonetheless, a writer who reads this passage carefully might be a bit confused by Frankenstein's reaction to his creation. After all he was using graveyard body parts to create a being. Did he really think "his limbs were in proportion" and that his features would be "beautiful?" How could that be? Why was he so shocked at how loathsome such a creature would be? During his nightmares, he sees a dead Elizabeth followed by the dead and decaying corpse of his mother in his arms. How was he shocked and revolted when he had spent years prowling around graveyards? Shelley offers as explanation, "The different accidents of life are not so changeable as the feelings of human nature." Basically, Victor spent years on this project, and now that he is finished, he has changed his mind. This is where the Crisis of the Beginning Hook occurs; this is a best bad choice situation, where he can either deal with the problem he's created or run away.
- Taking one step back from the scene itself, it may be useful to contemplate this phrase: "the demoniacal corpse to which I had so miserably given life." The process of giving life had apparently been enough to suck Frankenstein into a vortex of obsession. But when the vortex stopped whirling, he did not actually want the result itself. Frankenstein is face to face with the consequences of his actions. He had hitherto

only been interested in the creature's adoration toward him but had never considered the creature itself.

- It is particularly distressing to consider that Shelley's first pregnancy ended in a premature birth. The infant did not survive. This gives sad double meaning to the phrase quoted above, "the demoniacal corpse to which I had so miserably given life."

CHAPTER 5 – SCENE 14

Morning, dismal and wet, at length dawned and discovered to my sleepless and aching eyes the church of Ingolstadt, its white steeple and clock, which indicated the sixth hour. The porter opened the gates of the court, which had that night been my asylum, and I issued into the streets, pacing them with quick steps, as if I sought to avoid the wretch whom I feared every turning of the street would present to my view. **I did not dare return to the apartment which I inhabited**, but felt impelled to hurry on, although drenched by the rain which poured from a black and comfortless sky.

I continued walking in this manner for some time, endeavouring by bodily exercise to ease the load that weighed upon my mind. I traversed the streets without any clear conception of where I was or what I was doing. My heart palpitated in the sickness of fear, and I hurried on with irregular steps, not daring to look about me:

Like one who, on a lonely road,
Doth walk in fear and dread,
And, having once turned round, walks on,
And turns no more his head;
Because he knows a frightful fiend
Doth close behind him tread.

[Coleridge's "Ancient Mariner."]

Continuing thus, I came at length opposite to the inn at which the various diligences and carriages usually stopped. Here I paused, I knew not why; but I remained some minutes with my eyes fixed on a coach that was coming towards me from the other end of the street. As it drew nearer I observed that it was the Swiss diligence; it stopped just where I was standing, and on the door being opened, I perceived Henry Clerval, who, on seeing me, instantly sprung out. "My dear Frankenstein," exclaimed he, "how glad I am to see you! How fortunate that you should be here at the very moment of my alighting!" *[Just when Frankenstein is at the depths of despair, Clerval arrives.]*

Nothing could equal my delight on seeing Clerval; his presence brought back to my thoughts my father, Elizabeth, and all those scenes of home so dear to my recollection. I grasped his hand, and in a moment forgot my horror and misfortune; I felt suddenly, and for the first time during many months, calm and serene joy. I welcomed my friend, therefore, in the most cordial manner, and we walked towards my college. Clerval continued talking for some time about our mutual friends and his own good fortune in being permitted to come to Ingolstadt. "You may easily believe," said he, "how great was the difficulty to persuade my father that all necessary knowledge was not comprised in the noble art of book-keeping; and, indeed, I believe I left him incredulous to the last, for his constant answer to my unwearied entreaties was the same as that of the Dutch schoolmaster in The Vicar of Wakefield: 'I have ten thousand florins a year without Greek, I eat heartily without Greek.' But his affection for me at length overcame his dislike of learning, and he has permitted me to undertake a voyage of discovery to the land of knowledge."

"It gives me the greatest delight to see you; but tell me how you left my father, brothers, and Elizabeth."

"Very well, and very happy, only a little uneasy that they hear from you so seldom. By the by, I mean to lecture you a little upon their account myself. But, my dear Frankenstein," continued he, stopping short and gazing full in my face, "I did not before remark how very ill you appear; so thin and pale; you look as if you had been watching for several nights."

"You have guessed right; I have lately been so deeply engaged in one occupation that I have not allowed myself sufficient rest, as you see; but I hope, I sincerely hope, that all these employments are now at an end and that I am at length free."

I trembled excessively; I could not endure to think of, and far less to allude to, the occurrences of the preceding night. I walked with a quick pace, and we soon arrived at my college. **I then reflected, and the thought made me shiver, that the creature whom I had left in my apartment might still be there, alive and walking about. I dreaded to behold this monster, but I feared still more that Henry should see him.** Entreating him, therefore, to remain a few minutes at the bottom of the stairs, I darted up towards my own room. My hand was already on the lock of the door before I recollected myself. I then paused, and a cold shivering came over me. I threw the door forcibly open, as children are accustomed to do when they expect a spectre to stand in waiting for them on the other side; but nothing appeared. I stepped fearfully in: the apartment was empty, and my bedroom was also freed from its hideous guest. I could hardly believe that so great a good fortune could have befallen me, but when I became assured that my enemy had indeed fled, I clapped my hands for joy and ran down to Clerval.

We ascended into my room, and the servant presently brought breakfast; but I was unable to contain myself. It was not joy only that possessed me; I felt my flesh tingle with excess of sensitiveness, and my pulse beat rapidly. I was unable to remain for a single instant in the same place; I jumped over the chairs, clapped my hands, and laughed aloud. Clerval at first attributed my unusual spirits to joy on his arrival, but when he observed me more attentively, **he saw a wildness in my eyes for which he could not account, and my loud, unrestrained, heartless laughter frightened and astonished him.**

"My dear Victor," cried he, "what, for God's sake, is the matter? Do not laugh in that manner. How ill you are! What is the cause of all this?"

"Do not ask me," cried I, putting my hands before my eyes, for I thought I saw the dreaded spectre glide into the room; "HE can tell.

Oh, save me! Save me!" I imagined that the monster seized me; I struggled furiously and fell down in a fit.

Poor Clerval! What must have been his feelings? A meeting, which he anticipated with such joy, so strangely turned to bitterness. But I was not the witness of his grief, for **I was lifeless and did not recover my senses for a long, long time.**

This was the commencement of a nervous fever which confined me for several months. During all that time Henry was my only nurse. I afterwards learned that, knowing my father's advanced age and unfitness for so long a journey, and how wretched my sickness would make Elizabeth, he spared them this grief by concealing the extent of my disorder. He knew that I could not have a more kind and attentive nurse than himself; and, firm in the hope he felt of my recovery, he did not doubt that, instead of doing harm, he performed the kindest action that he could towards them.

But **I was in reality very ill, and surely nothing but the unbounded and unremitting attentions of my friend could have restored me to life. The form of the monster on whom I had bestowed existence was forever before my eyes, and I raved incessantly concerning him. Doubtless my words surprised Henry; he at first believed them to be the wanderings of my disturbed imagination, but the pertinacity with which I continually recurred to the same subject persuaded him that my disorder indeed owed its origin to some uncommon and terrible event.**

By very slow degrees, and with frequent relapses that alarmed and grieved my friend, I recovered. I remember the first time I became capable of observing outward objects with any kind of pleasure, I perceived that the fallen leaves had disappeared and that the young buds were shooting forth from the trees that shaded my window. It was a divine spring, and the season contributed greatly to my convalescence. I felt also sentiments of joy and affection revive in my bosom; my gloom disappeared, and in a short time I became as cheerful as before I was attacked by the fatal passion.

"Dearest Clerval," exclaimed I, "how kind, how very good you are to me. This whole winter, instead of being spent in study, as you promised yourself, has been consumed in my sick room. How shall I ever repay you? I feel the greatest remorse for the disappointment of which I have been the occasion, but you will forgive me."

"You will repay me entirely if you do not discompose yourself, but get well as fast as you can; and since you appear in such good spirits, I may speak to you on one subject, may I not?"

I trembled. One subject! What could it be? Could he allude to an object on whom I dared not even think? "Compose yourself," said Clerval, who observed my change of colour, "I will not mention it if it agitates you; but your father and cousin would be very happy if they received a letter from you in your own handwriting. They hardly know how ill you have been and are uneasy at your long silence."

"Is that all, my dear Henry? How could you suppose that my first thought would not fly towards those dear, dear friends whom I love and who are so deserving of my love?"

"If this is your present temper, my friend, you will perhaps be glad to see a letter that has been lying here some days for you; it is from your cousin, I believe."

• ANALYZING THE SCENE •
CHAPTER 5 – SCENE 14

A Story Event is an active change of universal human value for one or more characters as a result of conflict (one character's desires clash with another's or an environmental shift changes the universal human value).

A Working Scene contains at least one Story Event. To determine a scene's Story Event, answer these four questions:

1. What are the characters literally doing—that is, what are their micro on-the-ground actions?

Frankenstein's dear friend Henry Clerval arrives unexpectedly in Ingolstadt. Frankenstein is afraid he will see the creature, and when he finds that the creature has disappeared, he is so relieved he becomes incoherent and ill. Clerval nurses him throughout the winter and into the spring.

2. What is the essential tactic of the characters—that is, what macro behaviors are they employing that are linked to a universal human value?

Frankenstein cannot handle the burden of what he has done and loses his mind. Only the devoted nursing of his best friend restores him to life. Between the two of them, they go back and forth on the line between life and death.

3. What universal human values have changed for one or more characters in the scene? Which one of those value changes is most important and should be included in the Story Grid Spreadsheet?

Frankenstein goes through several extreme emotional shifts in this scene. He starts in fear, looking over his shoulder and wondering if the monster is following him. Then he zooms upward to delight when he sees his friend Clerval; then he tanks into fear that Clerval will see the monster. When he realizes the monster has fled, he collapses into babbling incoherence with relief. Meanwhile Clerval is a confused bystander, worried for his friend and unable to do more than take care of his physical collapse.

Fear to Relief

4. What is the Story Event that sums up the scene's on-the-ground actions, essential tactics, and value change? We will enter that event in the Story Grid Spreadsheet.

Victor's dear friend Clerval arrives unexpectedly in Ingolstadt for a visit. Frankenstein is afraid he will see the creature but when he realizes that the creature has disappeared, he is so relieved he becomes incoherent and ill.

HOW THE SCENE ABIDES BY THE FIVE COMMANDMENTS OF STORYTELLING

Inciting Incident: Henry Clerval arrives in Ingolstadt.

Turning Point Progressive Complication: Frankenstein returns with Clerval to the apartment and the creature is gone.

Crisis: Should he tell Clerval about the creature? Best bad choice.

Climax: He concludes he cannot and then Frankenstein collapses.

Resolution: Clerval nurses Henry back to health and encourages him to write to his family.

NOTES

- It is fascinating that Shelley, who didn't make much of the moment that Frankenstein discovered the secret of life, saw fit to torment the reader with so many emotional highs and lows in a single later chapter! This journey of approximately sixteen hundred words is equal to the most dramatic car chase scene where the hero "almost dies" multiple times.
- All it took to bring Victor "calm and serene joy" was seeing his old friend Clerval. How terrible that he has not been in touch with the only people who bring him joy and can be relied upon to support him. While Frankenstein blamed some evil influence for taking hold of him and forcing him to obsess on his mission, he clearly knew his family would disapprove of his experiment because he didn't tell them about it. He isn't about to tell Clerval about it, either. It is a reminder that human beings want what they want and will justify it even beyond rational logic.
- When Victor "loses it" with relief after discovering the creature gone, Henry rescues him and becomes his caregiver over the winter months until Victor recovers in the spring. Frankenstein says that "nothing but the unbounded and remitting attentions of my friend could have restored me to life." Once again we observe "morality" at work. Henry is a

truly good person, as Elizabeth is and Victor's parents were also. And yet when Victor sees his creation come to life, he flees. What a terrible contrast. Henry "parents" Victor back to life. Victor abandons his child. Where did Victor learn his parenting skills? Not his family and few friends, for sure.

CHAPTER 6 – SCENE 15

Clerval then put the following letter into my hands. It was from my own Elizabeth:

"My dearest Cousin,

"You have been ill, very ill, and even the constant letters of dear kind Henry are not sufficient to reassure me on your account. You are forbidden to write—to hold a pen; yet one word from you, dear Victor, is necessary to calm our apprehensions. For a long time I have thought that each post would bring this line, and my persuasions have restrained my uncle from undertaking a journey to Ingolstadt. I have prevented his encountering the inconveniences and perhaps dangers of so long a journey, yet how often have I regretted not being able to perform it myself! I figure to myself that the task of attending on your sickbed has devolved on some mercenary old nurse, who could never guess your wishes nor minister to them with the care and affection of your poor cousin. Yet that is over now: Clerval writes that indeed you are getting better. I eagerly hope that you will confirm this intelligence soon in your own handwriting.

"Get well—and return to us. **You will find a happy, cheerful home and friends who love you dearly.** Your father's health is vigorous, and he asks but to see you, but to be assured that you are well; and not a care will ever cloud his benevolent countenance. How pleased you would be to remark the improvement of our Ernest! He is now sixteen and full of activity and spirit. He is desirous to be a true Swiss and to enter into foreign service, but we cannot part with him, at least until his elder brother returns to us. My uncle is not pleased with the idea of a military career in a distant country, but Ernest never had your powers of application. He looks upon study as an odious fetter; his time is spent in the open air, climbing the hills or rowing on the lake. I fear that he will become an idler unless we yield the point and permit him to enter on the profession which he has selected.

"Little alteration, except the growth of our dear children, has taken place since you left us. The blue lake and snow-clad mountains—they never change; and I think our placid home and our contented hearts are regulated by the same immutable laws. My trifling occupations take up my time and amuse me, and I am rewarded for any exertions by seeing none but happy, kind faces around me. Since you left us, but one change has taken place in our little household. Do you remember on what occasion Justine Moritz entered our family? Probably you do not; I will relate her history, therefore in a few words. Madame Moritz, her mother, was a widow with four children, of whom Justine was the third. **This girl had always been the favourite of her father, but through a strange perversity, her mother could not endure her, and after the death of M. Moritz, treated her very ill.** *[A parallel with Frankenstein and his creature—he wasn't able to "endure" his creation, either.]* My aunt observed this, and when Justine was twelve years of age, prevailed on her mother to allow her to live at our house. *[Another example of virtue from Frankenstein's mother.]* The republican institutions of our country have produced simpler and happier manners than those which prevail in the great monarchies that surround it. Hence there is less distinction between the several classes of its inhabitants; and the lower orders, being neither so poor nor so despised, their manners are more refined and moral. A servant in Geneva does not mean the same thing as a servant in France and England. Justine, thus received in our family, learned the duties of a servant, a condition which, in our fortunate country, does not include the idea of ignorance and a sacrifice of the dignity of a human being.

"Justine, you may remember, was a great favourite of yours; and I recollect you once remarked that if you were in an ill humour, one glance from Justine could dissipate it, for the same reason that Ariosto gives concerning the beauty of Angelica—she looked so frank-hearted and happy. My aunt conceived a great attachment for her, by which she was induced to give her an education superior to that which she had at first intended. This benefit was fully repaid; Justine was the most grateful little creature in the world: I do not mean that she made any professions I never heard one pass her lips, but you could see by her eyes that she almost adored her protectress. Although her disposition was gay and in many respects inconsiderate, yet she paid the greatest attention to every gesture of my aunt. She thought her the model of all excellence and endeavoured to imitate her phraseology and manners, so that even now she often reminds me of her.

"When my dearest aunt died every one was too much occupied in their own grief to notice poor Justine, who had attended her during her illness with the most anxious affection. Poor Justine was very ill; but other trials were reserved for her.

"One by one, her brothers and sister died; and her mother, with the exception of her neglected daughter, was left childless. **The conscience of the woman was troubled; she began to think that the deaths of her favourites was a judgement from heaven to chastise her partiality. She was a Roman Catholic; and I believe her confessor confirmed the idea which she had conceived.** Accordingly, a few months after your departure for Ingolstadt, **Justine was called home by her repentant mother.** Poor girl! She wept when she quitted our house; she was much altered since the death of my aunt; grief had given softness and a winning mildness to her manners, which had before been remarkable for vivacity. Nor was her residence at her mother's house of a nature to restore her gaiety. The poor woman was very vacillating in her repentance. **She sometimes begged Justine to forgive her unkindness, but much oftener accused her of having caused the deaths of her brothers and sister.** *[Justine is blamed for deaths that she didn't actually cause—her mother thinks that God is punishing her for being cruel to Justine, but in the end she blames Justine.]* Perpetual fretting at length threw Madame Moritz into a decline, which at first increased her irritability, but she is now at peace for ever. She died on the first approach of cold weather, at the beginning of this last winter. Justine has just returned to us; and I assure you I love her tenderly. She is very clever and gentle, and extremely pretty; as I mentioned before, her mien and her expression continually remind me of my dear aunt.

"I must say also a few words to you, my dear cousin, of little darling William. I wish you could see him; he is very tall of his age, with sweet laughing blue eyes, dark eyelashes, and curling hair. When he smiles, two little dimples appear on each cheek, which are rosy with health. *[Oh dear, not a good sign!]* He has already had one or two little WIVES, but Louisa Biron is his favourite, a pretty little girl of five years of age.

"Now, dear Victor, I dare say you wish to be indulged in a little gossip concerning the good people of Geneva. The pretty Miss Mansfield has already received the congratulatory visits on her approaching marriage with a young Englishman, John Melbourne, Esq. Her ugly sister, Manon, married M. Duvillard, the rich banker, last autumn. Your favourite schoolfellow, Louis Manoir, has suffered several misfortunes since the departure of Clerval from Geneva. But he has already recovered his spirits, and is reported to be on the point of marrying a lively pretty Frenchwoman, Madame Tavernier. She is a widow, and much older than Manoir; but she is very much admired, and a favourite with everybody.

"I have written myself into better spirits, dear cousin; but my anxiety returns upon me as I conclude. Write, dearest Victor,—one line —one word will be a blessing to us. Ten thousand thanks to Henry for his kindness, his affection, and his many letters; we are sincerely grateful. Adieu! my cousin; take care of your self; and, I entreat you, write!

"Elizabeth Lavenza.

"Geneva, March 18, 17—."

"Dear, dear Elizabeth!" I exclaimed, when I had read her letter: "I will write instantly and relieve them from the anxiety they must feel." I wrote, and this exertion greatly fatigued me; but my convalescence had commenced, and proceeded regularly. In another fortnight I was able to leave my chamber.

• ANALYZING THE SCENE •
CHAPTER 6 – SCENE 15

A Story Event is an active change of universal human value for one or more characters as a result of conflict (one character's desires clash with another's or an environmental shift changes the universal human value).

A Working Scene contains at least one Story Event. To determine a scene's Story Event, answer these four questions:

1. What are the characters literally doing—that is, what are their micro on-the-ground actions?

This scene involves the contents of a letter from Elizabeth, Victor's foster sister. She tells him they are waiting for him and shares the family and local gossip.

2. What is the essential tactic of the characters—that is, what macro behaviors are they employing that are linked to a universal human value?

The main story in the letter concerns their servant Justine, whom they rescued from a sad family situation, much as Elizabeth was rescued and Victor's mother was rescued. Once again, examples of moral behavior abound. The Frankensteins rescue sad children and live a warm, happy life while Justine's mother is cruel to her child and ends up losing all of her other children.

3. What universal human values have changed for one or more characters in the scene? Which one of those value changes is most important and should be included in the Story Grid Spreadsheet?

Justine is the major player in this scene. Her state has gone from alienated/ignored as a child, to included in the Frankenstein family. Then she underwent another trajectory from stable in the Frankenstein family, to unstable when she returned to placate her mother.

Alienated to Included

4. What is the Story Event that sums up the scene's on-the-ground actions, essential tactics, and value change? We will enter that event in the Story Grid Spreadsheet.

Elizabeth writes to Victor about news from home. She tells him about their servant Justine, who was rescued from a bad family situation and now has had to return to her mother to keep her company after the deaths of her siblings.

HOW THE SCENE ABIDES BY THE FIVE COMMANDMENTS OF STORYTELLING

Inciting Incident: The Frankensteins take Justine into their family as a servant girl because she is neglected by her mother.

Turning Point Progressive Complication: Justine was the neglected, unloved child at home until she moved to live with the Frankensteins, and her mother blames herself, thinking God punished her for not loving Justine. She seeks to make amends.

Crisis: Should Justine return to her mother? Best bad choice.

Climax: It is the right thing to do, so Justine returns to her mother, who begins to blame Justine herself for causing the death of her siblings.

Resolution: Justine's mother eventually dies and Justine returns to live with the Frankensteins.

NOTES

- Here is a challenging story within a story within a story within a story! In order to credibly use the first-person narrative technique over a global geographic span, one must resort to a number of clever tools that don't stretch the reader's imagination too far! Let's go back to the original framework to make sure we understand how Shelley executed this. We have Margaret Saville, Robert Walton's sister in England, presumably the final recipient of the tale. She reads a letter written by her brother, who is on a ship near the North Pole. Her brother writes this letter after hearing the events from Victor Frankenstein himself, who has been rescued from the ice during his pursuit of the monster he created. He tells Walton the story of the monster. This part of the story, he receives from his sister Elizabeth, who receives it from Justine. Four levels of "hearing," all so this story can make its eventual way to you, the reader, without breaking faith with the first-person POV.

- We don't know Justine herself and it seems that Victor only knows her slightly. This is a heads-up scene; apparently, we need to know Justine's story in order to make sense of the greater global story. Warning to the writer: if you spend this much time explaining something, it had better be relevant.
- Note that we are headed into emotional territory with the story of Justine's mother: "through a strange perversity, her mother could not endure her." Elizabeth says that Justine is very pretty, as if that makes the story even harder to digest. Frankenstein's monster is definitely not pretty, but the parallel here is undeniable. From the child's point of view, whether she or he is pretty or ugly, the thought that your mother cannot "endure" you is unnatural and cruel.
- Justine's mother seemed to believe that the deaths of her children were to punish her for slighting her other child; however, she also held Justine responsible, as if Justine herself had wielded the weapon that did away her siblings. So we have been put on notice that emotionally abandoning your child has a moral component to it, and that a higher power may take you to task for it. Victor, beware!

CHAPTER 6 – SCENE 16

One of my first duties on my recovery was to introduce Clerval to the several professors of the university. In doing this, I underwent a kind of rough usage, ill befitting the wounds that my mind had sustained. Ever since the fatal night, the end of my labours, and the beginning of my misfortunes, I had conceived a violent antipathy even to the name of natural philosophy. When I was otherwise quite restored to health, the sight of a chemical instrument would renew all the agony of my nervous symptoms. Henry saw this, and had removed all my apparatus from my view. He had also changed my apartment; for he perceived that I had acquired a dislike for the room which had previously been my laboratory. But these cares of Clerval were made of no avail when I visited the professors. M. Waldman inflicted torture when he praised, with kindness and warmth, the astonishing progress I had made in the sciences. He soon perceived that I disliked the subject; but not guessing the real cause, he attributed my feelings to modesty, and changed the subject from my improvement, to the science itself, with a desire, as I evidently saw, of drawing me out. What could I do? He meant to please, and he tormented me. I felt as if he had placed carefully, one by one, in my view those instruments which were to be afterwards used in putting me to a slow and cruel death. I writhed under his words, yet dared not exhibit the pain I felt. Clerval, whose eyes and feelings were always quick in discerning the sensations of others, declined the subject, alleging, in excuse, his total ignorance; and the conversation took a more general turn. I thanked my friend from my heart, but I did not speak. I saw plainly that he was surprised, but he never attempted to draw my secret from me; and although I loved him with a mixture of affection and reverence that knew no bounds, **yet I could never persuade myself to confide in him that event which was so often present to my recollection, but which I feared the detail to another would only impress more deeply.**

M. Krempe was not equally docile; and in my condition at that time, of almost insupportable sensitiveness, his harsh blunt encomiums gave me even more pain than the benevolent approbation of M. Waldman. "D—n the fellow!" cried he; "why, M. Clerval, I assure you he has outstript us all. Ay, stare if you please; but it is nevertheless true. A youngster who, but a few years ago, believed in Cornelius Agrippa as firmly as in the gospel, has now set himself at the head of the university; and if he is not soon pulled down, we shall all be out of countenance.—Ay, ay," continued he, observing my face expressive of suffering, "M. Frankenstein is modest; an excellent quality in a young man. Young men should be diffident of themselves, you know, M. Clerval: I was myself when young; but that wears out in a very short time."

M. Krempe had now commenced an eulogy on himself, which happily turned the conversation from a subject that was so annoying to me.

Clerval had never sympathized in my tastes for natural science; and his literary pursuits differed wholly from those which had occupied me. He came to the university with the design of making himself complete master of the oriental languages, and thus he should open a field for the plan of life he had marked out for himself. Resolved to pursue no inglorious career, he turned his eyes toward the East, as affording scope for his spirit of enterprise. The Persian, Arabic, and Sanskrit languages engaged his attention, and I was easily induced to enter on the same studies. Idleness had ever been irksome to me, and now that I wished to fly from reflection, and hated my former studies, I felt great relief in being the fellow-pupil with my friend, and found not only instruction but consolation in the works of the orientalists. I did not, like him, attempt a critical knowledge of their dialects, for I did not contemplate making any other use of them than temporary amusement. I read merely to understand their meaning, and they well repaid my labours. Their melancholy is soothing, and their joy elevating, to a degree I never experienced in studying the authors of any other country. **When you read their writings, life appears to consist in a warm sun and a garden of roses,—in the smiles and frowns of a fair enemy, and the fire that consumes your own heart.** *[Frankenstein decides to study "happy" subjects instead of science.]* How different from the manly and heroical poetry of Greece and Rome!

Summer passed away in these occupations, and my return to Geneva was fixed for the latter end of autumn; but being delayed by several accidents, winter and snow arrived, the roads were deemed impassable, and my journey was retarded until the ensuing spring. I felt this delay very bitterly; for I longed to see my native town and my beloved friends. My return had only been delayed so long, from an unwillingness to leave Clerval in a strange place, before he had become acquainted with any of its inhabitants. The winter, however, was spent cheerfully; and although the spring was uncommonly late, when it came its beauty compensated for its dilatoriness.

The month of May had already commenced, and I expected the letter daily which was to fix the date of my departure, when **Henry proposed a pedestrian tour in the environs of Ingolstadt**, that I might bid a personal farewell to the country I had so long inhabited. I acceded with pleasure to this proposition: I was fond of exercise, and Clerval had always been my favourite companion in the ramble of this nature that I had taken among the scenes of my native country.

We passed a fortnight in these perambulations: my health and spirits had long been restored, and they gained additional strength from the salubrious air I breathed, the natural incidents of our progress, and the conversation of my friend. **Study had before secluded me from the intercourse of my fellow-creatures, and rendered me unsocial; but Clerval called forth the better feelings of my heart; he again taught me to love the aspect of nature, and the cheerful faces of children.** Excellent friend! how sincerely you did love me, and endeavour to elevate my mind until it was on a level with your own. **A selfish pursuit had cramped and narrowed me** *[He recognizes his selfishness.]*, **until your gentleness and affection warmed and opened my senses; I became the same happy creature who, a few years ago, loved and beloved by all, had no sorrow or care.** When happy, inanimate nature had the power of bestowing on me the most delightful sensations. A serene sky and verdant fields filled me with ecstasy. The present season was indeed divine; the flowers of spring bloomed in the hedges, while those of summer were already in bud. I was undisturbed by thoughts which during the preceding year had pressed upon me, notwithstanding my endeavours to throw them off, with an invincible burden.

Henry rejoiced in my gaiety, and sincerely sympathised in my feelings: he exerted himself to amuse me, while he expressed the sensations that filled his soul. The resources of his mind on this occasion were truly astonishing: his conversation was full of imagination; and very often, in imitation of the Persian and Arabic writers, he invented tales of wonderful fancy and passion. At other times he repeated my favourite poems, or drew me out into arguments, which he supported with great ingenuity. We returned to our college on a Sunday afternoon: the peasants were dancing, and every one we met appeared gay and happy. **My own spirits were high, and I bounded along with feelings of unbridled joy and hilarity.** *[Unconsciousness! He is in complete denial over what he has done.]*

• ANALYZING THE SCENE •
CHAPTER 6 – SCENE 16

A Story Event is an active change of universal human value for one or more characters as a result of conflict (one character's desires clash with another's or an environmental shift changes the universal human value).

A Working Scene contains at least one Story Event. To determine a scene's Story Event, answer these four questions:

1. What are the characters literally doing—that is, what are their micro on-the-ground actions?

Victor is spending time with Clerval, introducing him about the university and taking walks in the beautiful countryside around the area.

2. What is the essential tactic of the characters—that is, what macro behaviors are they employing that are linked to a universal human value?

Victor is in denial. He has turned his back on the study of science, to the confusion of his professors, and is now studying foreign languages along with Clerval. He surrounds himself with beauty.

3. What universal human values have changed for one or more characters in the scene? Which one of those value changes is most important and should be included in the Story Grid Spreadsheet?

Victor begins the scene in some degree of torment as his professors persist in talking about his talent in the sciences. He ends the scene in "gaiety" as he and Henry ramble through the countryside, waiting for the travel arrangements, which will take him back home to his family.

Victor begins this scene in angst and ends in joy. In terms of the global value, Victor's agony is at the suffering/death end of the spectrum. Meanwhile, his countryside walk in the midst of natural beauty pushes him to the life end of the spectrum.

Angst to Joy

4. What is the Story Event that sums up the scene's on-the-ground actions, essential tactics, and value change? We will enter that event in the Story Grid Spreadsheet.

Victor has abandoned science. He now studies languages with Clerval and refuses to engage with his science professors.

HOW THE SCENE ABIDES BY THE FIVE COMMANDMENTS OF STORYTELLING

Inciting Incident: Victor introduces Clerval around the university.

Turning Point Progressive Complication: Victor is no longer interested in science.

Crisis: After the catastrophic results of his science obsession, what should he study? How should he live? Best bad choice.

Climax: Even though he previously had no interest in this area, Victor opts to study Eastern languages with Clerval because "their melancholy is soothing, and their joy elevating," and Clerval brings back the happy person Victor had been before his experiments.

Resolution: Victor's mood undergoes a complete turnaround. He is joyful once more.

NOTES

- Shelley is the master of emotional torment, and her method is "simple but not easy." Before she takes the reader down a horrific emotional road, she makes sure that she puts you into a blithe, cheerful mental space. This scene does the job. On the Horror story trajectory, this scene would fall into "Unconsciousness." This scene is the last in the Beginning Hook. We are about to launch into the Middle Build.
- After Victor has been nursed back to health by his friend, he does not want to study science anymore. His professors continue to praise him, but he chooses instead to study Eastern languages with Clerval. These languages (Arabic, Sanskrit, Persian) portray a world of beauty that suits Frankenstein's fragile state of mind.
- Gradually, Victor's devoted friend manages to restore the old, happy Victor to himself. "A selfish pursuit had cramped

and narrowed me, until your gentleness and affection warmed and opened my senses; I became the same happy creature who, a few years ago, loved and beloved by all, had no sorrow or care."

- Always bear in mind that readers are smart; they know that they have not seen the last of the creature! So if Victor is happy and gay, this is just setting him up for a disaster. This is excellent scene writing—if you are going to spend time in narrative explanations, it helps if it sets a stage for a big emotional explosion. Your readers are waiting for it.

CHAPTER 7 – SCENE 17

On my return, I found the following letter from my father:—

"My dear Victor,

"You have probably waited impatiently for a letter to fix the date of your return to us; and I was at first tempted to write only a few lines, merely mentioning the day on which I should expect you. But that would be a cruel kindness, and I dare not do it. What would be your surprise, my son, when you expected a happy and glad welcome, to behold, on the contrary, tears and wretchedness? And how, Victor, can I relate our misfortune? Absence cannot have rendered you callous to our joys and griefs; and how shall I inflict pain on my long absent son? I wish to prepare you for the woeful news, but I know it is impossible; even now your eye skims over the page to seek the words which are to convey to you the horrible tidings.

"William is dead!—that sweet child, whose smiles delighted and warmed my heart, who was so gentle, yet so gay! Victor, he is murdered!

"I will not attempt to console you; but will simply relate the circumstances of the transaction.

"Last Thursday (May 7th), I, my niece, and your two brothers, went to walk in Plainpalais. The evening was warm and serene, and we prolonged our walk farther than usual. It was already dusk before we thought of returning; and then we discovered that William and Ernest, who had gone on before, were not to be found. We accordingly rested on a seat until they should return. Presently Ernest came, and enquired if we had seen his brother; he said, that he had been playing with him, that William had run away to hide himself, and that he vainly sought for him, and afterwards waited for a long time, but that he did not return.

"This account rather alarmed us, and we continued to search for him until night fell, when Elizabeth conjectured that he might have returned to the house. He was not there. We returned again, with torches; for I could not rest, when I thought that my sweet boy had lost himself, and was exposed to all the damps and dews of night; Elizabeth also suffered extreme anguish. About five in the morning I discovered my lovely boy, whom the night before I had seen blooming and active in health, stretched on the grass livid and motionless; the print of the murder's finger was on his neck.

"He was conveyed home, and the anguish that was visible in my countenance betrayed the secret to Elizabeth. She was very earnest to see the corpse. At first I attempted to prevent her but she persisted, and entering the room where it lay, hastily examined the neck of the victim, and clasping her hands exclaimed, 'O God! I have murdered my darling child!'

"She fainted, and was restored with extreme difficulty. When she again lived, it was only to weep and sigh. She told me, that that same evening William had teased her to let him wear a very valuable miniature that she possessed of your mother. This picture is gone, and was doubtless the temptation which urged the murderer to the deed. *[Out of love, Elizabeth readily accepts responsibility for something she did not do and can't be sure was even the case.]* We have no trace of him at present, although our exertions to discover him are unremitted; but they will not restore my beloved William!

"Come, dearest Victor; you alone can console Elizabeth. She weeps continually, and accuses herself unjustly as the cause of his death; her words pierce my heart. We are all unhappy; but will not that be an additional motive for you, my son, to return and be our comforter? Your dear mother! Alas, Victor! I now say, Thank God she did not live to witness the cruel, miserable death of her youngest darling!

"Come, Victor; not brooding thoughts of vengeance against the assassin, but with feelings of peace and gentleness, that will heal, instead of festering, the wounds of our minds. Enter the house of mourning, my friend, but with kindness and affection for those who love you, and not with hatred for your enemies.

"Your affectionate and afflicted father,

"Alphonse Frankenstein.

"Geneva, May 12th, 17—."

Clerval, who had watched my countenance as I read this letter, was surprised to observe the despair that succeeded the joy I at first expressed on receiving new from my friends. I threw the letter on the table, and covered my face with my hands.

"My dear Frankenstein," exclaimed Henry, when he perceived me weep with bitterness, "are you always to be unhappy? My dear friend, what has happened?"

I motioned him to take up the letter, while I walked up and down the room in the extremest agitation. Tears also gushed from the eyes of Clerval, as he read the account of my misfortune.

"I can offer you no consolation, my friend," said he; "your disaster is irreparable. What do you intend to do?"

"To go instantly to Geneva: come with me, Henry, to order the horses."

During our walk, Clerval endeavoured to say a few words of consolation; he could only express his heartfelt sympathy. "Poor William!" said he, "dear lovely child, he now sleeps with his angel mother! Who that had seen him bright and joyous in his young beauty, but must weep over his untimely loss! To die so miserably; to feel the murderer's grasp! How much more a murdered that could destroy radiant innocence! Poor little fellow! one only consolation have we; his friends mourn and weep, but he is at rest. The pang is over, his sufferings are at an end for ever. A sod covers his gentle form, and he knows no pain. He can no longer be a subject for pity; we must reserve that for his miserable survivors."

Clerval spoke thus as we hurried through the streets; the words impressed themselves on my mind and I remembered them afterwards in solitude. But now, as soon as the horses arrived, I hurried into a cabriolet, and bade farewell to my friend.

My journey was very melancholy. At first I wished to hurry on, for I longed to console and sympathise with my loved and sorrowing friends; but when I drew near my native town, I slackened my progress. I could hardly sustain the multitude of feelings that crowded into my mind. I passed through scenes familiar to my youth, but which I had not seen for nearly six years. How altered every thing might be during that time! One sudden and desolating change had taken place; but a thousand little circumstances might have by degrees worked other alterations, which, although they were done more tranquilly, might not be the less decisive. Fear overcame me; I dared no advance, dreading a thousand nameless evils that made me tremble, although I was unable to define them. I remained two days at Lausanne, in this painful state of mind. I contemplated the lake: the waters were placid; all around was calm; and the snowy mountains, 'the palaces of nature,' were not changed. By degrees the calm and heavenly scene restored me, and I continued my journey towards Geneva.

The road ran by the side of the lake, which became narrower as I approached my native town. I discovered more distinctly the black sides of Jura, and the bright summit of Mont Blanc. I wept like a child. "Dear mountains! my own beautiful lake! how do you welcome your wanderer? **Your summits are clear; the sky and lake are blue and placid. Is this to prognosticate peace, or to mock at my unhappiness?"**

I fear, my friend, that I shall render myself tedious by dwelling on these preliminary circumstances; but they were days of comparative happiness, and I think of them with pleasure. My country, my beloved country! who but a native can tell the delight I took in again beholding thy streams, thy mountains, and, more than all, thy lovely lake!

Yet, as I drew nearer home, grief and fear again overcame me. **Night also closed around; and when I could hardly see the dark mountains, I felt still more gloomily. The picture appeared a vast and dim scene of evil, and I foresaw obscurely that I was destined to become the most wretched of human beings.** Alas! I prophesied truly, and failed only in one single circumstance, that in all the misery I imagined and dreaded, I did not conceive the hundredth part of the anguish I was destined to endure. *[There is something worse than losing our adorable little brother to a murderer?]* It was completely dark when I arrived in the environs of Geneva; the gates of the town were already shut; and I was obliged to pass the night at Secheron, a village at the distance of half a league from the city. The sky was serene; and, as I was unable to rest, **I resolved to visit the spot where my poor William had been murdered.** As I could not pass through the town, I was obliged to cross the lake in a boat to arrive at Plainpalais. During this short voyage **I saw the lightning playing on the summit of Mont Blanc** in the most beautiful figures. **The storm appeared to approach rapidly**, and, on landing, I ascended a low hill, that I might observe its progress. It advanced; the heavens were clouded, and I soon felt the rain coming slowly in large drops, but its violence quickly increased. *[More cinematic beauty—how amazing that Shelley knows just what we need to see in our mind's eye, having never seen a movie herself.]*

I quitted my seat, and walked on, although **the darkness and storm increased every minute, and the thunder burst with a terrific crash over my head. It was echoed from Saleve, the Juras, and the Alps of Savoy; vivid flashes of lightning dazzled my eyes, illuminating the lake, making it appear like a vast sheet of fire; then for an instant every thing seemed of a pitchy darkness, until the eye recovered itself from the preceding flash.** The storm, as is often the case in Switzerland, appeared at once in various parts of the heavens. The most violent storm hung exactly north of the town, over the part of the lake which lies between the promontory of Belrive and the village of Copet. Another storm enlightened Jura with faint flashes; and another darkened and sometimes disclosed the Mole, a peaked mountain to the east of the lake.

While I watched the tempest, so beautiful yet terrific, I wandered on with a hasty step. This noble war in the sky elevated my spirits; **I clasped my hands, and exclaimed aloud, "William, dear angel! this is thy funeral, this thy dirge!" As I said these words, I perceived in the gloom a figure which stole from behind a clump of trees near me; I stood fixed, gazing intently: I could not be mistaken. A flash of**

lightning illuminated the object, and discovered its shape plainly to me; its gigantic stature, and the deformity of its aspect more hideous than belongs to humanity, instantly informed me that it was the wretch, the filthy daemon, to whom I had given life. What did he there? Could he be (I shuddered at the conception) the murderer of my brother? No sooner did that idea cross my imagination, than I became convinced of its truth; my teeth chattered, and I was forced to lean against a tree for support. The figure passed me quickly, and I lost it in the gloom.

Nothing in human shape could have destroyed the fair child. HE was the murderer! I could not doubt it. The mere presence of the idea was an irresistible proof of the fact. I thought of pursuing the devil; but it would have been in vain, for another flash discovered him to me hanging among the rocks of the nearly perpendicular ascent of Mont Saleve, a hill that bounds Plainpalais on the south. He soon reached the summit, and disappeared.

I remained motionless. The thunder ceased; but the rain still continued, and the scene was enveloped in an impenetrable darkness. I revolved in my mind the events which I had until now sought to forget: the whole train of my progress toward the creation; the appearance of the works of my own hands at my bedside; its departure. **Two years had now nearly elapsed since the night on which he first received life; and was this his first crime? Alas! I had turned loose into the world a depraved wretch, whose delight was in carnage and misery;** had he not murdered my brother?

No one can conceive the anguish I suffered during the remainder of the night, which I spent, cold and wet, in the open air. But I did not feel the inconvenience of the weather; my imagination was busy in scenes of evil and despair. **I considered the being whom I had cast among mankind, and endowed with the will and power to effect purposes of horror, such as the deed which he had now done, nearly in the light of my own vampire, my own spirit let loose from the grave, and forced to destroy all that was dear to me.**

• ANALYZING THE SCENE •
CHAPTER 7 – SCENE 17

A Story Event is an active change of universal human value for one or more characters as a result of conflict (one character's desires clash with another's or an environmental shift changes the universal human value).

A Working Scene contains at least one Story Event. To determine a scene's Story Event, answer these four questions:

1. What are the characters literally doing—that is, what are their micro on-the-ground actions?

Victor Frankenstein learns from a letter that his little brother William has been murdered; he journeys home immediately, and when he reaches the nearby countryside, he goes to see the place where the crime happened.

2. What is the essential tactic of the characters—that is, what macro behaviors are they employing that are linked to a universal human value?

Frankenstein drags his feet during the journey home; he is dreading even seeing Geneva after six years of absence. He reaches Geneva after the city gates are shut and is feeling restless, so he visits the scene of the crime. He then catches sight of the monster in the distance. He realizes suddenly that he had "turned loose into the world a depraved wretch, whose delight was in carnage and misery," and that this being likely murdered his brother. Frankenstein is confronted with this terrible possibility after he tries to numb himself to the news of his brother's murder. His effort to feel better has made him feel worse.

3. What universal human values have changed for one or more characters in the scene? Which one of those value changes is most important and should be included in the Story Grid Spreadsheet?

In a Horror story, the global value at stake is Life to Death. The global value here is mirrored in Frankenstein's emotional journey. He starts out as greatly saddened and distraught; there is no deeper well of sadness than the pit of despair over the death of a child. However, Shelley pushes us to contemplate several steps beyond this level of despair. Not only has a child died, but he has been murdered. Not only has he been murdered, but he has likely been murdered by a monster. Not only has he likely been murdered by a monster, but he has likely been murdered by a monster created by none other than his brother! Victor is now a murderer.

Dismay to Horror

4. What is the Story Event that sums up the scene's on-the-ground actions, essential tactics, and value change? We will enter that event in the Story Grid Spreadsheet.

Frankenstein learns from a letter that his little brother William has been murdered. He visits the scene of the crime and sees the creature in the distance.

HOW THE SCENE ABIDES BY THE FIVE COMMANDMENTS OF STORYTELLING

Inciting Incident: Frankenstein receives a letter from his father saying his brother has been murdered.

Turning Point Progressive Complication: A storm is brewing, and in a flash of lightning, he sees the grotesque monster of his creation.

Crisis: He can either believe that his brother was randomly murdered, or he can follow the logic right before his eyes. Best bad choice.

Climax: Victor suddenly is convinced that the monster has killed his brother.

Resolution: Victor realizes he has let loose a monster on the world.

NOTES

- We have entered the Middle Build with a thunderclap!
- Shelley allows Victor to believe for most of the chapter that his brother has been murdered by a random killer. However, she knows the reader is going to jump to—perfectly reasonable—conclusions about the identity of the killer, so she smirks at us from the shadows by giving us the image of Elizabeth (of all people! The sainted Elizabeth!) weeping and saying that she is at fault. Victor's father writes in his letter that obviously she is not at fault. How could she be at fault, when theft of a locket that she lent the child is such an indirect connection to his murder? But she put the emotion of "guilt" right there on page one of the scene so that we would have it available to us in our emotional toolbox later when Victor realizes his own indirect hand in his brother's murder. If you have a collection of core emotions to play with, it is a nice technique to introduce them in parallel or similar setups.
- Remember Justine? Her mother blamed her for causing her siblings' death. Talk about an indirect connection to a crime! Her mother "vacillates" between feeling guilty that perhaps the death of all of her other children is God's way of punishing her for her indifferent treatment of Justine, and blaming Justine herself for being the cause of this tragedy. After all, if Justine had not provoked her mother's antipathy, there never would have been a tragedy at all, right? In the previous scene we shook our heads at her mother's cruelty and convoluted logic, but now we can see exactly where Victor's mind is headed. He is thinking if only he had not indulged his ego by creating the monster, his brother might be alive. It doesn't say this anywhere in the scene, but we readers see it plainly nonetheless.
- Modern literature has gone in the direction of the personal, often providing the reader with an interior monologue for every POV character. Older literature often takes on an

omniscient POV, which has an almost cinematic quality to it. We watch as the narrator explains what is happening, and we laugh, cry, or gasp together as we spectate. There is sometimes even the air of a higher authority telling the story, and we allow this voice to dictate the lessons of the story. In *Frankenstein*, Shelley uses the cinematic voice brilliantly, even as she employs first-person narration, and a contemporary writer would do well to examine her technique, even if it seems dated. In this scene, when Victor first approaches Geneva, the sky is blue and the lake is calm. Then night closes in, and he arrives in a darkened Geneva, with the town gates shut. He then crosses the lake, and Shelley describes lightning on the summit of Mont Blanc, followed by a full, violent lightning storm. In the next paragraph Shelley takes care to describe the storm in detail, and as the flashes of lightning light up the sky, this is how we spy the figure of the monster. It is as if Shelley were planning the movie version in her mind, having never seen a movie in her life. It is brilliantly executed with Victor spending the night cold and wet in the nighttime rain. Don't forget that the environment and backdrop is virtually a character in the novel also, and it can help push the emotional temperature up or down for you.

CHAPTER 7 – SCENE 18

Day dawned; and I directed my steps towards the town. The gates were open, and I hastened to my father's house. My first thought was to discover what I knew of the murderer, and cause instant pursuit to be made. **But I paused when I reflected on the story that I had to tell. A being whom I myself had formed, and endued with life, had met me at midnight among the precipices of an inaccessible mountain. I remembered also the nervous fever with which I had been seized just at the time that I dated my creation, and which would give an air of delirium to a tale otherwise so utterly improbable.** I well knew that if any other had communicated such a relation to me, I should have looked upon it as the ravings of insanity. Besides, the strange nature of the animal would elude all pursuit, even if I were so far credited as to persuade my relatives to commence it. And then of what use would be pursuit? Who could arrest a creature capable of scaling the overhanging sides of Mont Saleve? These reflections determined me, and I resolved to remain silent. *[Was this the "moral" decision? We don't know.]*

It was about five in the morning when I entered my father's house. I told the servants not to disturb the family, and went into the library to attend their usual hour of rising.

Six years had elapsed, passed in a dream but for one indelible trace, and I stood in the same place where I had last embraced my father before my departure for Ingolstadt. Beloved and venerable parent! He still remained to me. **I gazed on the picture of my mother, which stood over the mantel-piece. It was an historical subject, painted at my father's desire, and represented Caroline Beaufort in an agony of despair, kneeling by the coffin of her dead father.** *[A visual representation of goodness.]* **Her garb was rustic, and her cheek pale; but there was an air of dignity and beauty, that hardly permitted the sentiment of pity.** Below this picture was a miniature of William; and my tears flowed when I looked upon it. While I was thus engaged, Ernest entered: he had heard me arrive, and hastened to welcome me: "Welcome, my dearest Victor," said he. "Ah! I wish you had come three months ago, and then you would have found us all joyous and delighted. You come to us now to share a misery which nothing can alleviate; yet your presence will, I hope, revive our father, who seems sinking under his misfortune; and your persuasions will induce poor Elizabeth to cease her vain and tormenting self-accusations.—Poor William! he was our darling and our pride!"

Tears, unrestrained, fell from my brother's eyes; a sense of mortal agony crept over my frame. Before, I had only imagined the wretchedness of my desolated home; the reality came on me as a new, and a not less terrible, disaster. I tried to calm Ernest; I enquired more minutely concerning my father, and here I named my cousin.

"She most of all," said Ernest, "requires consolation; she accused herself of having caused the death of my brother, and that made her very wretched. But since the murderer has been discovered—"

"The murderer discovered! Good God! how can that be? who could attempt to pursue him? It is impossible; one might as well try to overtake the winds, or confine a mountain-stream with a straw. I saw him too; he was free last night!"

"I do not know what you mean," replied my brother, in accents of wonder, "but to us the discovery we have made completes our misery. No one would believe it at first; and even now Elizabeth will not be convinced, notwithstanding all the evidence. Indeed, who would credit that Justine Moritz, who was so amiable, and fond of all the family, could suddenly become so capable of so frightful, so appalling a crime?"

"Justine Moritz! Poor, poor girl, is she the accused? But it is wrongfully; every one knows that; no one believes it, surely, Ernest?"

"No one did at first; but several circumstances came out, that have almost forced conviction upon us; and her own behaviour has been so confused, as to add to the evidence of facts a weight that, I fear, leaves no hope for doubt. But she will be tried today, and you will then hear all."

He then related that, the morning on which the murder of poor William had been discovered, Justine had been taken ill, and confined to her bed for several days. During this interval, one of the servants, happening to examine the apparel she had worn on the night of the murder, had discovered in her pocket the picture of my mother, which had been judged to be the temptation of the murderer. The servant instantly showed it to one of the others, who, without saying a word to any of the family, went to a magistrate; and, upon their deposition, Justine was apprehended. On being charged with the fact, the poor girl confirmed the suspicion in a great measure by her extreme confusion of manner.

This was a strange tale, but it did not shake my faith; and I replied earnestly, "You are all mistaken; I know the murderer. Justine, poor, good Justine, is innocent."

At that instant my father entered. I saw unhappiness deeply impressed on his countenance, but he endeavoured to welcome me cheerfully; and, after we had exchanged our mournful greeting, would have introduced some other topic than that of our disaster, had not Ernest exclaimed, "Good God, papa! Victor says that he knows who was the murderer of poor William."

"We do also, unfortunately," replied my father, "for indeed I had rather have been for ever ignorant than have discovered so much depravity and ungratitude in one I valued so highly."

"My dear father, you are mistaken; Justine is innocent."

"If she is, God forbid that she should suffer as guilty. She is to be tried today, and I hope, I sincerely hope, that she will be acquitted." *[The justice system will take care of everything, right?]*

This speech calmed me. I was firmly convinced in my own mind that Justine, and indeed every human being, was guiltless of this murder. I had no fear, therefore, that any circumstantial evidence could be brought forward strong enough to convict her. My tale was not one to announce publicly; its astounding horror would be looked upon as madness by the vulgar. Did any one indeed exist, except I, the creator, who would believe, unless his senses convinced him, in the existence of the living monument of presumption and rash ignorance which I had let loose upon the world?

We were soon joined by Elizabeth. Time had altered her since I last beheld her; it had endowed her with loveliness surpassing the beauty of her childish years. There was the same candour, the same vivacity, but it was allied to an expression more full of sensibility and intellect. She welcomed me with the greatest affection. "Your arrival, my dear cousin," said she, "fills me with hope. You perhaps will find some means to justify my poor guiltless Justine. Alas! **who is safe, if she be convicted of crime?** *[Elizabeth nails the unspoken uncertainty—if Justine is a murderer, who is safe?]* I rely on her innocence as certainly as I do upon my own. Our misfortune is doubly hard to us; we have not only lost that lovely darling boy, but this poor girl, whom I sincerely love, is to be torn away by even a worse fate. If she is condemned, I never shall know joy more. But she will not, I am sure she will not; and then I shall be happy again, even after the sad death of my little William."

"She is innocent, my Elizabeth," said I, "and that shall be proved; fear nothing, but let your spirits be cheered by the assurance of her acquittal."

"How kind and generous you are! every one else believes in her guilt, and that made me wretched, for I knew that it was impossible: and to see every one else prejudiced in so deadly a manner rendered me hopeless and despairing." She wept.

"Dearest niece," said my father, "dry your tears. If she is, as you believe, innocent, rely on the justice of our laws, and the activity with which I shall prevent the slightest shadow of partiality."

• ANALYZING THE SCENE •
CHAPTER 7 – SCENE 18

A Story Event is an active change of universal human value for one or more characters as a result of conflict (one character's desires clash with another's or an environmental shift changes the universal human value).

A Working Scene contains at least one Story Event. To determine a scene's Story Event, answer these four questions:

1. What are the characters literally doing—that is, what are their micro on-the-ground actions?

Victor arrives at his home in Geneva, and his family members explain the strange events behind Justine Moritz's arrest for William's murder.

2. What is the essential tactic of the characters—that is, what macro behaviors are they employing that are linked to a universal human value?

Frankenstein is confused and indecisive. How does he explain that he knows who the murderer is? How does he get people to understand that Justine is not the murderer?

3. What universal human values have changed for one or more characters in the scene? Which one of those value changes is most important and should be included in the Story Grid Spreadsheet?

Frankenstein moves from uncertain to certain. At the beginning of the scene, he is filled with confusion as to how to explain his role in this terrible crime. But when his brother says Justine has been accused of the murder, this confusion changes to bewilderment and then certainty, as he knows that Justine could not be the culprit.

After a few scenes of dramatic emotion, this scene begins with the agitation that Frankenstein brings with him from seeing the monster. He is wrapped up in his own mind: how does he convince everyone of his story? But new information changes his mental direction. Now he realizes that the misconception of Justine as the murderer must be cleared up. He decides he will trust the justice system, and his father echoes this at the end of the scene. This is the calm before the storm.

Agitation to Calm Assurance

4. What is the Story Event that sums up the scene's on-the-ground actions, essential tactics, and value change? We will enter that event in the Story Grid Spreadsheet.

Frankenstein arrives home in Geneva and learns that Justine has been arrested for William's murder, even though he knows the creature must have done it.

HOW THE SCENE ABIDES BY THE FIVE COMMANDMENTS OF STORYTELLING

Inciting Incident: Frankenstein arrives at his family home, uncertain as to how he can convince the world of his knowledge.

Turning Point Progressive Complication: His brother informs him that Justine Moritz is accused of the murder.

Crisis: Frankenstein knows Justine is innocent. Does he speak up? Best bad choice.

Climax: Frankenstein decides that Justine cannot possibly be convicted of a crime she did not commit. He can either trust the justice system or not, and he decides that she certainly will not be convicted.

Resolution: The entire Frankenstein family decides to trust the justice system.

NOTES

- First of all, note that Shelley begins the scene with analysis. We are inside Frankenstein's head as he grapples with the situation. She writes, "But I paused when I reflected on the story that I had to tell." She is trying to answer the question, "Why isn't Frankenstein telling anyone about the monster?" Notice that the seemingly exaggerated and almost random nervous breakdown suffered by Frankenstein upon discovery of the flight of the monster now has a role to play in the plot. If he tries to tell anyone anything about what might have transpired during that period, they will remember that he was in a state of delirium at that time. He won't be a very credible source. It's well worth remembering that in subsequent edits, the writer always has the opportunity to strengthen motivation and tighten the storyline so questions like these can be answered in a satisfying way. Don't worry about perfecting the plot in an early draft—doubtless, Shelley went through repeated iterations before she was satisfied.
- When Victor enters his home, he sees a portrait of his mother above the mantelpiece. It is "Caroline Beaufort in an agony of despair, kneeling by the coffin of her dead father." What a strange painting to display in the entrance to one's house, and what a strange way to even want to remember one's beloved wife or mother! However, it's a very effective reminder of the role of justice and moral goodness in the Frankenstein home.
- We are headed into what we, as readers, know will be a stressful episode. Justine has been accused of murder, and we know she is innocent. But it wouldn't make sense in a Horror novel to let her off the hook so lightly (remember the global value at stake? Life to Death), so we are bracing ourselves for more drama and turbulence. Don't forget that in order to feel the impact of a peak of emotion, it is more effective to start in a place of stability or moderation. At the

end of this scene, Frankenstein is comforted by the thought that surely the court will not convict an innocent person. This is how we know things will not bode well for poor Justine.

- Finally, note Shelley's choice of name: Justine. Will Justine receive justice?

CHAPTER 8 – SCENE 19

We passed a few sad hours until eleven o'clock, when the trial was to commence. My father and the rest of the family being obliged to attend as witnesses, I accompanied them to the court. During the whole of this wretched mockery of justice I suffered living torture. **It was to be decided whether the result of my curiosity and lawless devices would cause the death of two of my fellow beings:** one a smiling babe full of innocence and joy, the other far more dreadfully murdered, with every aggravation of infamy that could make the murder memorable in horror. Justine also was a girl of merit and possessed qualities which promised to render her life happy; now all was to be obliterated in an ignominious grave, and I the cause! A thousand times rather would I have confessed myself guilty of the crime ascribed to Justine, but I was absent when it was committed, and such a declaration would have been considered as the ravings of a madman and would not have exculpated her who suffered through me.

The appearance of Justine was calm. She was dressed in mourning, and her countenance, always engaging, was rendered, by the solemnity of her feelings, exquisitely beautiful. Yet she appeared confident in innocence and did not tremble, although gazed on and execrated by thousands, for all the kindness which her beauty might otherwise have excited was obliterated in the minds of the spectators by the imagination of the enormity she was supposed to have committed. She was tranquil, yet her tranquillity was evidently constrained; and as her confusion had before been adduced as a proof of her guilt, she worked up her mind to an appearance of courage. When she entered the court she threw her eyes round it and quickly discovered where we were seated. A tear seemed to dim her eye when she saw us, but she quickly recovered herself, and a look of sorrowful affection seemed to attest her utter guiltlessness.

The trial began, and after the advocate against her had stated the charge, several witnesses were called. Several strange facts combined against her, which might have staggered anyone who had not such proof of her innocence as I had. She had been out the whole of the night on which the murder had been committed and towards morning had been perceived by a market-woman not far from the spot where the body of the murdered child had been afterwards found. The woman asked her what she did there, but she looked very strangely and only returned a confused and unintelligible answer. She returned to the house about eight o'clock, and when one inquired where she had passed the night, she replied that she had been looking for the child and demanded earnestly if anything had been heard concerning him. When shown the body, she fell into violent hysterics and kept her bed for several days. The picture was then produced which the servant had found in her pocket; and when Elizabeth, in a faltering voice, proved that it was the same which, an hour before the child had been missed, she had placed round his neck, a murmur of horror and indignation filled the court.

Justine was called on for her defence. As the trial had proceeded, her countenance had altered. Surprise, horror, and misery were strongly expressed. Sometimes she struggled with her tears, but when she was desired to plead, she collected her powers and spoke in an audible although variable voice.

"God knows," she said, "how entirely I am innocent. But I do not pretend that my protestations should acquit me; I rest my innocence on a plain and simple explanation of the facts which have been adduced against me, and I hope the character I have always borne will incline my judges to a favourable interpretation where any circumstance appears doubtful or suspicious."

She then related that, by the permission of Elizabeth, she had passed the evening of the night on which the murder had been committed at the house of an aunt at Chene, a village situated at about a league from Geneva. On her return, at about nine o'clock, she met a man who asked her if she had seen anything of the child who was lost. She was alarmed by this account and passed several hours in looking for him, when the gates of Geneva were shut, and she was forced to remain several hours of the night in a barn belonging to a cottage, being unwilling to call up the inhabitants, to whom she was well known. Most of the night she spent here watching; towards morning she believed that she slept for a few minutes; some steps disturbed her, and she awoke. It was dawn, and she quitted her asylum, that she might again endeavour to find my brother. If she had gone near the spot where his body lay, it was without her knowledge. That she had been bewildered when questioned by the market-woman was not surprising, since she had passed a sleepless night and the fate of poor William was yet uncertain. Concerning the picture she could give no account.

"I know," continued the unhappy victim, "how heavily and fatally this one circumstance weighs against me, but I have no power of explaining it; and when I have expressed my utter ignorance, I am only left to conjecture concerning the probabilities by which it might have been placed in my pocket. But here also I am checked. I believe that I have no enemy on earth, and none surely would have been so wicked as to destroy me wantonly. Did the murderer place it there? I know of no opportunity afforded him for so doing; or, if I had, why should he have stolen the jewel, to part with it again so soon?

"I commit my cause to the justice of my judges, yet I see no room for hope. I beg permission to have a few witnesses examined concerning my character, and if their testimony shall not overweigh my supposed guilt, I must be condemned, although I would pledge my salvation on my innocence."

Several witnesses were called who had known her for many years, and they spoke well of her; but fear and hatred of the crime of which they supposed her guilty rendered them timorous and

unwilling to come forward. *[Quite a moral failing indeed! No one will attest to Justine's character. Elizabeth responds with a vengeance.]* Elizabeth saw even this last resource, her excellent dispositions and irreproachable conduct, about to fail the accused, when, although violently agitated, she desired permission to address the court.

"I am," said she, "the cousin of the unhappy child who was murdered, or rather his sister, for I was educated by and have lived with his parents ever since and even long before his birth. It may therefore be judged indecent in me to come forward on this occasion, but when **I see a fellow creature about to perish through the cowardice of her pretended friends,** *[Go Elizabeth!]* I wish to be allowed to speak, that I may say what I know of her character. I am well acquainted with the accused. I have lived in the same house with her, at one time for five and at another for nearly two years. During all that period she appeared to me the most amiable and benevolent of human creatures. She nursed Madame Frankenstein, my aunt, in her last illness, with the greatest affection and care and afterwards attended her own mother during a tedious illness, in a manner that excited the admiration of all who knew her, after which she again lived in my uncle's house, where she was beloved by all the family. She was warmly attached to the child who is now dead and acted towards him like a most affectionate mother. For my own part, I do not hesitate to say that, notwithstanding all the evidence produced against her, I believe and rely on her perfect innocence. She had no temptation for such an action; as to the bauble on which the chief proof rests, if she had earnestly desired it, I should have willingly given it to her, so much do I esteem and value her."

A murmur of approbation followed Elizabeth's simple and powerful appeal, but it was excited by her generous interference, and not in favour of poor Justine, on whom the public indignation was turned with renewed violence, charging her with the blackest ingratitude. *[The general public comes off quite poorly here.]* She herself wept as Elizabeth spoke, but she did not answer. My own agitation and anguish was extreme during the whole trial. I believed in her innocence; I knew it. Could the demon who had (I did not for a minute doubt) murdered my brother also in his hellish sport have betrayed the innocent to death and ignominy? I could not sustain the horror of my situation, and when

I perceived that the popular voice and the countenances of the judges had already condemned my unhappy victim, I rushed out of the court in agony. **The tortures of the accused did not equal mine; she was sustained by innocence, but the fangs of remorse tore my bosom and would not forgo their hold.**

• ANALYZING THE SCENE •
CHAPTER 8 – SCENE 19

A Story Event is an active change of universal human value for one or more characters as a result of conflict (one character's desires clash with another's or an environmental shift changes the universal human value).

A Working Scene contains at least one Story Event. To determine a scene's Story Event, answer these four questions:

1. What are the characters literally doing—that is, what are their micro on-the-ground actions?

Justine Moritz is on trial for the murder of William Frankenstein, Victor's little brother.

2. What is the essential tactic of the characters—that is, what macro behaviors are they employing that are linked to a universal human value?

This scene demonstrates what we might possibly regard as one of the blackest aspects of the human heart. Justine is accused of murder based on circumstantial evidence. She was apparently in the wrong place at the wrong time, and for some reason a piece of jewelry that the child had worn around his neck was found in her pocket. Since the case rested on her word versus the conjecture of the prosecution, she asks witnesses to come forward and testify as to her character. However, they refuse to come forward. Similarly, Victor does not come forward with the truth, thinking no one would believe him. So the essential tactic in this scene is *lying*. Victor and Justine's supposed friends lie, while Justine and Elizabeth tell the truth.

3. What universal human values have changed for one or more characters in the scene? Which one of those value changes is most important and should be included in the Story Grid Spreadsheet?

Justine moves from innocent to condemned; Frankenstein moves from anxious to devastated.

Normally it makes sense to track the main protagonist's value change, but in this case, Justine serves as a stand-in for the main story problem, so we will track her position from merely accused to accused and condemned, bringing the story closer to "death."

Innocent to Condemned

4. What is the Story Event that sums up the scene's on-the-ground actions, essential tactics, and value change? We will enter that event in the Story Grid Spreadsheet.

Justine is now wrongly on trial for the murder of William, and her friends refuse to speak up for her.

HOW THE SCENE ABIDES BY THE FIVE COMMANDMENTS OF STORYTELLING

Inciting Incident: Frankenstein goes with his family to watch Justine's trial for murder.

Turning Point Progressive Complication: Justine asks for character witnesses to speak for her, but no one comes forward.

Crisis: Will Elizabeth speak for Justine or not? Best bad choice.

Climax: "Although violently agitated" Elizabeth bravely steps forward to speak.

Resolution: Frankenstein can see what the verdict will be and rushes out of the courtroom in agony.

NOTES

- Even though in the previous scene Frankenstein feels that justice will surely prevail for poor Justine, at the opening of this scene, he is back in the voice of the older, wiser, sadder Frankenstein who is telling the entire tale to Walton in retrospect. It is clear he knows the outcome, and he refers to "this wretched mockery of justice." Why might it be useful to jump ahead in time and view the trial from a different vantage point? First of all, we aren't able to get into Justine's head during the trial since we are restricted to Frankenstein's first-person POV. In addition, we are unable to get into the head of Elizabeth or any of the other bystanders. If we were to rely on Frankenstein's in-the-moment observations alone, the events of the trial would likely be confusing, as the circumstantial evidence against Justine needs to be weighed against what Justine says and what Frankenstein knows in order to make sense. So when Frankenstein explains these events to Walton in the future, he is applying both knowledge of a variety of facts and also a degree of analysis to the situation.
- In order to remain on track with the global value of the story, Shelley needs Justine to be convicted at the end of this trial, but she also needs it to be believable. Accordingly, she gives Justine a story that is potentially believable, but she counterbalances it with the discovery of William's jewelry in her pocket and some odd, nervous behavior on the part of Justine. Really, Justine's innocence looks about fifty-fifty, based purely on the facts. What is needed to tip the scales in favor of innocence is evidence of Justine's unimpeachable character, and here Shelley makes a brilliant move by having Justine's friends refuse to speak honestly about her. This mirrors Frankenstein's lie, and the result of Justine's

friends' refusing to speak the truth is death. The result of Frankenstein's lie, we can conclude, will be death as well.

- Last, the only person who speaks in defense of Justine is Elizabeth. Once again, we are shown the moral example in the women in Frankenstein's life.

CHAPTER 8 – SCENE 20

I passed a night of unmingled wretchedness. In the morning I went to the court; my lips and throat were parched. I dared not ask the fatal question, but I was known, and the officer guessed the cause of my visit. The ballots had been thrown; they were all black, and Justine was condemned.

I cannot pretend to describe what I then felt. I had before experienced sensations of horror, and I have endeavoured to bestow upon them adequate expressions, but words cannot convey an idea of the heart-sickening despair that I then endured. The person to whom I addressed myself added that Justine had already confessed her guilt. "That evidence," he observed, "was hardly required in so glaring a case, but I am glad of it, and, indeed, none of our judges like to condemn a criminal upon circumstantial evidence, be it ever so decisive."

This was strange and unexpected intelligence; what could it mean? Had my eyes deceived me? And was I really as mad as the whole world would believe me to be if I disclosed the object of my suspicions? I hastened to return home, and Elizabeth eagerly demanded the result.

"My cousin," replied I, "it is decided as you may have expected; all judges had rather that ten innocent should suffer than that one guilty should escape. But she has confessed."

This was a dire blow to poor Elizabeth, who had relied with

firmness upon Justine's innocence. "Alas!" said she. "How shall I ever again believe in human goodness? Justine, whom I loved and esteemed as my sister, how could she put on those smiles of innocence only to betray? Her mild eyes seemed incapable of any severity or guile, and yet she has committed a murder."

Soon after we heard that the poor victim had expressed a desire to see my cousin. My father wished her not to go but said that he left it to her own judgment and feelings to decide. "Yes," said Elizabeth, "I will go, although she is guilty; and you, Victor, shall accompany me; I cannot go alone." The idea of this visit was torture to me, yet I could not refuse. We entered the gloomy prison chamber and beheld Justine sitting on some straw at the farther end; her hands were manacled, and her head rested on her knees. She rose on seeing us enter, and when we were left alone with her, she threw herself at the feet of Elizabeth, weeping bitterly. My cousin wept also.

"Oh, Justine!" said she. "Why did you rob me of my last consolation? I relied on your innocence, and although I was then very wretched, I was not so miserable as I am now."

"And do you also believe that I am so very, very wicked? Do you also join with my enemies to crush me, to condemn me as a murderer?" Her voice was suffocated with sobs.

"Rise, my poor girl," said Elizabeth; "why do you kneel, if you are innocent? I am not one of your enemies, I believed you guiltless, notwithstanding every evidence, until I heard that you had yourself declared your guilt. That report, you say, is false; and be assured, dear Justine, that nothing can shake my confidence in you for a moment, but your own confession."

"I did confess, but I confessed a lie. **I confessed, that I might obtain absolution; but now that falsehood lies heavier at my heart than all my other sins.** The God of heaven forgive me! Ever since I was condemned, **my confessor has besieged me; he threatened and menaced, until I almost began to think that I was the monster that he said I was. He threatened excommunication and hell fire in my last moments if I continued obdurate.** Dear lady, I had none to support me; all looked on me as a wretch doomed to ignominy and perdition. What could I do? In an evil hour I subscribed to a lie; and now only am I truly miserable." *[This act of evil is beyond comprehension —this poor girl has been betrayed and manipulated by both church and state. Nothing, no one is safe, even if your character is unimpeachable.]*

She paused, weeping, and then continued, "I thought with horror, my sweet lady, that you should believe your Justine, whom your blessed aunt had so highly honoured, and whom you loved, was a creature capable of a crime which none but the devil himself could have perpetrated. Dear William! dearest blessed child! I soon shall see you again in heaven, where we shall all be happy; and that consoles me, going as I am to suffer ignominy and death."

"Oh, Justine! Forgive me for having for one moment distrusted you. Why did you confess? But do not mourn, dear girl. Do not fear. I will proclaim, I will prove your innocence. I will melt the stony hearts of your enemies by my tears and prayers. You shall not die! You, my playfellow, my companion, my sister, perish on the scaffold! No! No! I never could survive so horrible a misfortune."

Justine shook her head mournfully. "I do not fear to die," she said; "that pang is past. God raises my weakness and gives me courage to endure the worst. I leave a sad and bitter world; and if you remember me and think of me as of one unjustly condemned, I am resigned to the fate awaiting me. Learn from me, dear lady, to submit in patience to the will of heaven!"

During this conversation I had retired to a corner of the prison room, where I could conceal the horrid anguish that possessed me. Despair! Who dared talk of that? **The poor victim, who on the morrow was to pass the awful boundary between life and death**, felt not, as I did, such deep and bitter agony. I gnashed my teeth and ground them together, uttering a groan that came from my inmost soul. Justine started. When she saw who it was, she approached me and said, "Dear sir, you are very kind to visit me; you, I hope, do not believe that I am guilty?"

I could not answer. "No, Justine," said Elizabeth; "he is more convinced of your innocence than I was, for even when he heard that you had confessed, he did not credit it."

"I truly thank him. In these last moments I feel the sincerest gratitude towards those who think of me with kindness. How sweet is the affection of others to such a wretch as I am! It removes more than half my misfortune, and I feel as if I could die in peace now that my innocence is acknowledged by you, dear lady, and your cousin." *[Here is another example of the morality of the women in the Frankenstein household.]*

Thus the poor sufferer tried to comfort others and herself. She indeed gained the resignation she desired. But **I, the true murderer, felt the never-dying worm alive in my bosom, which allowed of no hope or consolation.** Elizabeth also wept and was unhappy, but hers also was the misery of innocence, which, like a cloud that passes over the fair moon, for a while hides but cannot tarnish its brightness. **Anguish and despair had penetrated into the core of my heart; I bore a hell within me which nothing could extinguish.** We stayed several hours with Justine, and it was with great difficulty that Elizabeth could tear herself away. "I wish," cried she, "that I were to die with you; I cannot live in this world of misery."

Justine assumed an air of cheerfulness, while she with difficulty repressed her bitter tears. She embraced Elizabeth and said in a voice of half-suppressed emotion, "Farewell, sweet lady, dearest Elizabeth, my beloved and only friend; may heaven, in its bounty, bless and preserve you; may this be the last misfortune that you will ever suffer! Live, and be happy, and make others so."

And on the morrow Justine died. Elizabeth's heart-rending eloquence failed to move the judges from their settled conviction in the criminality of the saintly sufferer. My passionate and indignant appeals were lost upon them. And when I received their cold answers and heard the harsh, unfeeling reasoning of these men, my purposed avowal died away on my lips. Thus I might proclaim myself a madman, but not revoke the sentence passed upon my wretched victim. She perished on the scaffold as a murderess!

From the tortures of my own heart, I turned to contemplate the deep and voiceless grief of my Elizabeth. This also was my doing! And my father's woe, and the desolation of that late so smiling home all was the work of my thrice-accursed hands! Ye weep, unhappy ones, but these are not your last tears! Again shall you raise the funeral wail, and the sound of your lamentations shall again and again be heard! Frankenstein, your son, your kinsman, your early, much-loved friend; he who would spend each vital drop of blood for your sakes, who has no thought nor sense of joy except as it is mirrored also in your dear countenances, who would fill the air with blessings and spend his life in serving you—he bids you weep, to shed countless tears; happy beyond his hopes, if thus inexorable fate be satisfied, and if the destruction pause before the peace of the grave have succeeded to your sad torments!

Thus spoke my prophetic soul, as, torn by remorse, horror, and despair, I beheld those I loved spend vain sorrow upon the graves of William and Justine, the first hapless victims to my unhallowed arts. *[Not only has Frankenstein sent two people to the grave, he torments the lives of his loved ones.]*

• ANALYZING THE SCENE •
CHAPTER 8 – SCENE 20

A Story Event is an active change of universal human value for one or more characters as a result of conflict (one character's desires clash with another's or an environmental shift changes the universal human value).

A Working Scene contains at least one Story Event. To determine a scene's Story Event, answer these four questions:

1. What are the characters literally doing—that is, what are their micro on-the-ground actions?

Victor and Elizabeth visit Justine in prison after she is condemned.

2. What is the essential tactic of the characters—that is, what macro behaviors are they employing that are linked to a universal human value?

Justine tells Elizabeth that she was coerced into confessing to the crime. Elizabeth says she believes in her innocence. Frankenstein contemplates his own lie and his role in the death of first his brother, and soon, Justine.

3. What universal human values have changed for one or more characters in the scene? Which one of those value changes is most important and should be included in the Story Grid Spreadsheet?

Frankenstein's universal human value doesn't change very much from the beginning to the end of the scene. He starts out in agony and ends in agony. Justine, however, starts out alive and ends up dead.

Life to Death

4. What is the Story Event that sums up the scene's on-the-ground actions, essential tactics, and value change? We will enter that event in the Story Grid Spreadsheet.

Justine is condemned to death for William's murder.

HOW THE SCENE ABIDES BY THE FIVE COMMANDMENTS OF STORYTELLING

Inciting Incident: Justine has confessed to the crime; Elizabeth is devastated, as she had believed Justine was innocent.

Turning Point Progressive Complication: Justine tells Elizabeth that her confessor badgered her until she confessed to the crime.

Crisis: Whom should Elizabeth believe? If Justine is innocent, both the church and state systems are corrupt. If Justine is guilty but lied about it, Elizabeth's trust was violated. Best bad choice.

Climax: Elizabeth believes Justine, so by definition the court and the church are corrupt. Elizabeth promises to save Justine, but Justine prefers to die, as the world is "sad and bitter." Elizabeth cries out that she wishes she were going to die also, saying, "I cannot live in this world of misery."

Resolution: Elizabeth and Victor are unable to convince the judges that Justine is innocent, and she dies.

NOTES

- This is an interesting scene—it almost seems a little flat. Victor starts out distraught and ends distraught, but the main character of this scene is actually the unfortunate Justine, who starts out alive and ends up dead.
- Sometimes a writer may wonder whether a scene needs to actually be "on the page" if it concerns a tertiary character or perhaps involves an outcome that is obvious. Here, we might be tempted to cut a scene whose only purpose seems to be that of a tear-jerker. However, the execution of Justine plays a major role in both the book's plot (i.e., the actual events of the story) and its emotional trajectory. Shelley takes advantage of this moment to have Justine talk about coercion and lies. Elizabeth shows her humanity by first, believing her, and second, saying she will fight for Justine's life. Justine shows her own humanity by saying that she isn't afraid to die, because she leaves behind an evil world.
- And last, Frankenstein gets to count the number of victims he is responsible for thus far. William and Justine are dead, but he is also responsible for the profound grief experienced by Elizabeth, his father, and the rest of the people at home. "Anguish and despair had penetrated into the core of my heart; I bore a hell within me which nothing could extinguish."

CHAPTER 9 – SCENE 21

Nothing is more painful to the human mind than, after the feelings have been worked up by a quick succession of events, the dead calmness of inaction and certainty which follows and deprives the soul both of hope and fear. Justine died, she rested, and I was alive. The blood flowed freely in my veins, but a weight of despair and remorse pressed on my heart which nothing could remove. **Sleep fled from my eyes; I wandered like an evil spirit, for I had committed deeds of mischief beyond description horrible, and more, much more (I persuaded myself) was yet behind.** Yet my heart overflowed with kindness and the love of virtue. I had begun life with benevolent intentions and thirsted for the moment when I should put them in practice and make myself useful to my fellow beings. Now all was blasted; instead of that serenity of conscience which allowed me to look back upon the past with self-satisfaction, and from thence to gather promise of new hopes, I was seized by remorse and the sense of guilt, which hurried me away to a hell of intense tortures such as no language can describe.

This state of mind preyed upon my health, which had perhaps never entirely recovered from the first shock it had sustained. **I shunned the face of man; all sound of joy or complacency was**

torture to me; solitude was my only consolation—deep, dark, deathlike solitude.

My father observed with pain the alteration perceptible in my disposition and habits and endeavoured by arguments deduced from the feelings of his serene conscience and guiltless life to inspire me with fortitude and awaken in me the courage to dispel the dark cloud which brooded over me. "Do you think, Victor," said he, "that I do not suffer also? No one could love a child more than I loved your brother"—tears came into his eyes as he spoke—"but is it not a duty to the survivors that we should refrain from augmenting their unhappiness by an appearance of immoderate grief? It is also a duty owed to yourself, for excessive sorrow prevents improvement or enjoyment, or even the discharge of daily usefulness, without which no man is fit for society."

This advice, although good, was totally inapplicable to my case; I should have been the first to hide my grief and console my friends if remorse had not mingled its bitterness, and terror its alarm, with my other sensations. Now I could only answer my father with a look of despair and endeavour to hide myself from his view.

About this time we retired to our house at Belrive. This change was particularly agreeable to me. The shutting of the gates regularly at ten o'clock and the impossibility of remaining on the lake after that hour had rendered our residence within the walls of Geneva very irksome to me. I was now free. Often, after the rest of the family had retired for the night, I took the boat and passed many hours upon the water. Sometimes, with my sails set, I was carried by the wind; and sometimes, after rowing into the middle of the lake, I left the boat to pursue its own course and gave way to my own miserable reflections. I was often tempted, when all was at peace around me, and I the only unquiet thing that wandered restless in a scene so beautiful and heavenly—if I except some bat, or the frogs, whose harsh and interrupted croaking was heard only when I approached the shore —**often, I say, I was tempted to plunge into the silent lake, that the waters might close over me and my calamities forever.** But I was restrained, when I thought of the heroic and suffering Elizabeth, whom

I tenderly loved, and whose existence was bound up in mine. I thought also of my father and surviving brother; should I by my base desertion leave them exposed and unprotected to the malice of the fiend whom I had let loose among them? *[This is a living hell! Frankenstein can't even commit suicide, as the monster is still wandering the earth.]*

At these moments I wept bitterly and wished that peace would revisit my mind only that I might afford them consolation and happiness. But that could not be. Remorse extinguished every hope. I had been the author of unalterable evils, and I lived in daily fear lest the monster whom I had created should perpetrate some new wickedness. I had an obscure feeling that all was not over and that he would still commit some signal crime, which by its enormity should almost efface the recollection of the past. There was always scope for fear so long as anything I loved remained behind. **My abhorrence of this fiend cannot be conceived. When I thought of him I gnashed my teeth, my eyes became inflamed, and I ardently wished to extinguish that life which I had so thoughtlessly bestowed. When I reflected on his crimes and malice, my hatred and revenge burst all bounds of moderation.** I would have made a pilgrimage to the highest peak of the Andes, could I when there have precipitated him to their base. I wished to see him again, that I might wreak the utmost extent of abhorrence on his head and avenge the deaths of William and Justine. Our house was the house of mourning. My father's health was deeply shaken by the horror of the recent events. Elizabeth was sad and desponding; she no longer took delight in her ordinary occupations; all pleasure seemed to her sacrilege toward the dead; eternal woe and tears she then thought was the just tribute she should pay to innocence so blasted and destroyed. She was no longer that happy creature who in earlier youth wandered with me on the banks of the lake and talked with ecstasy of our future prospects. The first of those sorrows which are sent to wean us from the earth had visited her, and its dimming influence quenched her dearest smiles.

"When I reflect, my dear cousin," said she, "on the miserable death of Justine Moritz, I no longer see the world and its works as they before appeared to me. Before, I looked upon the accounts of vice and injustice that I read in books or heard from others as tales of ancient days or imaginary evils; at least they were remote and more familiar to reason than to the imagination; but now misery has come home, and men appear to me as monsters thirsting for each other's blood. Yet I am certainly unjust. Everybody believed that poor girl to be guilty; and if she could have committed the crime for which she suffered, assuredly she would have been the most depraved of human creatures. For the sake of a few jewels, to have murdered the son of her benefactor and friend, a child whom she had nursed from its birth, and appeared to love as if it had been her own! I could not consent to the death of any human being, but certainly I should have thought such a creature unfit to remain in the society of men. But she was innocent. I know, I feel she was innocent; you are of the same opinion, and that confirms me. **Alas! Victor, when falsehood can look so like the truth, who can assure themselves of certain happiness?** I feel as if I were walking on the edge of a precipice, towards which thousands are crowding and endeavouring to plunge me into the abyss. William and Justine were assassinated, and the murderer escapes; he walks about the world free, and perhaps respected. But even if I were condemned to suffer on the scaffold for the same crimes, I would not change places with such a wretch."

I listened to this discourse with the extremest agony. I, not in deed, but in effect, was the true murderer. Elizabeth read my anguish in my countenance, and kindly taking my hand, said, "My dearest friend, you must calm yourself. These events have affected me, God knows how deeply; but I am not so wretched as you are. There is an expression of despair, and sometimes of revenge, in your countenance that makes me tremble. Dear Victor, banish these dark passions. Remember the friends around you, who centre all their hopes in you. Have we lost the power of rendering you happy? Ah! **While we love, while we are true to each other, here in this land of peace and beauty, your native country, we may reap every tranquil blessing—what can disturb our peace?"**

And could not such words from her whom I fondly prized before every other gift of fortune suffice to chase away the fiend that lurked in my heart? Even as she spoke I drew near to her, as if in terror, lest at that very moment the destroyer had been near to rob me of her.

Thus not the tenderness of friendship, nor the beauty of earth, nor of heaven, could redeem my soul from woe; the very accents of love were ineffectual. I was encompassed by a cloud which no beneficial influence could penetrate. The wounded deer dragging its fainting limbs to some untrodden brake, there to gaze upon the arrow which had pierced it, and to die, was but a type of me.

Sometimes I could cope with the sullen despair that overwhelmed me, but sometimes the whirlwind passions of my soul drove me to seek, by bodily exercise and by change of place, some relief from my intolerable sensations. It was during an access of this kind that **I suddenly left my home, and bending my steps towards the near Alpine valleys, sought in the magnificence, the eternity of such scenes, to forget myself and my ephemeral, because human, sorrows.** My wanderings were directed towards the valley of Chamounix. I had visited it frequently during my boyhood. Six years had passed since then: I was a wreck, but nought had changed in those savage and enduring scenes.

I performed the first part of my journey on horseback. I afterwards hired a mule, as the more sure-footed and least liable to receive injury on these rugged roads. The weather was fine; it was about the middle of the month of August, nearly two months after the death of Justine, that miserable epoch from which I dated all my woe. The weight upon my spirit was sensibly lightened as I plunged yet deeper in the ravine of Arve. The immense mountains and precipices that overhung me on every side, the sound of the river raging among the rocks, and the dashing of the waterfalls around spoke of a power mighty as Omnipotence—and I ceased to fear or to bend before any being less almighty than that which had created and ruled the elements, here displayed in their most terrific guise. Still, as I ascended higher, the valley assumed a more magnificent and astonishing character. Ruined castles hanging on the precipices of piny mountains, the impetuous Arve, and cottages every here and there peeping forth from among the trees formed a scene of singular beauty. But it was augmented and rendered sublime by the mighty Alps, whose white and shining pyramids and domes towered above all, as belonging to another earth, the habitations of another race of beings.

I passed the bridge of Pelissier, where the ravine, which the river forms, opened before me, and I began to ascend the mountain that overhangs it. Soon after, I entered the valley of Chamounix. This valley is more wonderful and sublime, but not so beautiful and picturesque as that of Servox, through which I had just passed. The high and snowy mountains were its immediate boundaries, but I saw no more ruined castles and fertile fields. Immense glaciers approached the road; I heard the rumbling thunder of the falling avalanche and marked the smoke of its passage. Mont Blanc, the supreme and magnificent Mont Blanc, raised itself from the surrounding aiguilles, and its tremendous dome overlooked the valley. *[This is a wonderful description; it also serves as a sort of "labyrinth" for the monster because it isn't easy to access these spots.]*

A tingling long-lost sense of pleasure often came across me during this journey. Some turn in the road, some new object suddenly perceived and recognized, reminded me of days gone by, and were associated with the lighthearted gaiety of boyhood. The very winds whispered in soothing accents, and maternal Nature bade me weep no more. Then again the kindly influence ceased to act—I found myself fettered again to grief and indulging in all the misery of reflection. Then I spurred on my animal, striving so to forget the world, my fears, and more than all, myself—or, in a more desperate fashion, **I alighted and threw myself on the grass, weighed down by horror and despair.**

At length I arrived at the village of Chamounix. Exhaustion succeeded to the extreme fatigue both of body and of mind which I had endured. For a short space of time I remained at the window watching the pallid lightnings that played above Mont Blanc and listening to the rushing of the Arve, which pursued its noisy way beneath. The same lulling sounds acted as a lullaby to my too keen sensations; when I placed my head upon my pillow, sleep crept over me; **I felt it as it came and blessed the giver of oblivion.**

• ANALYZING THE SCENE •
CHAPTER 9 – SCENE 21

A Story Event is an active change of universal human value for one or more characters as a result of conflict (one character's desires clash with another's or an environmental shift changes the universal human value).

A Working Scene contains at least one Story Event. To determine a scene's Story Event, answer these four questions:

1. What are the characters literally doing—that is, what are their micro on-the-ground actions?

Frankenstein is agonizing over the knowledge that his creation most likely murdered his brother and had a major hand in Justine's death.

2. What is the essential tactic of the characters—that is, what macro behaviors are they employing that are linked to a universal human value?

Frankenstein has become physically ill and mentally unstable under the stress. He seeks "relief from my intolerable sensations" by traveling for distraction and exercise to a nearby valley.

3. What universal human values have changed for one or more characters in the scene? Which one of those value changes is most important and should be included in the Story Grid Spreadsheet?

In this scene, Frankenstein's emotional temperature doesn't seem to change very much. He starts out agonizing and ends up agonizing. However, at the beginning of the scene, he is home. Trying to cope with the unhappy people at home is part of his own unhappiness. He finally can't stand it anymore and leaves. By immersing himself in nature, he is able to fall into a state of unconsciousness.

Home to Away

4. What is the Story Event that sums up the scene's on-the-ground actions, essential tactics, and value change? We will enter that event in the Story Grid Spreadsheet.

Frankenstein is now in agony over what he has done and what the creature has done. He leaves home and hikes to a nearby village in order to distract himself.

HOW THE SCENE ABIDES BY THE FIVE COMMANDMENTS OF STORYTELLING

Inciting Incident: The Frankenstein family leaves Geneva for Belrive, where they have a country home. This is where Frankenstein witnessed the lightning strike that caused him to drop his fascination with the outdated natural philosophers.

Turning Point Progressive Complication: Elizabeth tells Victor that she is tormented at the thought of innocent Justine being executed while the murderer still roams freely. She is filled with despair over the state of the world, that truth and falsehood can be mistaken for each other.

Crisis: Victor is in agony. He feels he is the true murderer. His violent feelings of guilt cause him to swing between leaving home and staying with his family. Both options seem intolerable. Best bad choice.

Climax: Victor leaves home.

Resolution: Victor arrives at the village of Chamounix.

NOTES

- This scene is a difficult one to analyze according to the Five Commandments of Storytelling. There isn't any clear inciting incident, as Frankenstein's mood has not changed from the previous scene, and it hasn't changed by the end of the scene, either. Everyone is still in exactly the same emotional place as previously. There aren't any big decisions or externalities happening.

- However, Shelley needed to get Frankenstein away from Geneva and into the countryside. Key events in his early life happen in the countryside where he spent time boating on the lake and reading works by his early idols, Agrippa and Paracelsus. This is also where Frankenstein learned about electricity and ditched his idols accordingly as not having the answers to his questions. Shelley uses the despondent mood of the family and the summer season as a way to move them to the country. Accordingly, we can view their departure from Geneva as the inciting incident here.
- The progressive complications are also a bit unclear because it seems his life is exactly as complicated at the end of the scene as it was at the beginning. It is perhaps helpful to bear in mind Shelley's writerly goal, which is to get Victor to the village of Chamounix, where she has some excitement planned for the reader. In that case, the progressive complications can be anything that helps eventually drive Victor to leave. Shelley continues to point out Victor's high level of personal torment and adds a "zinger" by having Elizabeth make a devastating speech about whether it is even possible to achieve happiness in such a terrible world. "Alas! Victor, when falsehood can look so like the truth, who can assure themselves of certain happiness?" Victor is acutely aware of his dishonesty, so this speech must have emotionally destroyed him even further, coming from the lips of his beloved Elizabeth.
- Then to make it worse, Elizabeth expresses kindness and pity for Victor's sadness: "Ah! While we love, while we are true to each other, here in this land of peace and beauty, your native country, we may reap every tranquil blessing—

what can disturb our peace?" The last thing in the world Victor feels is that he is "true" to anyone!

- At this point, Victor acknowledges that he is done for. There is no salve for his soul. In an effort to save his sanity during a dark moment of despair, he launches on a journey to Chamounix, a boyhood haunt in a nearby valley.

CHAPTER 10 – SCENE 22

I spent the following day roaming through the valley. I stood beside the sources of the Arveiron, which take their rise in a glacier, that with slow pace is advancing down from the summit of the hills to barricade the valley. **The abrupt sides of vast mountains were before me; the icy wall of the glacier overhung me; a few shattered pines were scattered around; and the solemn silence of this glorious presence-chamber of imperial nature was broken only by the brawling waves or the fall of some vast fragment, the thunder sound of the avalanche or the cracking, reverberated along the mountains, of the accumulated ice, which, through the silent working of immutable laws, was ever and anon rent and torn, as if it had been but a plaything in their hands.** These sublime and magnificent scenes afforded me the greatest consolation that I was capable of receiving. They elevated me from all littleness of feeling, and although they did not remove my grief, they subdued and tranquillized it. In some degree, also, they diverted my mind from the thoughts over which it had brooded for the last month. I retired to rest at night; my slumbers, as it were, waited on and ministered to by the assemblance of grand shapes which I had contemplated during the day. They congregated round me; the unstained snowy mountain-top, the glittering pinnacle, the pine woods, and ragged bare ravine, the eagle, soaring amidst the clouds—they all gathered round me and bade me be at peace.

Where had they fled when the next morning I awoke? All of soul-inspiriting fled with sleep, and dark melancholy clouded every thought. The rain was pouring in torrents, and thick mists hid the summits of the mountains, so that I even saw not the faces of those mighty friends. Still I would penetrate their misty veil and seek them in their cloudy retreats. What were rain and storm to me? My mule was brought to the door, and I resolved to ascend to the summit of Montanvert. I remembered the effect that the view of the tremendous and ever-moving glacier had produced upon my mind when I first saw it. **It had then filled me with a sublime ecstasy that gave wings to the soul and allowed it to soar from the obscure world to light and joy.** The sight of the awful and majestic in nature had indeed always the effect of solemnizing my mind and causing me to forget the passing cares of life. I determined to go without a guide, for I was well acquainted with the path, and the presence of another would destroy the solitary grandeur of the scene.

The ascent is precipitous, but the path is cut into continual and short windings, which enable you to surmount the perpendicularity of the mountain. It is a scene terrifically desolate. *[This is a parallel for the Arctic.]* In a thousand spots the traces of the winter avalanche may be perceived, where trees lie broken and strewed on the ground, some entirely destroyed, others bent, leaning upon the jutting rocks of the mountain or transversely upon other trees. The path, as you ascend higher, is intersected by ravines of snow, down which stones continually roll from above; one of them is particularly dangerous, as the slightest sound, such as even speaking in a loud voice, produces a concussion of air sufficient to draw destruction upon the head of the speaker. The pines are not tall or luxuriant, but they are sombre and add an air of severity to the scene. I looked on the valley beneath; vast mists were rising from the rivers which ran through it and curling in thick wreaths around the opposite mountains, whose summits were hid in the uniform clouds, while rain poured from the dark sky and added to the melancholy impression I received from the objects around me. Alas! Why does man boast of sensibilities superior to those apparent in the brute; it only renders them more necessary beings. If our impulses were confined to hunger, thirst, and desire, we might be nearly free; but now we are moved by every wind that blows and a chance word or scene that that word may convey to us.

> We rest; a dream has power to poison sleep.
> We rise; one wand'ring thought pollutes the day.
> We feel, conceive, or reason; laugh or weep,
> Embrace fond woe, or cast our cares away;
> It is the same: for, be it joy or sorrow,
> The path of its departure still is free.
> Man's yesterday may ne'er be like his morrow;
> Nought may endure but mutability!

It was nearly noon when I arrived at the top of the ascent. For some time I sat upon the rock that overlooks the sea of ice. A mist covered both that and the surrounding mountains. Presently a breeze dissipated the cloud, and I descended upon the glacier. The surface is very uneven, rising like the waves of a troubled sea, descending low, and interspersed by rifts that sink deep. The field of ice is almost a league in width, but I spent nearly two hours in crossing it. *[Frankenstein crosses ice, another parallel for his Arctic travels.]* The opposite mountain is a bare perpendicular rock. From the side where I now stood Montanvert was exactly opposite, at the distance of a league; and above it rose Mont Blanc, in awful majesty. I remained in a recess of the rock, gazing on this wonderful and stupendous scene. The sea, or rather the vast river of ice, wound among its dependent mountains, whose aerial summits hung over its recesses. Their icy and glittering peaks shone in the sunlight over the clouds. **My heart, which was before sorrowful, now swelled with something like joy**; I exclaimed, "Wandering spirits, if indeed ye wander, and do not rest in your narrow beds, allow me this faint happiness, or take me, as your companion, away from the joys of life."

As I said this I suddenly beheld the figure of a man, at some distance, advancing towards me with superhuman speed. He bounded over the crevices in the ice, among which I had walked with caution; his stature, also, as he approached, seemed to exceed that of man. I was troubled; a mist came over my eyes, and I felt a faintness seize me, but I was quickly restored by the cold gale of the mountains. I perceived, as the shape came nearer (sight tremendous and abhorred!) that it was the wretch whom I had created. **I trembled with rage and horror, resolving to wait his approach and then close with him in mortal combat.** He approached; his countenance bespoke bitter anguish, combined with disdain and malignity, while its unearthly ugliness rendered it almost too horrible for human eyes. But I scarcely observed this; rage and hatred had at first deprived me of utterance, and I recovered only to overwhelm him with words expressive of furious detestation and contempt.

"Devil," I exclaimed, "do you dare approach me? And do not you fear the fierce vengeance of my arm wreaked on your miserable head? Begone, vile insect! Or rather, stay, that I may trample you to dust! And, oh! That I could, with the extinction of your miserable existence, restore those victims whom you have so diabolically murdered!"

"I expected this reception," said the daemon. "**All men hate the wretched**; how, then, must I be hated, who am miserable beyond all living things! Yet you, my creator, detest and spurn me, thy creature, to whom thou art bound by ties only dissoluble by the annihilation of one of us. **You purpose to kill me. How dare you sport thus with life? Do your duty towards me, and I will do mine towards you and the rest of mankind. If you will comply with my conditions, I will leave them and you at peace; but if you refuse, I will glut the maw of death, until it be satiated with the blood of your remaining friends.**"

"Abhorred monster! Fiend that thou art! The tortures of hell are too mild a vengeance for thy crimes. Wretched devil! You reproach me with your creation, come on, then, that I may extinguish the spark which I so negligently bestowed."

My rage was without bounds; I sprang on him, impelled by all the feelings which can arm one being against the existence of another.

He easily eluded me and said, "Be calm! I entreat you to hear me before you give vent to your hatred on my devoted head. Have I not suffered enough, that you seek to increase my misery? **Life, although it may only be an accumulation of anguish, is dear to me, and I will**

defend it. Remember, thou hast made me more powerful than thyself; my height is superior to thine, my joints more supple. But I will not be tempted to set myself in opposition to thee. **I am thy creature, and I will be even mild and docile to my natural lord and king if thou wilt also perform thy part, the which thou owest me.** *[Aha, here is where we ask ourselves who the true villain is. Frankenstein reneged on his responsibilities and created this problem, but the monster is still a monster.]* Oh, Frankenstein, be not equitable to every other and trample upon me alone, to whom thy justice, and even thy clemency and affection, is most due. **Remember that I am thy creature; I ought to be thy Adam, but I am rather the fallen angel, whom thou drivest from joy for no misdeed. Everywhere I see bliss, from which I alone am irrevocably excluded. I was benevolent and good; misery made me a fiend. Make me happy, and I shall again be virtuous.**"

"Begone! I will not hear you. There can be no community between you and me; we are enemies. Begone, or let us try our strength in a fight, in which one must fall."

"How can I move thee? Will no entreaties cause thee to turn a favourable eye upon thy creature, who implores thy goodness and compassion? Believe me, Frankenstein, **I was benevolent; my soul glowed with love and humanity; but am I not alone, miserably alone? You, my creator, abhor me; what hope can I gather from your fellow creatures, who owe me nothing? They spurn and hate me. The desert mountains and dreary glaciers are my refuge.** I have wandered here many days; the caves of ice, which I only do not fear, are a dwelling to me, and the only one which man does not grudge. These bleak skies I hail, for they are kinder to me than your fellow beings. If the multitude of mankind knew of my existence, they would do as you do, and arm themselves for my destruction. Shall I not then hate them who abhor me? I will keep no terms with my enemies. I am miserable, and they shall share my wretchedness. Yet it is in your power to recompense me, and deliver them from an evil which it only remains for you to make so great, that not only you and your family, but thousands of others, shall be swallowed up in the whirlwinds of its rage. Let your compassion be moved, and do not disdain me. Listen to my tale; when you have heard that, abandon or commiserate me, as you shall judge that I deserve. But hear me. **The guilty are allowed, by human laws, bloody as they are, to speak in their own defence before they are condemned.** Listen to me, Frankenstein. **You accuse me of murder, and yet you would, with a satisfied conscience, destroy your own creature. Oh, praise the eternal justice of man!** *[This speech works particularly well in light of the events involving Justine.]* Yet I ask you not to spare me; listen to me, and then, if you can, and if you will, destroy the work of your hands."

"Why do you call to my remembrance," I rejoined, "circumstances of which I shudder to reflect, that I have been the miserable origin and author? Cursed be the day, abhorred devil, in which you first saw light! Cursed (although I curse myself) be the hands that formed you! You have made me wretched beyond expression. You have left me no power to consider whether I am just to you or not. Begone! Relieve me from the sight of your detested form."

"Thus I relieve thee, my creator," he said, and placed his hated hands before my eyes, which I flung from me with violence; "thus I take from thee a sight which you abhor. Still thou canst listen to me and grant me thy compassion. By the virtues that I once possessed, I demand this from you. Hear my tale; it is long and strange, and the temperature of this place is not fitting to your fine sensations; come to the hut upon the mountain. The sun is yet high in the heavens; before it descends to hide itself behind your snowy precipices and illuminate another world, you will have heard my story and can decide. **On you it rests, whether I quit forever the neighbourhood of man and lead a harmless life, or become the scourge of your fellow creatures and the author of your own speedy ruin.**"

As he said this he led the way across the ice; I followed. My heart was full, and I did not answer him, but as I proceeded, I weighed the various arguments that he had used and determined at least to listen to his tale. I was partly urged by curiosity, and compassion confirmed my resolution. I had hitherto supposed him to be the murderer of my brother, and I eagerly sought a confirmation or denial of this opinion. **For the first time, also, I felt what the duties of a creator towards his creature were, and that I ought to render him happy before I complained of his wickedness.** *[Frankenstein is actually in agreement* *about his duties as a creator. Is it too late for him to fix the problem he started?]* These motives urged me to comply with his demand. We crossed the ice, therefore, and ascended the opposite rock. The air was cold, and the rain again began to descend; we entered the hut, the fiend with an air of exultation, I with a heavy heart and depressed spirits. But I consented to listen, and seating myself by the fire which my odious companion had lighted, he thus began his tale.

• ANALYZING THE SCENE •
CHAPTER 10 – SCENE 22

A Story Event is an active change of universal human value for one or more characters as a result of conflict (one character's desires clash with another's or an environmental shift changes the universal human value).

A Working Scene contains at least one Story Event. To determine a scene's Story Event, answer these four questions:

1. What are the characters literally doing—that is, what are their micro on-the-ground actions?

Frankenstein has gone for a hike up onto a glacier when his creature emerges and begins to talk to him.

2. What is the essential tactic of the characters—that is, what macro behaviors are they employing that are linked to a universal human value?

Frankenstein's instinct is to try to kill the monster, but the monster begins to speak to him. They argue over Frankenstein's responsibility toward the life he has created. Frankenstein tries to claim that the monster's crimes are too great. The monster argues that he had begun life as a benevolent creature and was made wretched by Frankenstein's neglect and the cruelty of mankind.

3. What universal human values have changed for one or more characters in the scene? Which one of those value changes is most important and should be included in the Story Grid Spreadsheet?

Frankenstein moves from delight in nature's spectacle, to anger or rage about the monster's speech, to resignation regarding his own role in the monster's tragedy.

In this case, the monster's state does not change although you could say he starts out unheard and then becomes heard, but Frankenstein's value starts with the thrill of seeing nature's wonders and then plummets into rage toward the monster. So we record Calm to Enraged. There is also a change at the resolution of the scene where Frankenstein decides to hear the monster out. The scene ends with resignation.

Calm to Enraged to Resignation

4. What is the Story Event that sums up the scene's on-the-ground actions, essential tactics, and value change? We will enter that event in the Story Grid Spreadsheet.

Frankenstein goes for a hike on a glacier where the creature appears and starts to talk to him. He leads Frankenstein to his hut.

HOW THE SCENE ABIDES BY THE FIVE COMMANDMENTS OF STORYTELLING

Inciting Incident: Frankenstein has climbed up onto a glacier and spent the night.

Turning Point Progressive Complication: Frankenstein's creature appears.

Crisis: Frankenstein's instinct is to try to kill him, but the monster points out that he will lose such a confrontation and instead tries to strike a bargain. He would like something from Frankenstein. Does he try to kill the creature or hear him out? Best bad choice.

Climax: Victor is curious and also feels compassion for the creature, even though he still loathes him. Victor agrees to listen and follows the creature to his hut.

Resolution: The creature begins to tell his tale.

NOTES

- Notice the landscape! Shelley was living in Switzerland when she wrote the novel, so these place names are real, and the descriptions are likely the result of her own travels in the area. Recall that she starts the novel in a stark, icy landscape, and here we are again in a stark, icy landscape.
- The natural landscape manages to fill Frankenstein with joy, a "sublime ecstasy that gave wings to the soul."
- At one point Shelley quotes from a poem by her lover, Percy Bysshe Shelley. The poem is "Mutability," an interesting reflection on the idea that only change is permanent.
- Just as Frankenstein exclaims that he feels happy, the monster appears! Very nicely done. If you are going to bring out a monster, it can be very effective to make sure that the character in your scene is feeling as happy as can be right when the monster appears. Think of it as a roller coaster drop!
- Frankenstein makes an instant decision—mortal combat. He's going to kill him.
- The monster utters possibly the most important words in the book: "How dare you sport thus with life?"
- The monster also admits that he is the killer. He threatens to kill Frankenstein's "remaining friends" if his conditions are not met.
- Here the creature is setting up the story problem for the rest of the book. He acknowledges Frankenstein as his "natural lord and king" and says he will accept him as such if Frankenstein himself performs his own obligations as

master. He demands that Frankenstein hear his story and make the ultimate decision over his fate.

- Frankenstein is curious, but he also claims to be "compassionate." He feels his responsibility toward this creature for the first time and accompanies him to his hut.

CHAPTER 11 – SCENE 23

"It is with considerable difficulty that I remember the original era of my being; all the events of that period appear confused and indistinct. A strange multiplicity of sensations seized me, and I saw, felt, heard, and smelt at the same time; and **it was, indeed, a long time before I learned to distinguish between the operations of my various senses.** By degrees, I remember, a stronger light pressed upon my nerves, so that I was obliged to shut my eyes. Darkness then came over me and troubled me, but hardly had I felt this when, by opening my eyes, as I now suppose, the light poured in upon me again. I walked and, I believe, descended, but I presently found a great alteration in my sensations. Before, dark and opaque bodies had surrounded me, impervious to my touch or sight; but I now found that I could wander on at liberty, with no obstacles which I could not either surmount or avoid. The light became more and more oppressive to me, and the heat wearying me as I walked, I sought a place where I could receive shade. This was the forest near Ingolstadt; and here I lay by the side of a brook resting from my fatigue, until I felt tormented by hunger and thirst. This roused me from my nearly dormant state, and I ate some berries which I found hanging on the trees or lying on the ground. I slaked my thirst at the brook, and then lying down, was overcome by sleep.

"It was dark when I awoke; I felt cold also, and half frightened, as it were, instinctively, finding myself so desolate. Before I had quitted your apartment, on a sensation of cold, I had covered myself with some clothes, but these were insufficient to secure me from the dews of night. **I was a poor, helpless, miserable wretch; I knew, and could distinguish, nothing; but feeling pain invade me on all sides, I sat down and wept.**

"Soon a gentle light stole over the heavens and gave me a sensation of pleasure. I started up and beheld a radiant form rise from among the trees. [The moon] I gazed with a kind of wonder. It moved slowly, but it enlightened my path, and I again went out in search of berries. I was still cold when under one of the trees I found a huge cloak, with which I covered myself, and sat down upon the ground. **No distinct ideas occupied my mind; all was confused. I felt light, and hunger, and thirst, and darkness; innumerable sounds rang in my ears, and on all sides various scents saluted me; the only object that I could distinguish was the bright moon, and I fixed my eyes on that with pleasure.**

"Several changes of day and night passed, and the orb of night had greatly lessened, when I began to distinguish my sensations from each other. I gradually saw plainly the clear stream that supplied me with drink and the trees that shaded me with their foliage. I was delighted when I first discovered that a pleasant sound, which often saluted my ears, proceeded from the throats of the little winged animals who had often intercepted the light from my eyes. I began also to observe, with greater accuracy, the forms that surrounded me and to perceive the boundaries of the radiant roof of light which canopied me. Sometimes I tried to imitate the pleasant songs of the birds but was unable. Sometimes I wished to express my sensations in my own mode, but the uncouth and inarticulate sounds which broke from me frightened me into silence again.

"The moon had disappeared from the night, and again, with a lessened form, showed itself, while I still remained in the forest. My sensations had by this time become distinct, and my mind received every day additional ideas. My eyes became accustomed to the light and to perceive objects in their right forms; I distinguished the insect from the herb, and by degrees, one herb from another. I found that the sparrow uttered none but harsh notes, whilst those of the blackbird and thrush were sweet and enticing.

"One day, when I was oppressed by cold, I found a fire which had been left by some wandering beggars, and was overcome with delight at the warmth I experienced from it. In my joy I thrust my hand into the live embers, but quickly drew it out again with a cry of pain. How strange, I thought, that the same cause should produce such opposite effects! I examined the materials of the fire, and to my joy found it to be composed of wood. I quickly collected some branches, but they were wet and would not burn. I was pained at this and sat still watching the operation of the fire. The wet wood which I had placed near the heat dried and itself became inflamed. I reflected on this, and by touching the various branches, I discovered the cause and busied myself in collecting a great quantity of wood, that I might dry it and have a plentiful supply of fire. When night came on and brought sleep with it, I was in the greatest fear lest my fire should be extinguished. I covered it carefully with dry wood and leaves and placed wet branches upon it; and then, spreading my cloak, I lay on the ground and sank into sleep.

"It was morning when I awoke, and my first care was to visit the fire. I uncovered it, and a gentle breeze quickly fanned it into a flame. I observed this also and contrived a fan of branches, which roused the embers when they were nearly extinguished. When night came again I found, with pleasure, that the fire gave light as well as heat and that the discovery of this element was useful to me in my food, for **I found some of the offals that the travellers had left had been roasted, and tasted much more savoury than the berries I gathered from the trees.** I tried, therefore, to dress my food in the same manner, placing it on the live embers. I found that the berries were spoiled by this operation, and the nuts and roots much improved.

"Food, however, became scarce, and I often spent the whole day searching in vain for a few acorns to assuage the pangs of hunger. When I found this, I resolved to quit the place that I had hitherto inhabited, to seek for one where the few wants I experienced would be more easily satisfied. In this emigration I exceedingly lamented the loss of the fire which I had obtained through accident and knew not how to reproduce it. I gave several hours to the serious consideration of this difficulty, but I was obliged to relinquish all attempt to supply it, and wrapping myself up in my cloak, I struck across the wood towards the setting sun. I passed three days in these rambles and at length discovered the open country. A great fall of snow had taken place the night before, and the fields were of one uniform white; the appearance was disconsolate, and I found my feet chilled by the cold damp substance that covered the ground.

"It was about seven in the morning, and I longed to obtain food and shelter; **at length I perceived a small hut**, on a rising ground, which had doubtless been built for the convenience of some shepherd. This was a new sight to me, and I examined the structure with great curiosity. Finding the door open, I entered. An old man sat in it, near a fire, over which he was preparing his breakfast. He turned on hearing a noise, and perceiving me, shrieked loudly, and quitting the hut, ran across the fields with a speed of which his debilitated form hardly appeared capable. His appearance, different from any I had ever before seen, and his flight somewhat surprised me. But I was enchanted by the appearance of the hut; here the snow and rain could not penetrate; the ground was dry; and it presented to me then as exquisite and divine a retreat as Pandemonium appeared to the demons of hell after their sufferings in the lake of fire. I greedily devoured the remnants of the shepherd's breakfast, which consisted of bread, cheese, milk, and wine; the latter, however, I did not like. Then, overcome by fatigue, I lay down among some straw and fell asleep.

• ANALYZING THE SCENE •
CHAPTER 11 – SCENE 23

A Story Event is an active change of universal human value for one or more characters as a result of conflict (one character's desires clash with another's or an environmental shift changes the universal human value).

A Working Scene contains at least one Story Event. To determine a scene's Story Event, answer these four questions:

1. What are the characters literally doing—that is, what are their micro on-the-ground actions?

The creature is telling the story of the first days of his existence after having left Frankenstein's apartment.

2. What is the essential tactic of the characters—that is, what macro behaviors are they employing that are linked to a universal human value?

When the creature left Frankenstein's apartment, he was in effect a brand-new human being. Several metaphors work for what the creature was going through. One might say he was an infant human, or even that he was metaphorically going through the human experience writ large (caveman to modern person). Shelley uses what we know and assume about the human experience to show the progression of the creature from raw creation to sentient human being. At this point, the creature wants to survive. Only after he is able to see, hear, and take care of his physical needs does he then want more (love, belonging, learning, etc.).

3. What universal human values have changed for one or more characters in the scene? Which one of those value changes is most important and should be included in the Story Grid Spreadsheet?

The major change for the creature in this scene is from homeless to sheltered. He starts out sleeping on the ground and unable to do much more than gather berries and ends up in a shepherd's hut with a fire, food, and straw for a bed.

Homeless to Sheltered

4. What is the Story Event that sums up the scene's on-the-ground

actions, essential tactics, and value change? We will enter that event in the Story Grid Spreadsheet.

The creature tells the story of his life after leaving Frankenstein's apartment. He learns how to handle external stimuli and manages to find food and shelter.

HOW THE SCENE ABIDES BY THE FIVE COMMANDMENTS OF STORYTELLING

Inciting Incident: The creature leaves Frankenstein's apartment and walks out into the light.

Turning Point Progressive Complication: The creature discovers fire and cooking. It becomes more and more difficult for him to find food in the area.

Crisis: Does he leave his fire and possibly encounter more hostility? Best bad choice.

Climax: He decides to leave the fire even though he doesn't know how to create another; he ends up finding a small shepherd's hut.

Resolution: The resident shepherd runs away in fear and the creature is able to inhabit it.

NOTES

- As a writer, Shelley had a practical problem. She has a (more or less) convincing tale of an ambitious science student who is interested in the very edges of the life-death transition, and who decides to attempt to animate a being as part of his exploration of this question. But after you "animate" a creature, what do you have? How will it interact with people? How will you use this setup to explore the questions that are uppermost in your mind as a novelist?

- Obviously the main problem here is you can't suddenly have a being that is walking, talking, and sentient, unless the being has supernatural origins. Shelley never says that the monster has been inhabited by any kind of demon or spirit. In fact, she never says anything about the method by which the monster is animated! Despite the popular conception that Frankenstein's monster was brought to life by a zap of electricity, Shelley never says this, and on the occasions where Frankenstein mentions the act of animating the creature, he steadfastly refuses to explain exactly how he did it.
- Instead, Shelley portrays the newly animated creature almost as a newborn infant, unable to tolerate excessive stimulation and utterly ignorant of the practical world. As mentioned above, another way of looking at the development of Frankenstein's creature is to place him against a backdrop of the larger human experience. He feels cold and covers himself. The light disturbs him so he seeks shade. He drinks and eats whatever he finds. He lies down to sleep. At first he has a hard time telling one sort of stimulation from the other, but gradually he understands how to respond to each kind of sensation.
- At the next level, he discovers fire. He doesn't know how to reproduce it, but he figures out how to keep it going. He also appreciates the value of the shepherd's hut as shelter.
- The role of this scene in the story cannot be overemphasized. If we don't accept that the creature is sentient, there is no story. Shelley needs to convince her readers that it makes sense for a newly animated human being to become the creature who eventually torments Frankenstein and becomes his obsession. Unless he is evil personified, we need to understand why he is the being that he is—and since Shelley hasn't gone in the direction of creating a Satanic monster, we know she is exploring some other question that requires a relatively innocent start in life for Frankenstein's creature.

CHAPTER 11 – SCENE 24

"It was noon when I awoke, and allured by the warmth of the sun, which shone brightly on the white ground, I determined to recommence my travels; and, depositing the remains of the peasant's breakfast in a wallet I found, I proceeded across the fields for several hours, until at sunset I arrived at a village. How miraculous did this appear! The huts, the neater cottages, and stately houses engaged my admiration by turns. The vegetables in the gardens, the milk and cheese that I saw placed at the windows of some of the cottages, allured my appetite. One of the best of these I entered, but I had hardly placed my foot within the door before the children shrieked, and one of the women fainted. **The whole village was roused; some fled, some attacked me, until, grievously bruised by stones and many other kinds of missile weapons, I escaped to the open country and fearfully took refuge in a low hovel**, quite bare, and making a wretched appearance after the palaces I had beheld in the village. **This hovel however, joined a cottage of a neat and pleasant appearance, but after my late dearly bought experience, I dared not enter it.** My place of refuge was constructed of wood, but so low that I could with difficulty sit upright in it. No wood, however, was placed on the earth, which formed the floor, but it was dry; and although the wind entered it by innumerable chinks, I found it an agreeable asylum from the snow and rain.

"Here, then, I retreated and lay down happy to have found a shelter, however miserable, from the inclemency of the season, and still more from the barbarity of man. As soon as morning dawned I crept from my kennel, that I might view the adjacent cottage and discover if I could remain in the habitation I had found. It was situated against the back of the cottage and surrounded on the sides which were exposed by a pig sty and a clear pool of water. One part was open, and by that I had crept in; but now I covered every crevice by which I might be perceived with stones and wood, yet in such a manner that I might move them on occasion to pass out; all the light I enjoyed came through the sty, and that was sufficient for me.

"Having thus arranged my dwelling and carpeted it with clean straw, I retired, for I saw the figure of a man at a distance, and I remembered too well my treatment the night before to trust myself in his power. I had first, however, provided for my sustenance for that day by a loaf of coarse bread, which I purloined, and a cup with which I could drink more conveniently than from my hand of the pure water which flowed by my retreat. The floor was a little raised, so that it was kept perfectly dry, and by its vicinity to the chimney of the cottage it was tolerably warm.

"Being thus provided, I resolved to reside in this hovel until something should occur which might alter my determination. It was indeed a paradise compared to the bleak forest, my former residence, the rain-dropping branches, and dank earth. I ate my breakfast with pleasure and was about to remove a plank to procure myself a little water when I heard a step, and looking through a small chink, I beheld a young creature, with a pail on her head, passing before my hovel. The girl was young and of gentle demeanour, unlike what I have since found cottagers and farmhouse servants to be. Yet she was meanly dressed, a coarse blue petticoat and a linen jacket being her only garb; her fair hair was plaited but not adorned: she looked patient yet sad. I lost sight of her, and in about a quarter of an hour she returned bearing the pail, which was now partly filled with milk. As she walked along, seemingly incommoded by the burden, a young man met her, whose countenance expressed a deeper despondence. Uttering a few sounds with an air of melancholy, he took the pail from her head and bore it to the cottage himself. She followed, and they disappeared. Presently I saw the young man again, with some tools in his hand, cross the field behind the cottage; and the girl was also busied, sometimes in the house and sometimes in the yard. *[We are about to hear a story.]*

"On examining my dwelling, I found that one of the windows of the cottage had formerly occupied a part of it, but the panes had been filled up with wood. In one of these was a small and almost imperceptible chink through which the eye could just penetrate. Through this crevice a small room was visible, whitewashed and clean but very bare of furniture. In one corner, near a small fire, sat an old man, leaning his head on his hands in a disconsolate attitude. The young girl was occupied in arranging the cottage; but presently she took something out of a drawer, which employed her hands, and she sat down beside the old man, who, taking up an instrument, began to play and to produce sounds sweeter than the voice of the thrush or the nightingale. It was a lovely sight, even to me, poor wretch who had never beheld aught beautiful before. The silver hair and benevolent countenance of the aged cottager won my reverence, while the gentle manners of the girl enticed my love. He played a sweet mournful air which I perceived drew tears from the eyes of his amiable companion, of which the old man took no notice, until she sobbed audibly; he then pronounced a few sounds, and the fair creature, leaving her work, knelt at his feet. He raised her and smiled with such kindness and affection that I felt sensations of a peculiar and overpowering nature; they were a mixture of pain and pleasure, such as I had never before experienced, either from hunger or cold, warmth or food; and I withdrew from the window, unable to bear these emotions.

"Soon after this the young man returned, bearing on his shoulders a load of wood. The girl met him at the door, helped to relieve him of his burden, and taking some of the fuel into the cottage, placed it on the fire; then she and the youth went apart into a nook of the cottage, and he showed her a large loaf and a piece of cheese. She seemed pleased and went into the garden for some roots and plants, which she placed in water, and then upon the fire. She afterwards continued her work, whilst the young man went into the garden and appeared busily employed in digging and pulling up roots. After he had been employed thus about an hour, the young woman joined him and they entered the cottage together.

"The old man had, in the meantime, been pensive, but on the appearance of his companions he assumed a more cheerful air, and they sat down to eat. The meal was quickly dispatched. The young woman was again occupied in arranging the cottage, the old man walked before the cottage in the sun for a few minutes, leaning on the arm of the youth. **Nothing could exceed in beauty the contrast between these two excellent creatures. One was old, with silver hairs and a countenance beaming with benevolence and love; the younger was slight and graceful in his figure, and his features were moulded with the finest symmetry, yet his eyes and attitude expressed the utmost sadness and despondency**. The old man returned to the cottage, and the youth, with tools different from those he had used in the morning, directed his steps across the fields.

"Night quickly shut in, but to my extreme wonder, I found that the cottagers had a means of prolonging light by the use of tapers, and was delighted to find that the setting of the sun did not put an end to the pleasure I experienced in watching my human neighbours. In the evening the young girl and her companion were employed in various occupations which I did not understand; and the old man again took up the instrument which produced the divine sounds that had enchanted me in the morning. So soon as he had finished, the youth began, not to play, but to utter sounds that were monotonous, and neither resembling the harmony of the old man's instrument nor the songs of the birds; I since found that he read aloud, but at that time I knew nothing of the science of words or letters.

"The family, after having been thus occupied for a short time, extinguished their lights and retired, as I conjectured, to rest."

• ANALYZING THE SCENE •
CHAPTER 11 – SCENE 24

A Story Event is an active change of universal human value for one or more characters as a result of conflict (one character's desires clash with another's or an environmental shift changes the universal human value).

A Working Scene contains at least one Story Event. To determine a scene's Story Event, answer these four questions:

1. What are the characters literally doing—that is, what are their micro on-the-ground actions?

Frankenstein's creature decides to leave the hut where he has found shelter; after a few hours of travel he arrives at a village where the terrified inhabitants chase him away. He takes up residence in a hovel in the countryside that is connected to a cottage, and he begins to spy on the residents of the cottage.

2. What is the essential tactic of the characters—that is, what macro behaviors are they employing that are linked to a universal human value?

The creature is learning about human nature. First, he learns (again) that he is so terrifyingly different and ugly compared to humans, they will attack him rather than help him. Second, he observes the residents of the adjacent cottage and begins to learn about relationships among humans in a family.

3. What universal human values have changed for one or more characters in the scene? Which one of those value changes is most important and should be included in the Story Grid Spreadsheet?

The creature has gone from Attacked to Safe. One might also use a value of "in public" versus "in hiding." Both options describe changes in condition or state that happen in the scene, but when the global spectrum of value is as extreme as Damnation to Death to Life, perhaps Attacked to Safe is a little closer to that global value.

Attacked to Safe

4. What is the Story Event that sums up the scene's on-the-ground actions, essential tactics, and value change? We will enter that event in the Story Grid Spreadsheet.

The creature wanders about the countryside and is chased by humans when they see his horrific countenance. He finally finds shelter in a hovel attached to a cottage with three residents.

HOW THE SCENE ABIDES BY THE FIVE COMMANDMENTS OF STORYTELLING

Inciting Incident: The creature leaves the hut where he has been sheltered and travels through the countryside.

Turning Point Progressive Complication: The creature finds a hovel where he takes shelter but discovers that a family lives in a cottage connected to the hovel.

Crisis: Should the creature remain, after his frightening experience with other human beings? Should he approach them? Should he flee? Best bad choice.

Climax: He decides to remain and observe without revealing himself.

Resolution: The three members of the family are beautiful and sad. The creature is fascinated by them and decides to spy on them through a hole in the wall.

NOTES

- Recollect that we are still listening to the creature's tale. The story is so fascinating that it is easy to forget the quotation marks at the beginning of each paragraph, which are there to remind us that we are reading a story within a story within a story! Bear in mind that this is Walton writing to his sister, the substance of which is Victor telling the story, which was told to him by the creature.

- In the previous scene, we saw the creature start out as an innocent being wandering in the woods, unable to process the barest stimulation. The creature then learns to protect himself from cold, seek shelter, seek food, and avail himself of the warmth of fire. We are now at the next level of consciousness where the creature wanders into a village, presumably to see if he can join a community. Naturally this doesn't go over very well, and he is chased away.
- He is alone once more (remember Walton's loneliness? another parallel!) and too afraid to venture into public. That's logical, given his experience. However, Shelley-the-writer needs to keep him progressing along the continuum of human development, so she gives him the ability to spy on a family. Perfect! Remember, she needs to get this creature to the point where it's logical and possible for him to make a claim on Victor Frankenstein as his creator. He needs to be able to reason in a way that makes it possible for him to be a sympathetic character. This is what makes Frankenstein such a compelling horror story: we actually understand the motivations of the monster.

CHAPTER 12 – SCENE 25

"I lay on my straw, but I could not sleep. I thought of the occurrences of the day. What chiefly struck me was the gentle manners of these people, and I longed to join them, but dared not. I remembered too well the treatment I had suffered the night before from the barbarous villagers, and resolved, whatever course of conduct I might hereafter think it right to pursue, that for the present I would remain quietly in my hovel, watching and endeavouring to discover the motives which influenced their actions.

"The cottagers arose the next morning before the sun. The young woman arranged the cottage and prepared the food, and the youth departed after the first meal.

"This day was passed in the same routine as that which preceded it. The young man was constantly employed out of doors, and the girl in various laborious occupations within. The old man, whom I soon perceived to be blind, employed his leisure hours on his instrument or in contemplation. **Nothing could exceed the love and respect which the younger cottagers exhibited towards their venerable companion. They performed towards him every little office of affection and duty with gentleness, and he rewarded them by his benevolent smiles.**

"They were not entirely happy. The young man and his companion often went apart and appeared to weep. I saw no cause for their unhappiness, but I was deeply affected by it. **If such lovely creatures were miserable, it was less strange that I, an imperfect and solitary being, should be wretched.** Yet why were these gentle beings unhappy? They possessed a delightful house (for such it was in my eyes) and every luxury; they had a fire to warm them when chill and delicious viands when hungry; they were dressed in excellent clothes; and, still more, they enjoyed one another's company and speech, interchanging each day looks of affection and kindness. What did their tears imply? Did they really express pain? I was at first unable to solve these questions, but perpetual attention and time explained to me many appearances which were at first enigmatic.

"**A considerable period elapsed before I discovered one of the causes of the uneasiness of this amiable family: it was poverty**, and they suffered that evil in a very distressing degree. Their nourishment consisted entirely of the vegetables of their garden and the milk of one cow, which gave very little during the winter, when its masters could scarcely procure food to support it. They often, I believe, suffered the pangs of hunger very poignantly, especially the two younger cottagers, for **several times they placed food before the old man when they reserved none for themselves.**

"This trait of kindness moved me sensibly. I had been accustomed, during the night, to steal a part of their store for my own consumption, but when I found that in doing this I inflicted pain on the cottagers, I abstained and satisfied myself with berries, nuts, and roots which I gathered from a neighbouring wood.

"I discovered also another means through which I was enabled to assist their labours. I found that the youth spent a great part of each day in collecting wood for the family fire, and during the night I often took his tools, the use of which I quickly discovered, and brought home firing sufficient for the consumption of several days.

"I remember, the first time that I did this, the young woman, when she opened the door in the morning, appeared greatly astonished on seeing a great pile of wood on the outside. She uttered some words in a loud voice, and the youth joined her, who also expressed surprise. I observed, with pleasure, that he did not go to the forest that day, but spent it in repairing the cottage and cultivating the garden.

"By degrees I made a discovery of still greater moment. **I found that these people possessed a method of communicating their experience and feelings to one another by articulate sounds.** I perceived that the words they spoke sometimes produced pleasure or pain, smiles or sadness, in the minds and countenances of the hearers. This was indeed a godlike science, and I ardently desired to become acquainted with it. But I was baffled in every attempt I made for this purpose. Their pronunciation was quick, and the words they uttered, not having any apparent connection with visible objects, I was unable to discover any clue by which I could unravel the mystery of their reference. **By great application, however, and after having remained during the space of several revolutions of the moon in my hovel, I discovered the names that were given to some of the most familiar objects of discourse**; I learned and applied the words, 'fire,' 'milk,' 'bread,' and 'wood.' I learned also the names of the cottagers themselves. The youth and his companion had each of them several names, but the old man had only one, which was 'father.' The girl was called 'sister' or 'Agatha,' and the youth 'Felix,' 'brother,' or 'son.' I cannot describe the delight I felt when I learned the ideas appropriated to each of these sounds and was able to pronounce them. I distinguished several other words without being able as yet to understand or apply them, such as 'good,' 'dearest,' 'unhappy.'

• ANALYZING THE SCENE •
CHAPTER 12 – SCENE 25

A Story Event is an active change of universal human value for one or more characters as a result of conflict (one character's desires clash with another's or an environmental shift changes the universal human value).

A Working Scene contains at least one Story Event. To determine a scene's Story Event, answer these four questions:

1. What are the characters literally doing—that is, what are their micro on-the-ground actions?

Frankenstein's creature is observing the family living in the cottage next to his hovel.

2. What is the essential tactic of the characters—that is, what macro behaviors are they employing that are linked to a universal human value?

The creature is learning about the causes of human suffering and how people communicate; he is also learning language.

3. What universal human values have changed for one or more characters in the scene? Which one of those value changes is most important and should be included in the Story Grid Spreadsheet?

The creature starts the scene relatively ignorant of how human interactions work and how people affect each other. By the end of the scene, he has figured out that poverty causes suffering, that people can play a role in alleviating suffering (as in when the son and daughter give up food for their father, and when the creature cuts wood for the cottagers), and that they communicate their feelings to each other by way of speech. His state has changed from Ignorant to Knowledgeable. This transition greatly affects the overall story journey of the creature.

Ignorant to Knowledgeable

4. What is the Story Event that sums up the scene's on-the-ground actions, essential tactics, and value change? We will enter that event in the Story Grid Spreadsheet.

The creature begins to spy on his neighbors; he doesn't understand them but can see they are poor and struggling. He begins to understand language.

HOW THE SCENE ABIDES BY THE FIVE COMMANDMENTS OF STORYTELLING

Inciting Incident: The creature spies on the cottagers.

Turning Point Progressive Complication: The creature figures out they are poor and struggling.

Crisis: What should the creature do? Should he help them? Irreconcilable goods choice.

Climax: The creature decides to help them by cutting wood for them, which confuses and astonishes the cottagers.

Resolution: The creature begins to understand that the cottagers are able to communicate by way of sounds. He learns their names and names of objects.

NOTES

- This is a complex scene. Let's think about the role it plays in the greater story arc. We have several practical problems that need to be resolved. First of all, how shall we get the creature to learn language? Second, how do we teach the creature about human interactions? Third, how do we demonstrate the creature's humanity and capacity for the emotions that make him human rather than monster?
- We can see an example of Shelley's planning and careful structuring of the story in this scene. She already knows what kind of story she wants to tell with regard to the cottagers. This part of the story is a morality tale; she wants to explore the question of what it means to be human. Within the context of a morality tale, she has produced a creature that is brought into the world as a result of bypassing the "natural order" of things, so we aren't sure he qualifies as "human." However, if she had wanted a two-dimensional "monster," she could have had him systematically preying on the people he comes across, snatching what he pleases and taking advantage of his great

height and strength. Many Horror stories have a monster that plays that role. Instead, she has the creature spend hours observing a high level of moral human behavior and allowing him to draw conclusions.

- Since he goes from Ignorant to Knowledgeable in this scene, what can we conclude about the creature as a being? Is he human? He certainly seems human in the best possible way. He not only absorbs what is going on with the family, but he understands his role in prolonging their suffering and stops stealing their food. He also decides to improve their lives by providing firewood. These are the calculations of a human being, not a monster; they are also the calculation of a compassionate human being, not an indifferent human being.
- In this scene, Shelley is telling us to watch closely as this supposedly "unnatural" being behaves not only like a human, but learns the meaning of "humanity" at a very high level and emulates it. What does this say about the people who are born human in the "normal" way but who do not demonstrate these virtues? What does this say about the creature with his suspect origins?
- It seems we have more questions than answers here, but these are the most important questions in the book. When the creature's humanity is questioned in future scenes, keep in mind that he studied humanity by observing the highest examples of moral behavior.

CHAPTER 12 – SCENE 26

"I spent the winter in this manner. **The gentle manners and beauty of the cottagers greatly endeared them to me; when they were unhappy, I felt depressed; when they rejoiced, I sympathized in their joys.** I saw few human beings besides them, and if any other happened to enter the cottage, their harsh manners and rude gait only enhanced to me the superior accomplishments of my friends. The old man, I could perceive, often endeavoured to encourage his children, as sometimes I found that he called them, to cast off their melancholy. He would talk in a cheerful accent, with an expression of goodness that bestowed pleasure even upon me. Agatha listened with respect, her eyes sometimes filled with tears, which she endeavoured to wipe away unperceived; but I generally found that her countenance and tone were more cheerful after having listened to the exhortations of her father. It was not thus with Felix. He was always the saddest of the group, and even to my unpractised senses, he appeared to have suffered more deeply than his friends. But if his countenance was more sorrowful, his voice was more cheerful than that of his sister, especially when he addressed the old man.

"I could mention innumerable instances which, although slight, marked the dispositions of these amiable cottagers. In the midst of poverty and want, Felix carried with pleasure to his sister the first little white flower that peeped out from beneath the snowy ground. Early in the morning, before she had risen, he cleared away the snow that obstructed her path to the milk-house, drew water from the well, and brought the wood from the outhouse, where, to his perpetual astonishment, he found his store always replenished by an invisible hand. In the day, I believe, he worked sometimes for a neighbouring farmer, because he often went forth and did not return until dinner, yet brought no wood with him. At other times he worked in the garden, but as there was little to do in the frosty season, he read to the old man and Agatha.

"This reading had puzzled me extremely at first, but by degrees I discovered that he uttered many of the same sounds when he read as when he talked. I conjectured, therefore, that he found on the paper signs for speech which he understood, and I ardently longed to comprehend these also; but how was that possible when I did not even understand the sounds for which they stood as signs? I improved, however, sensibly in this science, but not sufficiently to follow up any kind of conversation, although I applied my whole mind to the endeavour, for I easily perceived that, **although I eagerly longed to discover myself to the cottagers, I ought not to make the attempt until I had first become master of their language, which knowledge might enable me to make them overlook the deformity of my figure, for with this also the contrast perpetually presented to my eyes had made me acquainted.**

"I had admired the perfect forms of my cottagers—their grace, beauty, and delicate complexions; but how was I terrified when I viewed myself in a transparent pool! At first I started back, unable to believe that it was indeed I who was reflected in the mirror; and when I became fully convinced that I was in reality the monster that I am, I was filled with the bitterest sensations of despondence and mortification. Alas! I did not yet entirely know the fatal effects of this miserable deformity.

"As the sun became warmer and the light of day longer, the snow vanished, and I beheld the bare trees and the black earth. From this time Felix was more employed, and the heart-moving indications of impending famine disappeared. Their food, as I afterwards found, was coarse, but it was wholesome; and they procured a sufficiency of it. Several new kinds of plants sprang up in the garden, which they dressed; and these signs of comfort increased daily as the season advanced.

"The old man, leaning on his son, walked each day at noon, when it did not rain, as I found it was called when the heavens poured forth its waters. This frequently took place, but a high wind quickly dried the earth, and the season became far more pleasant than it had been.

"My mode of life in my hovel was uniform. During the morning I attended the motions of the cottagers, and when they were dispersed in various occupations, I slept; the remainder of the day was spent in observing my friends. When they had retired to rest, if there was any moon or the night was star-light, I went into the woods and collected my own food and fuel for the cottage. **When I returned, as often as it was necessary, I cleared their path from the snow and performed those offices that I had seen done by Felix.** I afterwards found that these labours, performed by an invisible hand, greatly astonished them; and once or twice I heard them, on these occasions, utter the words 'good spirit,' 'wonderful'; but I did not then understand the signification of these terms.

"My thoughts now became more active, and I longed to discover the motives and feelings of these lovely creatures; I was inquisitive to know why Felix appeared so miserable and Agatha so sad. **I thought (foolish wretch!) that it might be in my power to restore happiness to these deserving people.** *[The monster is a virtuous being; he wants to make people happy.]* When I slept or was absent, the forms of the venerable blind father, the gentle Agatha, and the excellent Felix flitted before me. **I looked upon them as superior beings who would be the arbiters of my future destiny. I formed in my imagination a thousand pictures of presenting myself to them, and their reception of me. I imagined that they would be disgusted, until, by my gentle demeanour and conciliating words, I should first win their favour and afterwards their love.**

"These thoughts exhilarated me and led me to apply with fresh ardour to the acquiring the art of language. My organs were indeed harsh, but supple; and although my voice was very unlike the soft music of their tones, yet I pronounced such words as I understood with tolerable ease. It was as the ass and the lap-dog; yet surely the gentle ass whose intentions were affectionate, although his manners were rude, deserved better treatment than blows and execration.

"The pleasant showers and genial warmth of spring greatly altered the aspect of the earth. Men who before this change seemed to have been hid in caves dispersed themselves and were employed in various arts of cultivation. The birds sang in more cheerful notes, and the leaves began to bud forth on the trees. Happy, happy earth! Fit habitation for gods, which, so short a time before, was bleak, damp, and unwholesome. **My spirits were elevated by the enchanting appearance of nature; the past was blotted from my memory, the present was tranquil, and the future gilded by bright rays of hope and anticipations of joy."**

• ANALYZING THE SCENE •
CHAPTER 12 – SCENE 26

A Story Event is an active change of universal human value for one or more characters as a result of conflict (one character's desires clash with another's or an environmental shift changes the universal human value).

A Working Scene contains at least one Story Event. To determine a scene's Story Event, answer these four questions:

1. What are the characters literally doing—that is, what are their micro on-the-ground actions?

The creature is spending the winter watching the cottagers and studying them.

2. What is the essential tactic of the characters—that is, what macro behaviors are they employing that are linked to a universal human value?

The creature is learning aspects of what it means to be human. He improves in his ability to understand their language and learns about reading. He aspires to join their family and decides he must learn their language well.

3. What universal human values have changed for one or more characters in the scene? Which one of those value changes is most important and should be included in the Story Grid Spreadsheet?

In this scene, the season changes from winter to spring. As the days grow longer, green leaves appear, and people emerge from their simple homes, the creature feels more and more optimistic about his future.

This scene starts with winter and ends with spring, so at the most basic level, the value really is Death to Life (winter to spring). In order to tie the emotional shift to the character, it is probably more useful to characterize it as Despair to Hope. However, the initial emotion is not quite at the level of despair, so perhaps we should say Sadness to Joy or Adrift to Focused as the creature decides on a plan to gain the love and affection of the cottagers.

Adrift to Focused

4. What is the Story Event that sums up the scene's on-the-ground actions, essential tactics, and value change? We will enter that event in the Story Grid Spreadsheet.

The creature spends the winter watching the family in the cottage and learning what it means to be human; he secretly helps with chores and studies their language.

HOW THE SCENE ABIDES BY THE FIVE COMMANDMENTS OF STORYTELLING

Inciting Incident: The creature observes the life of the cottagers throughout the winter.

Turning Point Progressive Complication: He wants to join their family.

Crisis: What plan should he create that would enable him to become accepted as one of their household? He can learn language if he stays quiet and spies; he can also contribute to the work of the household. Irreconcilable goods.

Climax: The creature helps the family by clearing snow and cutting wood but decides language acquisition is most important.

Resolution: He applies himself to the study of language.

NOTES

- Chapter 12 is a little difficult to separate into scenes. Much of what is happening is the creature simply observing the little family. At this stage in his life, he does not yet understand language, so he isn't able to explain to Frankenstein exactly what is happening with the cottagers. The major takeaway here is that the creature states his intention to eventually reveal himself to the family, and because of their gentle behavior with each other, he expects they will accept and love him.
- We've expected all along that the family is going to eventually discover that he is hiding next door. They are the family that Victor Frankenstein refused to be for his creature, so they are of paramount importance. Everything he knows about human nature and how people relate to one another comes from this family. How will they receive him? This is the new anxiety that Shelley has introduced to us.

CHAPTER 13 – SCENE 27

"I now hasten to the more moving part of my story. **I shall relate events that impressed me with feelings which, from what I had been, have made me what I am.**

"Spring advanced rapidly; the weather became fine and the skies cloudless. It surprised me that what before was desert and gloomy should now bloom with the most beautiful flowers and verdure. My senses were gratified and refreshed by a thousand scents of delight and a thousand sights of beauty.

"It was on one of these days, when my cottagers periodically rested from labour—the old man played on his guitar, and the children listened to him—that I observed the countenance of Felix was melancholy beyond expression; he sighed frequently, and once his father paused in his music, and I conjectured by his manner that he inquired the cause of his son's sorrow. Felix replied in a cheerful accent, and the old man was recommencing his music when someone tapped at the door.

"It was a lady on horseback, accompanied by a country-man as a guide. The lady was dressed in a dark suit and covered with a thick black veil. Agatha asked a question, to which the stranger only replied by pronouncing, in a sweet accent, the name of Felix. Her voice was musical but unlike that of either of my friends. On hearing this word,

Felix came up hastily to the lady, who, when she saw him, threw up her veil, and I beheld a countenance of angelic beauty and expression. Her hair of a shining raven black, and curiously braided; her eyes were dark, but gentle, although animated; her features of a regular proportion, and her complexion wondrously fair, each cheek tinged with a lovely pink.

"Felix seemed ravished with delight when he saw her, every trait of sorrow vanished from his face, and it instantly expressed a degree of ecstatic joy, of which I could hardly have believed it capable; his eyes sparkled, as his cheek flushed with pleasure; and at that moment I thought him as beautiful as the stranger. She appeared affected by different feelings; wiping a few tears from her lovely eyes, she held out her hand to Felix, who kissed it rapturously and called her, as well as I could distinguish, his sweet Arabian. She did not appear to understand him, but smiled. He assisted her to dismount, and dismissing her guide, conducted her into the cottage. Some conversation took place between him and his father, and the young stranger knelt at the old man's feet and would have kissed his hand, but he raised her and embraced her affectionately.

"I soon perceived that **although the stranger uttered articulate sounds and appeared to have a language of her own, she was neither understood by nor herself understood the cottagers**. They made many signs which I did not comprehend, but I saw that her presence diffused gladness through the cottage, dispelling their sorrow as the sun dissipates the morning mists. Felix seemed peculiarly happy and with smiles of delight welcomed his Arabian. Agatha, the ever-gentle Agatha, kissed the hands of the lovely stranger, and pointing to her brother, made signs which appeared to me to mean that he had been sorrowful until she came. Some hours passed thus, while they, by their countenances, expressed joy, the cause of which I did not comprehend. Presently I found, by the frequent recurrence of some sound which the stranger repeated after them, that she was endeavouring to learn their language; and the idea instantly occurred to me that I should make use of the same instructions to the same end. The stranger learned about twenty words at the first lesson; most of them, indeed, were those which I had before understood, but I profited by the others.

"As night came on, Agatha and the Arabian retired early. When they separated Felix kissed the hand of the stranger and said, 'Good night sweet Safie.' He sat up much longer, conversing with his father, and by the frequent repetition of her name I conjectured that their lovely guest was the subject of their conversation. I ardently desired to understand them, and bent every faculty towards that purpose, but found it utterly impossible.

"The next morning Felix went out to his work, and after the usual occupations of Agatha were finished, the Arabian sat at the feet of the old man, and taking his guitar, played some airs so entrancingly beautiful that they at once drew tears of sorrow and delight from my eyes. She sang, and her voice flowed in a rich cadence, swelling or dying away like a nightingale of the woods.

"When she had finished, she gave the guitar to Agatha, who at first declined it. She played a simple air, and her voice accompanied it in sweet accents, but unlike the wondrous strain of the stranger. The old man appeared enraptured and said some words which Agatha endeavoured to explain to Safie, and by which he appeared to wish to express that she bestowed on him the greatest delight by her music.

"The days now passed as peaceably as before, with the sole alteration that joy had taken place of sadness in the countenances of my friends. **Safie was always gay and happy; she and I improved rapidly in the knowledge of language, so that in two months I began to comprehend most of the words uttered by my protectors.**

"In the meanwhile also the black ground was covered with herbage, and the green banks interspersed with innumerable flowers, sweet to the scent and the eyes, stars of pale radiance among the moonlight woods; the sun became warmer, the nights clear and balmy; and my nocturnal rambles were an extreme pleasure to me, although they were considerably shortened by the late setting and early rising of the sun, for I never ventured abroad during daylight, fearful of meeting with the same treatment I had formerly endured in the first village which I entered.

• ANALYZING THE SCENE •
CHAPTER 13 – SCENE 27

A Story Event is an active change of universal human value for one or more characters as a result of conflict (one character's desires clash with another's or an environmental shift changes the universal human value).

A Working Scene contains at least one Story Event. To determine a scene's Story Event, answer these four questions:

1. What are the characters literally doing—that is, what are their micro on-the-ground actions?

A new arrival changes the dynamic of the cottagers' simple household. The arrival is an "Arabian" named Safie who clearly has some kind of romantic past with Felix.

2. What is the essential tactic of the characters—that is, what macro behaviors are they employing that are linked to a universal human value?

Safie is unable to speak the language of the cottagers. Shelley shows that it is possible for Safie to communicate feeling to the cottagers by playing music on the old man's guitar, but she needs to learn the cottagers' language, and by doing so the creature also has the opportunity to learn. It appears that everyone in this scene wants to hear and be heard.

3. What universal human values have changed for one or more characters in the scene? Which one of those value changes is most important and should be included in the Story Grid Spreadsheet?

This scene starts with the words "spring advanced rapidly." At the end of the scene spring is in full force. Safie's arrival has given the creature an opportunity to rapidly study and learn the cottagers' language.

Spring is a metaphor for life, and in this scene, the creature's optimism expands as he improves so rapidly in his study of the cottagers' language he says he could now understand most of what they said. One could highlight the value of any of the cottagers or of Safie, as all of them are much happier after her arrival. To remain consistent, however, let's track the creature's state, which goes from uncomprehending to comprehending (of language).

Uncomprehending to Comprehending

4. What is the Story Event that sums up the scene's on-the-ground actions, essential tactics, and value change? We will enter that event in the Story Grid Spreadsheet.

The cottagers welcome Safie, an "Arabian." She studies their language and the creature studies along with her.

HOW THE SCENE ABIDES BY THE FIVE COMMANDMENTS OF STORYTELLING

Inciting Incident: A stranger arrives at the cottagers' hut.

Turning Point Progressive Complication: She does not know their language, so how will they communicate?

Crisis: She plays the old man's instrument and otherwise communicates her emotions that way, but it's clearly insufficient. Will she be able to stay?

Climax: Safie studies the cottagers' language over time.

Resolution: The creature learns rapidly along with her.

NOTES

- At the very beginning of this scene, the creature makes an important pronouncement: "I shall relate events that impressed me with feelings which, from what I had been, have made me what I am." That's quite an attention-getter! We'd better pay close attention to the emotional swings here.

- Safie the "Arabian" shows up. She seems to be a previous love interest of Felix's, but strangely she doesn't speak his language!
- Nonetheless everyone is thrilled that she has arrived. Her lack of understanding doesn't seem to get in the way of their happiness, but she doesn't understand a word of what is said and cannot make herself understood. There is a lovely moment where she plays the guitar and sings, and it is clear that she can communicate emotion through music.
- After Safie's arrival, the creature's language ability skyrockets.

CHAPTER 13 – SCENE 28

"My days were spent in close attention, that I might more speedily master the language; and I may boast that I improved more rapidly than the Arabian, who understood very little and conversed in broken accents, whilst I comprehended and could imitate almost every word that was spoken.

"While I improved in speech, I also learned the science of letters as it was taught to the stranger, and this opened before me a wide field for wonder and delight.

"The book from which Felix instructed Safie was Volney's Ruins of Empires. I should not have understood the purport of this book had not Felix, in reading it, given very minute explanations. He had chosen this work, he said, because the declamatory style was framed in imitation of the Eastern authors. **Through this work I obtained a cursory knowledge of history and a view of the several empires at present existing in the world; it gave me an insight into the manners, governments, and religions of the different nations of the earth.** I heard of the slothful Asiatics, of the stupendous genius and mental activity of the Grecians, of the wars and wonderful virtue of the early Romans—of their subsequent degenerating—of the decline of that mighty empire, of chivalry, Christianity, and kings. **I heard of the discovery of the American hemisphere and wept with Safie over the**

hapless fate of its original inhabitants. *[Again, the monster shows his humanity.]*

"These wonderful narrations inspired me with strange feelings. **Was man, indeed, at once so powerful, so virtuous and magnificent, yet so vicious and base? He appeared at one time a mere scion of the evil principle and at another as all that can be conceived of noble and godlike.** To be a great and virtuous man appeared the highest honour that can befall a sensitive being; to be base and vicious, as many on record have been, appeared the lowest degradation, a condition more abject than that of the blind mole or harmless worm. **For a long time I could not conceive how one man could go forth to murder his fellow, or even why there were laws and governments; but when I heard details of vice and bloodshed, my wonder ceased and I turned away with disgust and loathing.**

"Every conversation of the cottagers now opened new wonders to me. While I listened to the instructions which Felix bestowed upon the Arabian, the strange system of human society was explained to me. I heard of the division of property, of immense wealth and squalid poverty, of rank, descent, and noble blood.

"The words induced me to turn towards myself. **I learned that the possessions most esteemed by your fellow creatures were high and unsullied descent united with riches.** A man might be respected with only one of these advantages, but without either he was considered, except in very rare instances, as a vagabond and a slave, doomed to waste his powers for the profits of the chosen few! And what was I? Of my creation and creator I was absolutely ignorant, but I knew that I possessed no money, no friends, no kind of property. I was, besides, endued with a figure hideously deformed and loathsome; I was not even of the same nature as man. I was more agile than they and could subsist upon coarser diet; I bore the extremes of heat and cold with less injury to my frame; my stature far exceeded theirs. When I looked around I saw and heard of none like me. **Was I, then, a monster, a blot upon the earth, from which all men fled and whom all men disowned?** *[What is the nature of humankind? Does being alone equal being a monster?]*

"I cannot describe to you the agony that these reflections inflicted upon me; I tried to dispel them, but sorrow only increased with knowledge. Oh, that I had forever remained in my native wood, nor known nor felt beyond the sensations of hunger, thirst, and heat!

"**Of what a strange nature is knowledge! It clings to the mind when it has once seized on it like a lichen on the rock.** I wished sometimes to shake off all thought and feeling, but I learned that there was but one means to overcome the sensation of pain, and that was death—a state which I feared yet did not understand. I admired virtue and good feelings and loved the gentle manners and amiable qualities of my cottagers, but I was shut out from intercourse with them, except through means which I obtained by stealth, when I was unseen and unknown, and which rather increased than satisfied the desire I had of becoming one among my fellows. The gentle words of Agatha and the animated smiles of the charming Arabian were not for me. The mild exhortations of the old man and the lively conversation of the loved Felix were not for me. Miserable, unhappy wretch!

"Other lessons were impressed upon me even more deeply. I heard of the difference of sexes, and the birth and growth of children, how the father doted on the smiles of the infant, and the lively sallies of the older child, how all the life and cares of the mother were wrapped up in the precious charge, how the mind of youth expanded and gained knowledge, of brother, sister, and all the various relationships which bind one human being to another in mutual bonds.

"But **where were my friends and relations?** No father had watched my infant days, no mother had blessed me with smiles and caresses; or if they had, all my past life was now a blot, a blind vacancy in which I distinguished nothing. From my earliest remembrance I had been as I then was in height and proportion. I had never yet seen a being resembling me or who claimed any intercourse with me. **What was I?** The question again recurred, to be answered only with groans.

"I will soon explain to what these feelings tended, but allow me now to return to the cottagers, whose story excited in me such various feelings of indignation, delight, and wonder, but which all terminated in additional love and reverence for my protectors (for so I loved, in an innocent, half-painful self-deceit, to call them)."

• ANALYZING THE SCENE •
CHAPTER 13 – SCENE 28

A Story Event is an active change of universal human value for one or more characters as a result of conflict (one character's desires clash with another's or an environmental shift changes the universal human value).

A Working Scene contains at least one Story Event. To determine a scene's Story Event, answer these four questions:

1. What are the characters literally doing—that is, what are their micro on-the-ground actions?

The creature is studying both the language of the cottagers and learning to read. Because Felix is using a history book to instruct Safie in language, the creature is treated to lectures on history, government, religion, and other subjects.

2. What is the essential tactic of the characters—that is, what macro behaviors are they employing that are linked to a universal human value?

This is where Shelley introduces the creature to the evils of man and the complexities of human society. The creature's essential tactic in this scene revolves around studying and learning about the human race and its relationships and actions.

3. What universal human values have changed for one or more characters in the scene? Which one of those value changes is most important and should be included in the Story Grid Spreadsheet?

This knowledge, far from bringing feelings of happy enlightenment to the creature, causes him to become despondent as he contemplates questions that cannot be answered about his origins and his role in society.

In this scene, the creature goes from Ignorance to Awareness, but he also goes from pleasure in the act of learning to dismay at the substance of what he is learning. In this case, let's concentrate on emotional transition and highlight Hopeful Ignorance to Dismayed Knowledge.

Hopeful Ignorance to Dismayed Knowledge

4. What is the Story Event that sums up the scene's on-the-ground actions, essential tactics, and value change? We will enter that event in the Story Grid Spreadsheet.

Safie learns the language with the help of a history book. The creature learns about human relations and the history of the world and realizes he has been deprived of normal relationships.

HOW THE SCENE ABIDES BY THE FIVE COMMANDMENTS OF STORYTELLING

Inciting Incident: Felix begins to formally teach Safie his language, using a history book.

Turning Point Progressive Complication: The creature is confused and disgusted at man's obsession with power, wealth, and the harm he does to his fellow man, as well as the means by which men gain mutual respect. "Was I, then, a monster, a blot upon the earth, from which all men fled and whom all men disowned?" And if he is a man, where is the loving family described by the book as the source of learning for children?

Crisis: Should he choose to inhabit the identity of a man or a monster? Best bad choice.

Climax: The creature chooses to focus on his love for the cottagers.

Resolution: The creature continues his tale.

NOTES

- Once again, Shelley solves a practical problem. Safie arrives at the cottage and needs language instruction. Felix instructs her with a book about history and the affairs of men. This is how the creature learns about other civilizations, other cultures, and relationships between them.
- How fascinating that the creature specifically refers to the sad fate of American natives at the hands of European settlers.
- There is a conflict between what the creature sees in his gentle neighbors and the stories reported in the history book. This book is how he learns about murder, betrayal, corruption—everything "base and vicious." So the examples that Shelley gives of morals of the highest sort (Frankenstein's parents, his sister Elizabeth, and now the cottagers) are offset by this completely different set of examples of the damage that man can do.
- The history book also makes clear the terms by which men measure power and prestige, and this is the jumping-off point for the creature, who realizes he has none of the items that are required for respect. He realizes he does not have a status or a position in the world of men at all, and this knowledge crushes him.
- The last piece of information that the creature learns is that human beings grow from infancy to adulthood in the bosom of a family. He has no family and realizes he has never been an infant or a child. He ends this painful reflection with the question, "What am I?"

CHAPTER 14 – SCENE 29

"Some time elapsed before I learned the history of my friends. It was one which could not fail to impress itself deeply on my mind, unfolding as it did a number of circumstances, each interesting and wonderful to one so utterly inexperienced as I was.

"The name of the old man was De Lacey. He was descended from a good family in France, where he had lived for many years in affluence, respected by his superiors and beloved by his equals. His son was bred in the service of his country, and Agatha had ranked with ladies of the highest distinction. A few months before my arrival they had lived in a large and luxurious city called Paris, surrounded by friends and possessed of every enjoyment which virtue, refinement of intellect, or taste, accompanied by a moderate fortune, could afford.

"The father of Safie had been the cause of their ruin. He was a Turkish merchant and had inhabited Paris for many years, when, for some reason which I could not learn, he became obnoxious to the government. He was seized and cast into prison the very day that Safie arrived from Constantinople to join him. He was tried and condemned to death. The injustice of his sentence was very flagrant; all Paris was indignant; and it was judged that his religion and wealth rather than the crime alleged against him had been the cause of his condemnation.

"Felix had accidentally been present at the trial; his horror and indignation were uncontrollable when he heard the decision of the court. He made, at that moment, a solemn vow to deliver him and then looked around for the means. *[Another example of moral behavior, where you sacrifice yourself for justice.]* After many fruitless attempts to gain admittance to the prison, he found a strongly grated window in an unguarded part of the building, which lighted the dungeon of the unfortunate Muhammadan, who, loaded with chains, waited in despair the execution of the barbarous sentence. Felix visited the grate at night and made known to the prisoner his intentions in his favour. The Turk, amazed and delighted, endeavoured to kindle the zeal of his deliverer by promises of reward and wealth. Felix rejected his offers with contempt, yet when he saw the lovely Safie, who was allowed to visit her father and who by her gestures expressed her lively gratitude, the youth could not help owning to his own mind that the captive possessed a treasure which would fully reward his toil and hazard.

"The Turk quickly perceived the impression that his daughter had made on the heart of Felix and endeavoured to secure him more entirely in his interests by the promise of her hand in marriage so soon as he should be conveyed to a place of safety. Felix was too delicate to accept this offer, yet he looked forward to the probability of the event as to the consummation of his happiness.

"During the ensuing days, while the preparations were going forward for the escape of the merchant, the zeal of Felix was warmed by several letters that he received from this lovely girl, who found means to express her thoughts in the language of her lover by the aid of an old man, a servant of her father who understood French. She thanked him in the most ardent terms for his intended services towards her parent, and at the same time she gently deplored her own fate.

"I have copies of these letters, for I found means, during my residence in the hovel, to procure the implements of writing; and the letters were often in the hands of Felix or Agatha. Before I depart I will give them to you; they will prove the truth of my tale; but at present, as the sun is already far declined, I shall only have time to repeat the substance of them to you.

"Safie related that her mother was a Christian Arab, seized and made a slave by the Turks; recommended by her beauty, she had won

the heart of the father of Safie, who married her. The young girl spoke in high and enthusiastic terms of her mother, who, born in freedom, spurned the bondage to which she was now reduced. She instructed her daughter in the tenets of her religion and taught her to aspire to higher powers of intellect and an independence of spirit forbidden to the female followers of Muhammad. This lady died, but her lessons were indelibly impressed on the mind of Safie, who sickened at the prospect of again returning to Asia and being immured within the walls of a harem, allowed only to occupy herself with infantile amusements, ill-suited to the temper of her soul, now accustomed to grand ideas and a noble emulation for virtue. The prospect of marrying a Christian and remaining in a country where women were allowed to take a rank in society was enchanting to her.

"The day for the execution of the Turk was fixed, but on the night previous to it he quitted his prison and before morning was distant many leagues from Paris. Felix had procured passports in the name of his father, sister, and himself. He had previously communicated his plan to the former, who aided the deceit by quitting his house, under the pretence of a journey and concealed himself, with his daughter, in an obscure part of Paris.

"Felix conducted the fugitives through France to Lyons and across Mont Cenis to Leghorn, where the merchant had decided to wait a favourable opportunity of passing into some part of the Turkish dominions.

"Safie resolved to remain with her father until the moment of his departure, before which time the Turk renewed his promise that she should be united to his deliverer; and Felix remained with them in expectation of that event; and in the meantime he enjoyed the society of the Arabian, who exhibited towards him the simplest and tenderest affection. They conversed with one another through the means of an interpreter, and sometimes with the interpretation of looks; and Safie sang to him the divine airs of her native country.

"The Turk allowed this intimacy to take place and encouraged the hopes of the youthful lovers, while in his heart he had formed far other plans. He loathed the idea that his daughter should be united to a Christian, but he feared the resentment of Felix if he

should appear lukewarm, for he knew that he was still in the power of his deliverer if he should choose to betray him to the Italian state which they inhabited. He revolved a thousand plans by which he should be enabled to prolong the deceit until it might be no longer necessary, and secretly to take his daughter with him when he departed. His plans were facilitated by the news which arrived from Paris.

"The government of France were greatly enraged at the escape of their victim and spared no pains to detect and punish his deliverer. The plot of Felix was quickly discovered, and De Lacey and Agatha were thrown into prison. The news reached Felix and roused him from his dream of pleasure. His blind and aged father and his gentle sister lay in a noisome dungeon while he enjoyed the free air and the society of her whom he loved. This idea was torture to him. He quickly arranged with the Turk that if the latter should find a favourable opportunity for escape before Felix could return to Italy, Safie should remain as a boarder at a convent at Leghorn; and then, quitting the lovely Arabian, **he hastened to Paris and delivered himself up to the vengeance of the law, hoping to free De Lacey and Agatha by this proceeding.**

"He did not succeed. They remained confined for five months before the trial took place, the result of which deprived them of their fortune and condemned them to a perpetual exile from their native country.

"They found a miserable asylum in the cottage in Germany, where I discovered them. Felix soon learned that **the treacherous Turk, for whom he and his family endured such unheard-of oppression, on discovering that his deliverer was thus reduced to poverty and ruin, became a traitor to good feeling and honour and had quitted Italy with his daughter**, insultingly sending Felix a pittance of money to aid him, as he said, in some plan of future maintenance.

"Such were the events that preyed on the heart of Felix and rendered him, when I first saw him, the most miserable of his family. He could have endured poverty, and while this distress had been the meed of his virtue, he gloried in it; but the ingratitude of the Turk and the loss of his beloved Safie were misfortunes more bitter and irreparable. The arrival of the Arabian now infused new life into his soul.

"When the news reached Leghorn that Felix was deprived of his wealth and rank, the merchant commanded his daughter to think no more of her lover, but to prepare to return to her native country. The generous nature of Safie was outraged by this command; she attempted to expostulate with her father, but he left her angrily, reiterating his tyrannical mandate.

"A few days after, the Turk entered his daughter's apartment and told her hastily that he had reason to believe that his residence at Leghorn had been divulged and that he should speedily be delivered up to the French government; he had consequently hired a vessel to convey him to Constantinople, for which city he should sail in a few hours. He intended to leave his daughter under the care of a confidential servant, to follow at her leisure with the greater part of his property, which had not yet arrived at Leghorn.

"When alone, Safie resolved in her own mind the plan of conduct that it would become her to pursue in this emergency. A residence in Turkey was abhorrent to her; her religion and her feelings were alike averse to it. *[A fascinating setup; Shelley justifies her disobedience toward her father by creating a morally corrupt father figure and suggesting that Safie was faithful to her Christian religion.]* By some papers of her father which fell into her hands she heard of the exile of her lover and learnt the name of the spot where he then resided. She hesitated some time, but at length she formed her determination. Taking with her some jewels that belonged to her and a sum of money, she quitted Italy with an attendant, a native of Leghorn, but who understood the common language of Turkey, and departed for Germany.

"She arrived in safety at a town about twenty leagues from the cottage of De Lacey, when her attendant fell dangerously ill. Safie nursed her with the most devoted affection, but the poor girl died, and the Arabian was left alone, unacquainted with the language of the country and utterly ignorant of the customs of the world. She fell, however, into good hands. The Italian had mentioned the name of the spot for which they were bound, and after her death the woman of the house in which they had lived took care that Safie should arrive in safety at the cottage of her lover."

• ANALYZING THE SCENE • CHAPTER 14 – SCENE 29

A Story Event is an active change of universal human value for one or more characters as a result of conflict (one character's desires clash with another's or an environmental shift changes the universal human value).

A Working Scene contains at least one Story Event. To determine a scene's Story Event, answer these four questions:

1. What are the characters literally doing—that is, what are their micro on-the-ground actions?

The creature takes a moment to now explain Safie's background and how she came to know Felix and his family.

2. What is the essential tactic of the characters—that is, what macro behaviors are they employing that are linked to a universal human value?

In this scene, Felix takes several moral positions and is punished every time. He helps Safie's father escape from a wrongful prison sentence. He believes him when he says that Felix and Safie may get married. When his sister and father are imprisoned, he turns himself in to the French government, which results in all three being deprived of their wealth and exiled from France. The only person who receives what is due to her is Safie, who is a secret Christian in her Muslim family and who resolves to follow Felix to Germany after her father makes it clear that he will no longer permit her to marry her lover.

3. What universal human values have changed for one or more

characters in the scene? Which one of those value changes is most important and should be included in the Story Grid Spreadsheet?

There are several characters with different trajectories. Felix starts out the scene in a fit of rightful indignation and ends up a despondent exile in Germany. Because of the way in which the creature is telling this story to Frankenstein, we don't actually have a clear sense of Felix's emotional state. Felix's family also start as wealthy residents of Paris and end up in poverty in a hovel in Germany, but we don't actually see or experience this. The main character in this scene is actually Safie. She starts out frustrated by her cloistered existence as a female in Muslim Turkey and ends up free in Germany with her beloved.

Trapped to Free

4. What is the Story Event that sums up the scene's on-the-ground actions, essential tactics, and value change? We will enter that event in the Story Grid Spreadsheet.

The creature explains Safie's story to Frankenstein. Safie is Turkish and a secret Christian, who has escaped confinement in Turkey after her father escapes prison in France.

HOW THE SCENE ABIDES BY THE FIVE COMMANDMENTS OF STORYTELLING

Inciting Incident: Felix helps Safie's father escape prison in France; he falls in love with Safie.

Turning Point Progressive Complication: The French throw Felix and his family into prison after he turns himself in, and they are exiled from France.

Crisis: Should Safie obey her father and return to a confined life as a Muslim woman in Turkey, or should she run away? Best bad choice.

Climax: Safie goes in search of Felix and his family.

Resolution: Safie arrives in Germany.

NOTES

- As mentioned above, Felix is punished for every moral action he takes. He rescues Safie's father and his family is thrown into prison. He turns himself in to the French and is exiled. He wants to marry Safie, but her father goes back on his promise to help him and refuses to let them marry.
- Safie is the only person who ends up with what she wants, but in order to reach Felix, she has had to run away at great risk to herself. Shelley makes it clear that what she runs away from is a life as a closeted Muslim woman, and that her aim is to marry and live in Europe as a free Christian woman. In addition, her female companion dies on the way to Germany. Bad things have to happen in order for Safie to get what she wants.
- Note that Shelley's mother, Mary Wollstonecraft, was a celebrated feminist of her time, and she died when Shelley was born. The idea of fleeing a life of confinement as a Muslim woman was probably something Shelley thought of as a moral choice.
- Also note the strange contrast between Felix, who sacrificed in order to rescue Safie's father from prison in part because of his faith as a Muslim, and Safie, who was exercising her choice as a Christian woman not to return to a Muslim lifestyle.
- Safie's mother was born a Christian and enslaved by the Turks. This scene is full of images of freedom versus images of bondage. Safie's mother was enslaved. Safie's father was imprisoned. Felix and his family were imprisoned. Safie declined to re-enter a life of bondage by returning to Turkey.

CHAPTER 15 – SCENE 30

"Such was the history of my beloved cottagers. It impressed me deeply. I learned, from the views of social life which it developed, to admire their virtues and to deprecate the vices of mankind.

"As yet I looked upon crime as a distant evil, benevolence and generosity were ever present before me, inciting within me a desire to become an actor in the busy scene where so many admirable qualities were called forth and displayed. But in giving an account of the progress of my intellect, I must not omit a circumstance which occurred in the beginning of the month of August of the same year.

"One night during my accustomed visit to the neighbouring wood where I collected my own food and brought home firing for my protectors, I found on the ground a leathern portmanteau containing several articles of dress and some books. I eagerly seized the prize and returned with it to my hovel. Fortunately the books were written in the language, the elements of which I had acquired at the cottage; they consisted of ***Paradise Lost*, a volume of *Plutarch's Lives*, and the *Sorrows of Werter*** [sic]. The possession of these treasures gave me extreme delight; I now continually studied and exercised my mind upon these histories, whilst my friends were employed in their ordinary occupations.

"I can hardly describe to you the effect of these books. They produced in me an infinity of new images and feelings, that sometimes raised me to ecstasy, but more frequently sunk me into the lowest dejection. In the *Sorrows of Werter*, besides the interest of its simple and affecting story, so many opinions are canvassed and so many lights thrown upon what had hitherto been to me obscure subjects that I found in it a never-ending source of speculation and astonishment. The gentle and domestic manners it described, combined with lofty sentiments and feelings, which had for their object something out of self, accorded well with my experience among my protectors and with the wants which were forever alive in my own bosom. But I thought Werter himself a more divine being than I had ever beheld or imagined; his character contained no pretension, but it sank deep. The disquisitions upon death and suicide were calculated to fill me with wonder. I did not pretend to enter into the merits of the case, yet I inclined towards the opinions of the hero, whose extinction I wept, without precisely understanding it.

"**As I read, however, I applied much personally to my own feelings and condition. I found myself similar yet at the same time strangely unlike to the beings concerning whom I read and to whose conversation I was a listener. I sympathized with and partly understood them, but I was unformed in mind; I was dependent on none and related to none. 'The path of my departure was free,' and there was none to lament my annihilation. My person was hideous and my stature gigantic. What did this mean? Who was I? What was I? Whence did I come? What was my destination**? These questions continually recurred, but I was unable to solve them.

"The volume of *Plutarch's Lives* which I possessed contained the histories of the first founders of the ancient republics. This book had a far different effect upon me from the *Sorrows of Werter*. I learned from Werter's imaginations despondency and gloom, but **Plutarch taught me high thoughts; he elevated me above the wretched sphere of my own reflections, to admire and love the heroes of past ages.** Many things I read surpassed my understanding and experience. I had a very confused knowledge of kingdoms, wide extents of country, mighty rivers, and boundless seas. But I was perfectly unacquainted with towns and large assemblages of men. The cottage of my protectors had been the only school in which I had studied human nature, but this book developed new and mightier scenes of action. I read of men concerned in public affairs, governing or massacring their species. I felt the greatest ardour for virtue rise within me, and abhorrence for vice, as far as I understood the signification of those terms, relative as they were, as I applied them, to pleasure and pain alone. Induced by these feelings, I was of course led to admire peaceable lawgivers, Numa, Solon, and Lycurgus, in preference to Romulus and Theseus. The patriarchal lives of my protectors caused these impressions to take a firm hold on my mind; perhaps, if my first introduction to humanity had been made by a young soldier, burning for glory and slaughter, I should have been imbued with different sensations.

"But *Paradise Lost* excited different and far deeper emotions. I read it, as I had read the other volumes which had fallen into my hands, as a true history. It moved every feeling of wonder and awe that the picture of an omnipotent God warring with his creatures was capable of exciting. I often referred the several situations, as their similarity struck me, to my own. **Like Adam, I was apparently united by no link to any other being in existence; but his state was far different from mine in every other respect. He had come forth from the hands of God a perfect creature, happy and prosperous, guarded by the especial care of his Creator; he was allowed to converse with and acquire knowledge from beings of a superior nature, but I was wretched, helpless, and alone. Many times I considered Satan as the fitter emblem of my condition, for often, like him, when I viewed the bliss of my protectors, the bitter gall of envy rose within me.**

"Another circumstance strengthened and confirmed these feelings. Soon after my arrival in the hovel I discovered some papers in the pocket of the dress which I had taken from your laboratory. At first I had neglected them, but now that I was able to decipher the characters in which they were written, I began to study them with diligence. It was your journal of the four months that preceded my creation. You minutely described in these papers every step you took in the progress of your work; this history was mingled with accounts of domestic occurrences. You doubtless recollect these papers. Here they are. Everything is related in them which bears reference to my accursed origin; the whole detail of that series of disgusting circumstances which produced it is set in view; the minutest description of my odious and loathsome person is given, in language which painted your own horrors and rendered mine indelible. **I sickened as I read. 'Hateful day when I received life!' I exclaimed in agony. 'Accursed creator! Why did you form a monster so hideous that even YOU turned from me in disgust? God, in pity, made man beautiful and alluring, after his own image; but my form is a filthy type of yours, more horrid even from the very resemblance. Satan had his companions, fellow devils, to admire and encourage him, but I am solitary and abhorred.'**

"These were the reflections of my hours of despondency and solitude; but **when I contemplated the virtues of the cottagers, their amiable and benevolent dispositions, I persuaded myself that when they should become acquainted with my admiration of their virtues they would compassionate me and overlook my personal deformity.** Could they turn from their door one, however monstrous, who solicited their compassion and friendship? I resolved, at least, not to despair, but in every way to fit myself for an interview with them which would decide my fate. I postponed this attempt for some months longer, for the importance attached to its success inspired me with a dread lest I should fail. Besides, I found that my understanding improved so much with every day's experience that I was unwilling to commence this undertaking until a few more months should have added to my sagacity.

"Several changes, in the meantime, took place in the cottage. The presence of Safie diffused happiness among its inhabitants, and I also found that a greater degree of plenty reigned there. Felix and Agatha spent more time in amusement and conversation, and were assisted in their labours by servants. They did not appear rich, but they were contented and happy; their feelings were serene and peaceful, while mine became every day more tumultuous. **Increase of knowledge only discovered to me more clearly what a wretched outcast I was.** I cherished hope, it is true, but it vanished when I beheld my person reflected in water or my shadow in the moonshine, even as that frail image and that inconstant shade.

"I endeavoured to crush these fears and to fortify myself for the trial which in a few months I resolved to undergo; and **sometimes I allowed my thoughts, unchecked by reason, to ramble in the fields of Paradise, and dared to fancy amiable and lovely creatures sympathizing with my feelings and cheering my gloom; their angelic countenances breathed smiles of consolation. But it was all a dream; no Eve soothed my sorrows nor shared my thoughts; I was alone. I remembered Adam's supplication to his Creator. But where was mine? He had abandoned me, and in the bitterness of my heart I cursed him.**

• ANALYZING THE SCENE •
CHAPTER 15 – SCENE 30

A Story Event is an active change of universal human value for one or more characters as a result of conflict (one character's desires clash with another's or an environmental shift changes the universal human value).

A Working Scene contains at least one Story Event. To determine a scene's Story Event, answer these four questions:

1. What are the characters literally doing—that is, what are their micro on-the-ground actions?

The creature finds several books in the woods, which he studies. He also finds notes pertaining to the creation of the creature in the pocket of the clothes he took from Frankenstein's apartment.

2. What is the essential tactic of the characters—that is, what macro behaviors are they employing that are linked to a universal human value?

The creature learns more about humanity from his readings. Then he reads Frankenstein's notes and is angry when he understands that far from following the examples of the humane authors of these books,

Frankenstein operated in a realm of selfish lack of concern for the being he created.

3. What universal human values have changed for one or more characters in the scene? Which one of those value changes is most important and should be included in the Story Grid Spreadsheet?

At the beginning of this scene, the creature is delighted to find several books, presumably left by some traveler in the woods. At the end of the scene, he has not only read all three books (*Paradise Lost*, *Plutarch's Lives*, and *The Sorrows of Werter*), but he had also read Frankenstein's notes on his creation. He is appalled at Frankenstein because he now has read *Paradise Lost*, where Milton explains that God created man in his own image. Instead, Frankenstein created a horrifyingly ugly figure that disgusts him. So the creature's mental journey in this scene starts with Ignorance and ends in Knowledge. It also starts with Delight (at the prospect of Knowledge) and ends up with Despair. ("Increase of knowledge only discovered to me more clearly what a wretched outcast I was.")

Ignorant to Knowledgeable

4. What is the Story Event that sums up the scene's on-the-ground actions, essential tactics, and value change? We will enter that event in the Story Grid Spreadsheet.

When the creature finds several books in the woods and Frankenstein's journal in the pocket of clothes he took from the apartment, he learns more about the human condition and also about his own creation. He decides he will eventually reveal himself to the family next door so he can have a family.

HOW THE SCENE ABIDES BY THE FIVE COMMANDMENTS OF STORYTELLING

Inciting Incident: The creature finds books in the woods and Frankenstein's papers in his pocket.

Turning Point Progressive Complication: He reads the books and the papers and "applied much personally" to his own feelings and condition, as a creation who disgusted his own creator. He is wracked with doubt, indecision, and agony over his existence.

Crisis: Should he reveal himself to the cottagers and potentially be rejected? Or commit himself to spending his entire life alone? Best bad choice.

Climax: He resolves to reveal himself.

Resolution: He decides to procrastinate for a few months before doing the deed.

NOTES

- The particular books chosen by Shelley for Frankenstein give him a range of information about human nature. The creature says himself that, "The cottage of my protectors had been the only school in which I had studied human nature," and save for the history text used to teach Safie French, he has had no exposure to bigger ideas. This is where Shelley finishes pummeling the creature with examples of humanity and then introduces the truth about his own origins as well as doubts about his humanity.
- First of all, *The Sorrows of Werter* was a popular novel from the later 1700s about a young man in love with a married woman. At the end of the book, he commits suicide. Legend has it that this book "inspired" many copycat suicides all over Europe during the height of its popularity. Any contemporary reader would have certainly read this book and recognized it as a source of examples of "sensibility" and passion, versus practicality and common sense. The creature is both taken with the emotional angst described by the book and confused by it. He doesn't have that kind of tie to anyone, and he responds with the questions: "What did this

mean? Who was I? What was I? Whence did I come? What was my destination?"

- *Plutarch's Lives* is a different type of book; it contains biographies of Greek and Roman leaders and focuses on their characters. This book demonstrates the nature of high moral character and leadership to the creature, and the way in which humans can live together in societies. Until now, the creature has not witnessed any type of society but the villagers who attacked him and the cottagers next door. By reading Plutarch, he can see the intentional way in which a leader might choose either peace or violence as a way to direct a community, and he notes that he admires peaceable lawgivers more than he does lawgivers who prefer violence.
- *Paradise Lost* is a narrative poem by John Milton that describes man's fall from grace. It's essentially the story of Adam and Eve in the Garden of Eden, but there is a certain sympathetic, character-based quality to the poem, with roles for Satan, angels, and other side characters. "*Paradise Los*t" is the last book that the creature reads before he deciphers Frankenstein's notes on the creation of the monster, and the contrasts and similarities between the two are profound. The creature notes that he is like Adam, but unlike Adam he did not have the happy origin of a perfect creature made in the eyes of God. He also compares himself to Satan, experiencing envy as he spies on the cottagers next door.
- In the last part of this scene, after he expresses his anger and frustration toward Frankenstein for cruelly creating a creature such as himself and then abandoning it without love or regret, the creature again contemplates revealing himself to the cottagers. He decides he is going to go through with it but then decides to hold off for a few months. The cottagers are happier than before thanks to Safie's arrival, and the creature is sadder than before. "Increase of knowledge only discovered to me more clearly what a wretched outcast I was." Shelley has done everything she can to bring the creature to the point where he possesses

knowledge of humanity, human relationships, and family. He possesses enough knowledge to realize he has been deprived of the essential elements of humanity. All his hope is now pinned on the cottagers to pity him and love him as a member of their family. Indeed, Safie has appeared out of nowhere—without language and without any relationship to Felix, Agatha, and their father. Why should they treat the creature any differently? They are happier than before, with a stranger in their midst. Why would they not welcome a pitiable figure such as the creature into their home? We are at the climax of this story. Shelley has done her job. Now we will see what happens.

CHAPTER 15 – SCENE 31

"Autumn passed thus. I saw, with surprise and grief, the leaves decay and fall, and nature again assume the barren and bleak appearance it had worn when I first beheld the woods and the lovely moon. Yet I did not heed the bleakness of the weather; I was better fitted by my conformation for the endurance of cold than heat. But my chief delights were the sight of the flowers, the birds, and all the gay apparel of summer; when those deserted me, I turned with more attention towards the cottagers. Their happiness was not decreased by the absence of summer. They loved and sympathized with one another; and their joys, depending on each other, were not interrupted by the casualties that took place around them. The more I saw of them, the greater became my desire to claim their protection and kindness; my heart yearned to be known and loved by these amiable creatures; to see their sweet looks directed towards me with affection was the utmost limit of my ambition. I dared not think that they would turn them from me with disdain and horror. The poor that stopped at their door were never driven away. *[More evidence of their goodness/morality.]* I asked, it is true, for greater treasures than a little food or rest: I required kindness and sympathy; but I did not believe myself utterly unworthy of it.

"The winter advanced, and an entire revolution of the seasons had taken place since I awoke into life. My attention at this time was solely directed towards my plan of introducing myself into the cottage of my protectors. I revolved many projects, but that on which I finally fixed was to enter the dwelling when the blind old man should be alone. I had sagacity enough to discover that the unnatural hideousness of my person was the chief object of horror with those who had formerly beheld me. My voice, although harsh, had nothing terrible in it; I thought, therefore, that if in the absence of his children I could gain the good will and mediation of the old De Lacey, I might by his means be tolerated by my younger protectors.

"One day, when the sun shone on the red leaves that strewed the ground and diffused cheerfulness, although it denied warmth, Safie, Agatha, and Felix departed on a long country walk, and the old man, at his own desire, was left alone in the cottage. When his children had departed, he took up his guitar and played several mournful but sweet airs, more sweet and mournful than I had ever heard him play before. At first his countenance was illuminated with pleasure, but as he continued, thoughtfulness and sadness succeeded; at length, laying aside the instrument, he sat absorbed in reflection.

"My heart beat quick; this was the hour and moment of trial, which would decide my hopes or realize my fears. The servants were gone to a neighbouring fair. All was silent in and around the cottage; it was an excellent opportunity; yet, when I proceeded to execute my plan, my limbs failed me and I sank to the ground. Again I rose, and exerting all the firmness of which I was master, removed the planks which I had placed before my hovel to conceal my retreat. The fresh air revived me, and with renewed determination I approached the door of their cottage.

"I knocked. 'Who is there?' said the old man. 'Come in.'

"I entered. 'Pardon this intrusion,' said I; 'I am a traveller in want of a little rest; you would greatly oblige me if you would allow me to remain a few minutes before the fire.'

"'Enter,' said De Lacey, 'and I will try in what manner I can to relieve your wants; but, unfortunately, my children are from home, and as I am blind, I am afraid I shall find it difficult to procure food for you.'

"'Do not trouble yourself, my kind host; I have food; it is warmth and rest only that I need.'

"I sat down, and a silence ensued. I knew that every minute was precious to me, yet I remained irresolute in what manner to commence the interview, when the old man addressed me. 'By your language, stranger, I suppose you are my countryman; are you French?'

"'No; but I was educated by a French family and understand that language only. I am now going to claim the protection of some friends, whom I sincerely love, and of whose favour I have some hopes.'

"'Are they Germans?'

"'No, they are French. But let us change the subject. I am an unfortunate and deserted creature, I look around and I have no relation or friend upon earth. These amiable people to whom I go have never seen me and know little of me. I am full of fears, for if I fail there, I am an outcast in the world forever.'

"'Do not despair. To be friendless is indeed to be unfortunate, but the hearts of men, when unprejudiced by any obvious self-interest, are full of brotherly love and charity. Rely, therefore, on your hopes; and if these friends are good and amiable, do not despair.'

"'They are kind—they are the most excellent creatures in the world; but, unfortunately, they are prejudiced against me. I have good dispositions; my life has been hitherto harmless and in some degree beneficial; but a fatal prejudice clouds their eyes, and where they ought to see a feeling and kind friend, they behold only a detestable monster.'

"'That is indeed unfortunate; but if you are really blameless, cannot you undeceive them?'

"'I am about to undertake that task; and it is on that account that I feel so many overwhelming terrors. I tenderly love these friends; I have, unknown to them, been for many months in the habits of daily kindness towards them; but they believe that I wish to injure them, and it is that prejudice which I wish to overcome.'

"'Where do these friends reside?'

"'Near this spot.'

"The old man paused and then continued, 'If you will unreservedly confide to me the particulars of your tale, I perhaps may be of use in undeceiving them. I am blind and cannot judge of your countenance, but there is something in your words which persuades me that you are sincere. I am poor and an exile, but it will afford me true pleasure to be in any way serviceable to a human creature.'

"'Excellent man! I thank you and accept your generous offer. You raise me from the dust by this kindness; and I trust that, by your aid, I shall not be driven from the society and sympathy of your fellow creatures.'

"'Heaven forbid! Even if you were really criminal, for that can only drive you to desperation, and not instigate you to virtue. I also am unfortunate; I and my family have been condemned, although innocent; judge, therefore, if I do not feel for your misfortunes.'

"'How can I thank you, my best and only benefactor? From your lips first have I heard the voice of kindness directed towards me; I shall be forever grateful; and your present humanity assures me of success with those friends whom I am on the point of meeting.'

"'May I know the names and residence of those friends?'

"I paused. This, I thought, was the moment of decision, which was to rob me of or bestow happiness on me forever. I struggled vainly for firmness sufficient to answer him, but the effort destroyed all my remaining strength; I sank on the chair and sobbed aloud. At that moment I heard the steps of my younger protectors. I had not a moment to lose, but seizing the hand of the old man, I cried, 'Now is the time! Save and protect me! You and your family are the friends whom I seek. Do not you desert me in the hour of trial!'

"'Great God!' exclaimed the old man. 'Who are you?'

"At that instant the cottage door was opened, and Felix, Safie, and Agatha entered. Who can describe their horror and consternation on beholding me? Agatha fainted, and Safie, unable to attend to her friend, rushed out of the cottage. Felix darted forward, and with supernatural force tore me from his father, to whose knees I clung, in a transport of fury, he dashed me to the ground and struck me violently with a stick. I could have torn him limb from limb, as the lion rends the antelope. But my heart sank within me as with bitter sickness, and I refrained. I saw him on the point of repeating his blow, when, overcome by pain and anguish, I quitted the cottage, and in the general tumult escaped unperceived to my hovel."

• ANALYZING THE SCENE •
CHAPTER 15 – SCENE 31

A Story Event is an active change of universal human value for one or more characters as a result of conflict (one character's desires clash with another's or an environmental shift changes the universal human value).

A Working Scene contains at least one Story Event. To determine a scene's Story Event, answer these four questions:

1. What are the characters literally doing—that is, what are their micro on-the-ground actions?

The creature finally makes himself known. He first knocks on the door of the cottage when only the old man is home since he is blind and will not be afraid of the creature. He has a conversation with him, but is interrupted when Felix, Safie, and Agatha enter and are horrified at the sight of the creature. Felix beats him and chases him away.

2. What is the essential tactic of the characters—that is, what macro behaviors are they employing that are linked to a universal human value?

The creature has made his effort to connect with the family and find a place where he belongs. The creature's beloved cottagers, however, have now rejected him, just as he has been rejected by Frankenstein and every other human he has encountered.

3. What universal human values have changed for one or more characters in the scene? Which one of those value changes is most important and should be included in the Story Grid Spreadsheet?

The most important value at stake here is the creature's. He begins the scene included by the old man and ends the scene rejected by the family.

Included to Rejected

4. What is the Story Event that sums up the scene's on-the-ground actions, essential tactics, and value change? We will enter that event in the Story Grid Spreadsheet.

The creature makes his move. He goes to visit the cottage when only the blind old man is home; however, as he reveals himself, the son rushes in and begins to beat him, so he flees.

HOW THE SCENE ABIDES BY THE FIVE COMMANDMENTS OF STORYTELLING

Inciting Incident: The creature finally makes his move and knocks on the door of the cottage.

Turning Point Progressive Complication: The creature hears the steps of the rest of the family outside.

Crisis: Should he rely on the old man to protect him? Should he run? Best bad choice.

Climax: He begs the old man not to "desert me in the hour of trial," but before the old man can react, Felix rushes in and begins to beat the creature.

Resolution: The creature flees.

NOTES

- This is the moment of truth. Will the cottagers, who have been the example of the moral high ground for almost the entirety of the creature's tale, uphold the standards they have set for him? Are they superior beings to Frankenstein, who had no problem abandoning his creation at its birth?

- As long as the old man could not see him, he was willing to be of service. It is Felix who beats the creature and drives him away when he sees him with his father.
- During his conversation with the old man, the creature tells him that he has no friends or relations, and he is trying to connect with some "amiable people." The old man assures him that people are generally charitable and asks for the names and address of these people. All of this leads the narrative to the point where the creature hears footsteps outside and begs the old man for help. One can see that Shelley starts the scene with a story goal: she needs to create the big crisis where the creature is changed forever, and transitions from a creature filled with possible benevolence into a creature bent on angry destruction. She sets up a huge contrast; the creature has a conversation with the kind, sympathetic old man, and the situation appears to be headed in a positive direction for the creature until the rest of the family returns. The one difference between the old man and his family is that he cannot see the ugliness of the creature, while they can. This answers the creature's question definitively: human society will not accept him regardless of his hidden virtues.

CHAPTER 16 – SCENE 32

"Cursed, cursed creator! Why did I live? Why, in that instant, did I not extinguish the spark of existence which you had so wantonly bestowed? I know not; despair had not yet taken possession of me; my feelings were those of rage and revenge. I could with pleasure have destroyed the cottage and its inhabitants and have glutted myself with their shrieks and misery.

"When night came I quitted my retreat and wandered in the wood; and now, no longer restrained by the fear of discovery, I gave vent to my anguish in fearful howlings. I was like a wild beast that had broken the toils, destroying the objects that obstructed me and ranging through the wood with a stag-like swiftness. Oh! What a miserable night I passed! The cold stars shone in mockery, and the bare trees waved their branches above me; now and then the sweet voice of a bird burst forth amidst the universal stillness. All, save I, were at rest or in enjoyment; I, like the arch-fiend, bore a hell within me, and finding myself unsympathized with, wished to tear up the trees, spread havoc and destruction around me, and then to have sat down and enjoyed the ruin.

"But this was a luxury of sensation that could not endure; I became fatigued with excess of bodily exertion and sank on the damp grass in the sick impotence of despair. There was none among the myriads of men that existed who would pity or assist me; and should I feel kindness towards my enemies? No; **from that moment I declared everlasting war against the species, and more than all, against him who had formed me and sent me forth to this insupportable misery.**

"The sun rose; I heard the voices of men and knew that it was impossible to return to my retreat during that day. Accordingly I hid myself in some thick underwood, determining to devote the ensuing hours to reflection on my situation.

"The pleasant sunshine and the pure air of day restored me to some degree of tranquillity; and when I considered what had passed at the cottage, I could not help believing that I had been too hasty in my conclusions. I had certainly acted imprudently. It was apparent that my conversation had interested the father in my behalf, and I was a fool in having exposed my person to the horror of his children. I ought to have familiarized the old De Lacey to me, and by degrees to have discovered myself to the rest of his family, when they should have been prepared for my approach. But I did not believe my errors to be irretrievable, and after much consideration I resolved to return to the cottage, seek the old man, and by my representations win him to my party.

"These thoughts calmed me, and in the afternoon I sank into a profound sleep; but the fever of my blood did not allow me to be visited by peaceful dreams. The horrible scene of the preceding day was forever acting before my eyes; the females were flying and the enraged Felix tearing me from his father's feet. I awoke exhausted, and finding that it was already night, I crept forth from my hiding-place, and went in search of food.

"When my hunger was appeased, I directed my steps towards the well-known path that conducted to the cottage. All there was at peace. I crept into my hovel and remained in silent expectation of the accustomed hour when the family arose. That hour passed, the sun mounted high in the heavens, but the cottagers did not appear. I trembled violently, apprehending some dreadful misfortune. The inside of the cottage was dark, and I heard no motion; I cannot describe the agony of this suspense.

"Presently two countrymen passed by, but pausing near the cottage, they entered into conversation, using violent gesticulations; but I did not understand what they said, as they spoke the language of the country, which differed from that of my protectors. Soon after, however, Felix approached with another man; I was surprised, as I knew that he had not quitted the cottage that morning, and waited anxiously to discover from his discourse the meaning of these unusual appearances.

"'Do you consider,' said his companion to him, 'that you will be obliged to pay three months' rent and to lose the produce of your garden? I do not wish to take any unfair advantage, and I beg therefore that you will take some days to consider of your determination.'

"'It is utterly useless,' replied Felix; 'we can never again inhabit your cottage. The life of my father is in the greatest danger, owing to the dreadful circumstance that I have related. My wife and my sister will never recover from their horror. I entreat you not to reason with me any more. Take possession of your tenement and let me fly from this place.'

"Felix trembled violently as he said this. He and his companion entered the cottage, in which they remained for a few minutes, and then departed. I never saw any of the family of De Lacey more.

"I continued for the remainder of the day in my hovel in a state of utter and stupid despair. **My protectors had departed and had broken the only link that held me to the world. For the first time the feelings of revenge and hatred filled my bosom, and I did not strive to control them, but allowing myself to be borne away by the stream, I bent my mind towards injury and death.** When I thought of my friends, of the mild voice of De Lacey, the gentle eyes of Agatha, and the exquisite beauty of the Arabian, these thoughts vanished and a gush of tears somewhat soothed me. But again **when I reflected that they had spurned and deserted me, anger returned, a rage of anger, and unable to injure anything human, I turned my fury towards inanimate objects. As night advanced I placed a variety of combustibles around the cottage, and after having destroyed every vestige of cultivation in the garden, I waited with forced impatience until the moon had sunk to commence my operations.**

"As the night advanced, a fierce wind arose from the woods and quickly dispersed the clouds that had loitered in the heavens; the blast tore along like a mighty avalanche and produced a kind of insanity in my spirits that burst all bounds of reason and reflection. **I lighted the**

dry branch of a tree and danced with fury around the devoted cottage, my eyes still fixed on the western horizon, the edge of which the moon nearly touched. A part of its orb was at length hid, and I waved my brand; it sank, and with a loud scream I fired the straw, and heath, and bushes, which I had collected. The wind fanned the fire, and the cottage was quickly enveloped by the flames, which clung to it and licked it with their forked and destroying tongues.

"As soon as I was convinced that no assistance could save any part of the habitation, I quitted the scene and sought for refuge in the woods.

• ANALYZING THE SCENE •
CHAPTER 16 – SCENE 32

A Story Event is an active change of universal human value for one or more characters as a result of conflict (one character's desires clash with another's or an environmental shift changes the universal human value).

A Working Scene contains at least one Story Event. To determine a scene's Story Event, answer these four questions:

1. What are the characters literally doing—that is, what are their micro on-the-ground actions?

The creature runs away into the woods in a rage; he then returns to the hovel to await the cottagers, but they do not return.

2. What is the essential tactic of the characters—that is, what macro behaviors are they employing that are linked to a universal human value?

The creature decides how he will react to this event. When he thinks of the cottagers, he is filled with regret. He was too precipitous and frightened them. At the same time, he is angry at how he has been treated.

3. What universal human values have changed for one or more characters in the scene? Which one of those value changes is most important and should be included in the Story Grid Spreadsheet?

The most important value at stake here is the creature's. At the beginning of the scene, he has been attacked and brutalized, and he flees. He eventually returns, and when he realizes that the cottagers have abandoned him, he is furious and decides to take his anger out on the cottage itself.

The creature goes from Destroyed to Destroyer, which is another kind of Life to Death/Death to Life trajectory. He was "dead" in that he was a victim, but now he is no longer the victim.

Destroyed to Destroyer

4. What is the Story Event that sums up the scene's on-the-ground actions, essential tactics, and value change? We will enter that event in the Story Grid Spreadsheet.

The creature flees into the woods but decides to return to plead his case. He discovers that the cottagers have left for good. Angry, he burns down the cottage.

HOW THE SCENE ABIDES BY THE FIVE COMMANDMENTS OF STORYTELLING

Inciting Incident: The creature has fled into the woods, but after some reflection, decides that he had been hasty and returns to the cottage to await the return of the cottagers.

Turning Point Progressive Complication: The creature sees Felix and another man approach the cottage. Felix is notifying the landlord that they are quitting the cottage for good.

Crisis: The creature spends the rest of the day in despair. His beloved cottagers have left him. Should he think of them fondly, or should he be furious? Best bad choice.

Climax: He decides that they have spurned him, and he acts out his anger by burning down the cottage.

Resolution: The creature waits until the cottage is destroyed, then leaves.

NOTES

- Shelley could have skipped this scene; she could have had the cottagers and the creature flee the cottage, never to return. She has already indicated that creature never sees those people again. This is presumably the end of their role in this story. However, this scene is a great finishing touch as it gives the reader a nice, concrete end to the creature's fantasy that he is a human with a possibility of entering into human relationships. He torches the cottage. There is no going back.
- The spectacle of the cottage going up in flames is made all the more horrible by the fact that the creature spent his time in the woods reflecting on his own culpability and blaming himself for being hasty and frightening the family by appearing too precipitously. He admits that he did not handle the situation well and decides that he would try again with the old man. The realization that the cottagers would never return drives him into a fury precisely because he was still deluding himself into thinking a relationship was possible.

CHAPTER 16 – SCENE 33

"And now, with the world before me, whither should I bend my steps? I resolved to fly far from the scene of my misfortunes; but to me, hated and despised, every country must be equally horrible. At length the thought of you crossed my mind. I learned from your papers that **you were my father, my creator; and to whom could I apply with more fitness than to him who had given me life?** Among the lessons that Felix had bestowed upon Safie, geography had not been omitted; I had learned from these the relative situations of the different countries of the earth. You had mentioned Geneva as the name of your native town, and towards this place I resolved to proceed.

"But how was I to direct myself? I knew that I must travel in a southwesterly direction to reach my destination, but the sun was my only guide. I did not know the names of the towns that I was to pass through, nor could I ask information from a single human being; but I did not despair. **From you only could I hope for succour, although towards you I felt no sentiment but that of hatred. Unfeeling, heartless creator! You had endowed me with perceptions and passions and then cast me abroad an object for the scorn and horror of mankind.** But on you only had I any claim for pity and redress, and from you I determined to seek that **justice** which I vainly attempted to gain from any other being that wore the human form.

"My travels were long and the sufferings I endured intense. It was late in autumn when I quitted the district where I had so long resided. I travelled only at night, fearful of encountering the visage of a human being. Nature decayed around me, and the sun became heatless; rain and snow poured around me; mighty rivers were frozen; the surface of the earth was hard and chill, and bare, and I found no shelter. Oh, earth! How often did I imprecate curses on the cause of my being! **The mildness of my nature had fled, and all within me was turned to gall and bitterness. The nearer I approached to your habitation, the more deeply did I feel the spirit of revenge enkindled in my heart.** Snow fell, and the waters were hardened, but I rested not. A few incidents now and then directed me, and I possessed a map of the country; but I often wandered wide from my path. The agony of my feelings allowed me no respite; no incident occurred from which my rage and misery could not extract its food; but a circumstance that happened when I arrived on the confines of Switzerland, when the sun had recovered its warmth and the earth again began to look green, confirmed in an especial manner the bitterness and horror of my feelings.

"I generally rested during the day and travelled only when I was secured by night from the view of man. One morning, however, finding that my path lay through a deep wood, I ventured to continue my journey after the sun had risen; the day, which was one of the first of spring, cheered even me by the loveliness of its sunshine and the balminess of the air. I felt emotions of gentleness and pleasure, that had long appeared dead, revive within me. Half surprised by the novelty of these sensations, I allowed myself to be borne away by them, and forgetting my solitude and deformity, dared to be happy. Soft tears again bedewed my cheeks, and I even raised my humid eyes with thankfulness towards the blessed sun, which bestowed such joy upon me. *[Shelley often brings in nature as a source of healing.]*

"I continued to wind among the paths of the wood, until I came to its boundary, which was skirted by a deep and rapid river, into which many of the trees bent their branches, now budding with the fresh spring. Here I paused, not exactly knowing what path to pursue, when I heard the sound of voices, that induced me to conceal myself under the shade of a cypress. I was scarcely hid when a young girl came running towards the spot where I was concealed, laughing, as if she ran from someone in sport. She continued her course along the precipitous sides of the river, when suddenly her foot slipped, and she fell into the rapid stream. I rushed from my hiding-place and with extreme labour, from the force of the current, saved her and dragged her to shore. She was senseless, and I endeavoured by every means in my power to restore animation, when I was suddenly interrupted by the approach of a rustic, who was probably the person from whom she had playfully fled. On seeing me, he darted towards me, and tearing the girl from my arms, hastened towards the deeper parts of the wood. I followed speedily, I hardly knew why; but when the man saw me draw near, he aimed a gun, which he carried, at my body and fired. I sank to the ground, and my injurer, with increased swiftness, escaped into the wood.

"This was then the reward of my benevolence! I had saved a human being from destruction, and as a recompense I now writhed under the miserable pain of a wound which shattered the flesh and bone. The feelings of kindness and gentleness which I had entertained but a few moments before gave place to hellish rage and gnashing of teeth. **Inflamed by pain, I vowed eternal hatred and vengeance to all mankind.** But the agony of my wound overcame me; my pulses paused, and I fainted.

"For some weeks I led a miserable life in the woods, endeavouring to cure the wound which I had received. The ball had entered my shoulder, and I knew not whether it had remained there or passed through; at any rate I had no means of extracting it. My sufferings were augmented also by the oppressive sense of the injustice and ingratitude of their infliction. My daily vows rose for revenge—a deep and deadly revenge, such as would alone compensate for the outrages and anguish I had endured.

• ANALYZING THE SCENE •
CHAPTER 16 – SCENE 33

A Story Event is an active change of universal human value for one or more characters as a result of conflict (one character's desires clash with another's or an environmental shift changes the universal human value).

A Working Scene contains at least one Story Event. To determine a scene's Story Event, answer these four questions:

1. What are the characters literally doing—that is, what are their micro on-the-ground actions?

The creature decides to go in search of his creator and sets out to travel to Geneva. He rescues a young girl from drowning but her companion shoots him.

2. What is the essential tactic of the characters—that is, what macro behaviors are they employing that are linked to a universal human value?

Once again the creature is made aware of just how alienated he is. When he has fleeting benevolent feelings and engages in benevolent actions, he is always punished for his pains. This scene exists to remind him and us of the extent of his alienation. He performed the most humane gesture possible, that of rescuing a fellow human, but was treated like a monster.

3. What universal human values have changed for one or more characters in the scene? Which one of those value changes is most important and should be included in the Story Grid Spreadsheet?

In the past, the creature has been beaten and chased away by humans, but this is the first time anyone has actually used a lethal weapon against him. He is now injured and suffering great pain.

The creature starts out the scene in good health but ends the scene suffering a gunshot wound. We could track a value of Healthy to Injured, but it's worse than that. The creature is shot after saving someone's life. It's more accurate to say that the value goes from Savior to Villain.

Savior to Villain

4. What is the Story Event that sums up the scene's on-the-ground actions, essential tactics, and value change? We will enter that event in the Story Grid Spreadsheet.

The creature decides to try to find Frankenstein. During his travels he rescues a girl from drowning, only to be shot and injured by her companion. He vows vengeance on mankind.

HOW THE SCENE ABIDES BY THE FIVE COMMANDMENTS OF STORYTELLING

Inciting Incident: The creature decides to try to find his creator.

Turning Point Progressive Complication: He sees a young girl slip and fall into a stream.

Crisis: Should he rescue the girl even though he has committed himself to exacting revenge against humans? Irreconcilable goods choice.

Climax: He rescues her, only to be shot by a man who tears the girl from his arms.

Resolution: The creature vows "eternal hatred and vengeance to all mankind."

NOTES

- The creature sets out to find his creator. Having been shunned by the cottagers, he decides Frankenstein owes him justice.

- It is a long and arduous journey, and as time passes and the weather improves, his spirits rise. Of course, whenever people become too happy, we know Shelley is about to throw a monkey wrench into the plot. The creature rescues a girl from drowning and is punished for it with a gunshot wound. If the creature didn't hate humans before, he certainly does now. Until now, Shelley hasn't allowed anyone to really harm the creature, but he is powerless before firearms. The creature now has been abused in a manner that will be much too hard to forgive.

CHAPTER 16 – SCENE 34

"After some weeks my wound healed, and I continued my journey. The labours I endured were no longer to be alleviated by the bright sun or gentle breezes of spring; all joy was but a mockery which insulted my desolate state and made me feel more painfully that I was not made for the enjoyment of pleasure.

"But my toils now drew near a close, and in two months from this time I reached the environs of Geneva.

"It was evening when I arrived, and I retired to a hiding-place among the fields that surround it to meditate in what manner I should apply to you. I was oppressed by fatigue and hunger and far too unhappy to enjoy the gentle breezes of evening or the prospect of the sun setting behind the stupendous mountains of Jura.

"At this time a slight sleep relieved me from the pain of reflection, which was disturbed by the approach of a beautiful child, who came running into the recess I had chosen, with all the sportiveness of infancy. Suddenly, as I gazed on him, an idea seized me that **this little creature was unprejudiced and had lived too short a time to have imbibed a horror of deformity. If, therefore, I could seize him and educate him as my companion and friend, I should not be so desolate in this peopled earth.**

"Urged by this impulse, I seized on the boy as he passed and drew him towards me. As soon as he beheld my form, he placed his hands before his eyes and uttered a shrill scream; I drew his hand forcibly from his face and said, 'Child, what is the meaning of this? I do not intend to hurt you; listen to me.'

"He struggled violently. 'Let me go,' he cried; 'monster! Ugly wretch! You wish to eat me and tear me to pieces. You are an ogre. Let me go, or I will tell my papa.'

"'Boy, you will never see your father again; you must come with me.'

"'Hideous monster! Let me go. My papa is a syndic—he is M. Frankenstein—he will punish you. You dare not keep me.'

"'Frankenstein! you belong then to my enemy—to him towards whom I have sworn eternal revenge; you shall be my first victim.'

"The child still struggled and loaded me with epithets which carried despair to my heart; I grasped his throat to silence him, and in a moment he lay dead at my feet.

"I gazed on my victim, and my heart swelled with exultation and hellish triumph; clapping my hands, I exclaimed, 'I too can create desolation; my enemy is not invulnerable; this death will carry despair to him, and a thousand other miseries shall torment and destroy him.'

"As I fixed my eyes on the child, I saw something glittering on his breast. I took it; it was a portrait of a most lovely woman. In spite of my malignity, it softened and attracted me. For a few moments I gazed with delight on her dark eyes, fringed by deep lashes, and her lovely lips; but presently my rage returned; I remembered that I was forever deprived of the delights that such beautiful creatures could bestow and that she whose resemblance I contemplated would, in regarding me, have changed that air of divine benignity to one expressive of disgust and affright.

"Can you wonder that such thoughts transported me with rage? I only wonder that at that moment, instead of venting my sensations in exclamations and agony, I did not rush among mankind and perish in the attempt to destroy them.

"While I was overcome by these feelings, I left the spot where I had committed the murder, and seeking a more secluded hiding-place, I entered a barn which had appeared to me to be empty. A woman was sleeping on some straw; she was young, not indeed so beautiful as her whose portrait I held, but of an agreeable aspect and blooming in the loveliness of youth and health. Here, I thought, is one of those whose joy-imparting smiles are bestowed on all but me. And then I bent over her and whispered, 'Awake, fairest, thy lover is near—he who would give his life but to obtain one look of affection from thine eyes; my beloved, awake!'

"The sleeper stirred; a thrill of terror ran through me. Should she indeed awake, and see me, and curse me, and denounce the murderer? Thus would she assuredly act if her darkened eyes opened and she beheld me. The thought was madness; it stirred the fiend within me—**not I, but she, shall suffer; the murder I have committed because I am forever robbed of all that she could give me, she shall atone. The crime had its source in her; be hers the punishment! Thanks to the lessons of Felix and the sanguinary laws of man, I had learned now to work mischief.** I bent over her and placed the portrait securely in one of the folds of her dress. She moved again, and I fled.

"For some days I haunted the spot where these scenes had taken place, sometimes wishing to see you, sometimes resolved to quit the world and its miseries forever. At length I wandered towards these mountains, and have ranged through their immense recesses, consumed by a burning passion which you alone can gratify. We may not part until you have promised to comply with my requisition. **I am alone and miserable; man will not associate with me; but one as deformed and horrible as myself would not deny herself to me. My companion must be of the same species and have the same defects. This being you must create."**

• ANALYZING THE SCENE •
CHAPTER 16 – SCENE 34

A Story Event is an active change of universal human value for one or more characters as a result of conflict (one character's desires clash with

another's or an environmental shift changes the universal human value).

A Working Scene contains at least one Story Event. To determine a scene's Story Event, answer these four questions:

1. What are the characters literally doing—that is, what are their micro on-the-ground actions?

In this scene, the murder of Frankenstein's little brother takes place. The creature kills him almost by accident; he is trying to keep him because he thinks a child may not be as prejudiced against him as adults, but when the creature tries to keep him quiet, he chokes him to death. Then, he plants evidence on the body of a sleeping woman in a barn.

2. What is the essential tactic of the characters—that is, what macro behaviors are they employing that are linked to a universal human value?

The creature is now carrying through on his promise of vengeance against man.

3. What universal human values have changed for one or more characters in the scene? Which one of those value changes is most important and should be included in the Story Grid Spreadsheet?

There are two major value changes here. The child goes from Life to Death. The creature goes from Victim to Murderer.

In a Horror story, the global value at stake is Life to Death. Given that the creature is one of our protagonists, it makes more sense to track his emotional state than the child's brief life.

Victim to Murderer

4. What is the Story Event that sums up the scene's on-the-ground actions, essential tactics, and value change? We will enter that event in the Story Grid Spreadsheet.

The creature kills Frankenstein's younger brother William; he frames Justine when he sees her sleeping in a barn by putting William's necklace into her pocket.

HOW THE SCENE ABIDES BY THE FIVE COMMANDMENTS OF STORYTELLING

Inciting Incident: The creature is near Geneva. A child comes into his view, and he decides to capture the child.

Turning Point Progressive Complication: The child makes noise and resists, saying he is the child of M. Frankenstein.

Crisis: Should he let the child go? Should he try to keep the child? Best bad choice.

Climax: He tries to quiet the child and chokes him to death.

Resolution: As a way of working "mischief," he plants evidence on the body of a young woman he comes across sleeping in a barn. He then tells his listener (Frankenstein) that he demands a companion female for himself.

NOTES

- Now we are almost in the present. The creature has told his story leading up to the murder of Frankenstein's little brother, and now he is admitting that he is indeed the murderer. He is also admitting that he framed Justine for the murder.
- We now know why he has become a murderer, and the question is, what will Frankenstein do? Will he understand him and feel pity for him after hearing this same tale that we did?
- In the ending cliffhanger, he demands that Frankenstein create a female for him. He no longer has hope of human

companionship, and after all the reading and thinking he has done, he knows how human relationships are supposed to work. Therefore, he concludes that a female of the same species as him will solve his problem, and only his creator can make such a being. This cliffhanger is the Crisis question of the Middle Build.

CHAPTER 17 – SCENE 35

The being finished speaking and fixed his looks upon me in the expectation of a reply. But I was bewildered, perplexed, and unable to arrange my ideas sufficiently to understand the full extent of his proposition.

He continued, **"You must create a female for me with whom I can live in the interchange of those sympathies necessary for my being. This you alone can do, and I demand it of you as a right which you must not refuse to concede."**

The latter part of his tale had kindled anew in me the anger that had died away while he narrated his peaceful life among the cottagers, and as he said this I could no longer suppress the rage that burned within me.

"I do refuse it," I replied; "and no torture shall ever extort a consent from me. You may render me the most miserable of men, but you shall never make me base in my own eyes. Shall I create another like yourself, whose joint wickedness might desolate the world. Begone! I have answered you; you may torture me, but I will never consent."

"You are in the wrong," replied the fiend; "and instead of threatening, I am content to reason with you. **I am malicious because I am miserable.** Am I not shunned and hated by all mankind? You, my creator, would tear me to pieces and triumph; remember that, and tell me why I should pity man more than he pities me? You would not call it murder if you could precipitate me into one of those ice-rifts and destroy my frame, the work of your own hands. Shall I respect man when he condemns me? Let him live with me in the interchange of kindness, and instead of injury I would bestow every benefit upon him with tears of gratitude at his acceptance. But that cannot be; the human senses are insurmountable barriers to our union. Yet mine shall not be the submission of abject slavery. **I will revenge my injuries; if I cannot inspire love, I will cause fear, and chiefly towards you my arch-enemy, because my creator, do I swear inextinguishable hatred.** Have a care; **I will work at your destruction, nor finish until I desolate your heart, so that you shall curse the hour of your birth.**" *[This is borderline "Speech in Praise of the Monster" territory; however, it's only in the realm of the possible, because we don't know yet what Frankenstein will reply.]*

A fiendish rage animated him as he said this; his face was wrinkled into contortions too horrible for human eyes to behold; but presently he calmed himself and proceeded— "I intended to reason. This passion is detrimental to me, for you do not reflect that YOU are the cause of its excess. If any being felt emotions of benevolence towards me, I should return them a hundred and a hundredfold; for that one creature's sake I would make peace with the whole kind! But I now indulge in dreams of bliss that cannot be realized. What I ask of you is reasonable and moderate; I demand a creature of another sex, but as hideous as myself; the gratification is small, but it is all that I can receive, and it shall content me. It is true, we shall be monsters, cut off from all the world; but on that account we shall be more attached to one another. Our lives will not be happy, but they will be harmless and free from the misery I now feel. Oh! **My creator, make me happy; let me feel gratitude towards you for one benefit!** Let me see that I excite the sympathy of some existing thing; do not deny me my request!" *[At this point, "Speech in Praise of the Monster" doesn't fit, because he is trying to make himself agreeable with terms that might interest Frankenstein. The actual "Speech in Praise of the Monster" needs to be uncompromising in its defense of the monster.]*

I was moved. I shuddered when I thought of the possible

consequences of my consent, but I felt that there was some justice in his argument. His tale and the feelings he now expressed proved him to be a creature of fine sensations, and did I not as his maker owe him all the portion of happiness that it was in my power to bestow? *[Frankenstein actually sees his point!]* He saw my change of feeling and continued, "If you consent, neither you nor any other human being shall ever see us again; I will go to the vast wilds of South America. My food is not that of man; I do not destroy the lamb and the kid to glut my appetite; acorns and berries afford me sufficient nourishment. My companion will be of the same nature as myself and will be content with the same fare. We shall make our bed of dried leaves; the sun will shine on us as on man and will ripen our food. **The picture I present to you is peaceful and human, and you must feel that you could deny it only in the wantonness of power and cruelty.** Pitiless as you have been towards me, I now see compassion in your eyes; let me seize the favourable moment and persuade you to promise what I so ardently desire."

"You propose," replied I, "to fly from the habitations of man, to dwell in those wilds where the beasts of the field will be your only companions. **How can you, who long for the love and sympathy of man, persevere in this exile?** You will return and again seek their kindness, and you will meet with their detestation; your evil passions will be renewed, and you will then have a companion to aid you in the task of destruction. This may not be; cease to argue the point, for I cannot consent."

"How inconstant are your feelings! But a moment ago you were moved by my representations, and why do you again harden yourself to my complaints? I swear to you, by the earth which I inhabit, and by you that made me, that with the companion you bestow I will quit the neighbourhood of man and dwell, as it may chance, in the most savage of places. My evil passions will have fled, for I shall meet with sympathy! My life will flow quietly away, and in my dying moments I shall not curse my maker."

His words had a strange effect upon me. I compassionated him and sometimes felt a wish to console him, but when I looked upon him, when I saw the filthy mass that moved and talked, my heart sickened and my feelings were altered to those of horror and hatred. I tried to stifle these sensations; **I thought that as I could not sympathize with him, I had no right to withhold from him the small portion of happiness which was yet in my power to bestow.**

"You swear," I said, "to be harmless; but have you not already shown a degree of malice that should reasonably make me distrust you? May not even this be a feint that will increase your triumph by affording a wider scope for your revenge?"

"How is this? I must not be trifled with, and I demand an answer. If I have no ties and no affections, hatred and vice must be my portion; the love of another will destroy the cause of my crimes, and I shall become a thing of whose existence everyone will be ignorant. **My vices are the children of a forced solitude that I abhor, and my virtues will necessarily arise when I live in communion with an equal. I shall feel the affections of a sensitive being and become linked to the chain of existence and events from which I am now excluded.**"

I paused some time to reflect on all he had related and the various arguments which he had employed. I thought of the promise of virtues which he had displayed on the opening of his existence and the subsequent blight of all kindly feeling by the loathing and scorn which his protectors had manifested towards him. His power and threats were not omitted in my calculations; a creature who could exist in the ice caves of the glaciers and hide himself from pursuit among the ridges of inaccessible precipices was a being possessing faculties it would be vain to cope with. After a long pause of reflection I concluded that the justice due both to him and my fellow creatures demanded of me that I should comply with his request. *[Frankenstein is mentally applying some kind of moral code to all he has heard.]* Turning to him, therefore, I said, **"I consent to your demand, on your solemn oath to quit Europe forever, and every other place in the neighbourhood of man, as soon as I shall deliver into your hands a female who will accompany you in your exile."**

"I swear," he cried, "by the sun, and by the blue sky of heaven, and by the fire of love that burns my heart, that if you grant my prayer, while they exist you shall never behold me again. Depart to your home and commence your labours; I shall watch their progress with unutterable anxiety; and fear not but that when you are ready I shall appear."

Saying this, he suddenly quitted me, fearful, perhaps, of any change in my sentiments. I saw him descend the mountain with greater speed than the flight of an eagle, and quickly lost among the undulations of the sea of ice.

His tale had occupied the whole day, and the sun was upon the verge of the horizon when he departed. I knew that I ought to hasten my descent towards the valley, as I should soon be encompassed in darkness; but my heart was heavy, and my steps slow. The labour of winding among the little paths of the mountain and fixing my feet firmly as I advanced perplexed me, occupied as I was by the emotions which the occurrences of the day had produced. Night was far advanced when I came to the halfway resting-place and seated myself beside the fountain. The stars shone at intervals as the clouds passed from over them; the dark pines rose before me, and every here and there a broken tree lay on the ground; it was a scene of wonderful solemnity and stirred strange thoughts within me. I wept bitterly, and clasping my hands in agony, I exclaimed, "Oh! Stars and clouds and winds, ye are all about to mock me; if ye really pity me, crush sensation and memory; let me become as nought; but if not, depart, depart, and leave me in darkness."

These were wild and miserable thoughts, but I cannot describe to you how the eternal twinkling of the stars weighed upon me and how I listened to every blast of wind as if it were a dull ugly siroc on its way to consume me.

Morning dawned before I arrived at the village of Chamounix; I took no rest, but returned immediately to Geneva. Even in my own heart I could give no expression to my sensations—they weighed on me with a mountain's weight and their excess destroyed my agony beneath them. Thus I returned home, and entering the house, presented myself to the family. My haggard and wild appearance awoke intense alarm, but I answered no question, scarcely did I speak. I felt as if I were placed under a ban—as if I had no right to claim their sympathies—as if never more might I enjoy companionship with them. Yet even thus I loved them to adoration; and to save them, I resolved to dedicate myself to my most abhorred task. The prospect of such an occupation made every other circumstance of existence pass before me like a dream, and that thought only had to me the reality of life.

• ANALYZING THE SCENE •
CHAPTER 17 – SCENE 35

A Story Event is an active change of universal human value for one or more characters as a result of conflict (one character's desires clash with another's or an environmental shift changes the universal human value).

A Working Scene contains at least one Story Event. To determine a scene's Story Event, answer these four questions:

1. What are the characters literally doing—that is, what are their micro on-the-ground actions?

We are back to Frankenstein's first-person narration; the creature has finished his own storytelling. Now he attempts to convince Frankenstein to create a female being as his companion.

2. What is the essential tactic of the characters—that is, what macro behaviors are they employing that are linked to a universal human value?

Frankenstein and the creature are negotiating over the creature's future. The creature threatens to continue to kill people and create havoc unless Frankenstein creates a female companion for him. In this scene, Shelley lays out the story question that pulls us through to the climax of the entire book. Will Frankenstein obey the creature and create a female as part of a deal whereby the creature will disappear forever? Will the creature actually honor such a promise?

3. What universal human values have changed for one or more

characters in the scene? Which one of those value changes is most important and should be included in the Story Grid Spreadsheet?

The only two characters in this scene are Frankenstein and his creature; the creature's state or condition has not changed, but Frankenstein's has.

Frankenstein goes through several emotional states. He says that at the end of the monster's speech, he felt "bewildered, perplexed." Then he becomes angry as he remembers that this creature killed his brother and caused Justine's death; as the creature pleads, he calms down and considers his request. He agrees to the request, and after the creature leaves, he weeps. Even with the fit of anger, the general direction of his state is from Indecision/Confusion to Resolution/Clarity. He knows what he must do and resolves to do it.

Confusion to Clarity

4. What is the Story Event that sums up the scene's on-the-ground actions, essential tactics, and value change? We will enter that event in the Story Grid Spreadsheet.

The creature demands that Frankenstein build him a female, and Frankenstein agrees.

HOW THE SCENE ABIDES BY THE FIVE COMMANDMENTS OF STORYTELLING

Inciting Incident: The creature demands that Frankenstein create a female companion for him.

Turning Point Progressive Complication: Frankenstein refuses, but the creature threatens to cause destruction if he does not obey.

Crisis: Frankenstein knows that the creature is capable of doing what he says; he has already killed his brother and framed Justine for the murder. But can he trust the creature's promise? Best bad choice.

Climax: Frankenstein decides that the creature is both dangerous and deserving of help; he agrees to his request if he promises to leave human society.

Resolution: The creature agrees and leaves; Frankenstein returns to Geneva, his heart heavy with the knowledge of what he must do.

NOTES

- There are lots of holes in the creature's logic! Frankenstein is right to be worried, and he raises the points that the reader should be concerned about. This is how Shelley ensures that Frankenstein's eventual agreement to build yet another human being makes sense; she has him present the objections on the page and lets the creature respond.
- The holes in the logic, however, are part of the essential moral questions that Shelley is writing about in the book overall. First of all, is it true that he is malicious because he is miserable? The cottagers were miserable, yet not malicious. The creature blames the lack of human companionship for his misery, but can Frankenstein guarantee a female creature will want to remain with the male?
- Is the creature showing his humanity by his statement that, "if I cannot inspire love, I will cause fear"? How is this helpful to him? Why does he think that this makes sense? Is it a way of being noticed, paid attention to? Perhaps it is the logic of a child.
- Frankenstein eventually agrees, saying, "I concluded that the justice due both to him and my fellow creatures demanded of me that I should comply with his request." Frankenstein feels guilt toward this creature and acknowledges his role in this mess. What kind of justice is he referring to? Possibly a heavenly justice, as discussed in *Paradise Lost*? Is he concerned about being just because we have been shown that you cannot trust earthly justice?

CHAPTER 18 – SCENE 36

Day after day, week after week, passed away on my return to Geneva; and I could not collect the courage to recommence my work. I feared the vengeance of the disappointed fiend, yet I was unable to overcome my repugnance to the task which was enjoined me. I found that I could not compose a female without again devoting several months to profound study and laborious disquisition. I had heard of some discoveries having been made by an English philosopher, the knowledge of which was material to my success, and I sometimes thought of obtaining my father's consent to visit England for this purpose; but I clung to every pretence of delay and shrank from taking the first step in an undertaking whose immediate necessity began to appear less absolute to me. **A change indeed had taken place in me; my health, which had hitherto declined, was now much restored; and my spirits, when unchecked by the memory of my unhappy promise, rose proportionably.** My father saw this change with pleasure, and he turned his thoughts towards the best method of eradicating the remains of my melancholy, which every now and then would return by fits, and with a devouring blackness overcast the approaching sunshine. At these moments I took refuge in the most perfect solitude. I passed whole days on the lake alone in a little boat, watching the clouds and listening to the rippling of the waves, silent and listless. But the fresh air and bright sun seldom failed to restore me to some degree of composure, and on my return I met the salutations of my friends with a readier smile and a more cheerful heart.

It was after my return from one of these rambles that my father, calling me aside, thus addressed me, "I am happy to remark, my dear son, that you have resumed your former pleasures and seem to be returning to yourself. And yet you are still unhappy and still avoid our society. For some time I was lost in conjecture as to the cause of this, but yesterday an idea struck me, and if it is well founded, I conjure you to avow it. Reserve on such a point would be not only useless, but draw down treble misery on us all." *[Frankenstein is procrastinating and cheerful until his father brings up an important subject.]*

I trembled violently at his exordium, and my father continued—"I confess, my son, that I have always looked forward to your marriage with our dear Elizabeth as the tie of our domestic comfort and the stay of my declining years. You were attached to each other from your earliest infancy; you studied together, and appeared, in dispositions and tastes, entirely suited to one another. But so blind is the experience of man that what I conceived to be the best assistants to my plan may have entirely destroyed it. **You, perhaps, regard her as your sister, without any wish that she might become your wife. Nay, you may have met with another whom you may love; and considering yourself as bound in honour to Elizabeth, this struggle may occasion the poignant misery which you appear to feel.**"

"My dear father, reassure yourself. I love my cousin tenderly and sincerely. I never saw any woman who excited, as Elizabeth does, my warmest admiration and affection. My future hopes and prospects are entirely bound up in the expectation of our union." *[This is a strange response. He's never given the least indication that he is in love with Elizabeth. Perhaps he merely "admires" her and that's enough for marriage in their social class.]*

"The expression of your sentiments of this subject, my dear Victor, gives me more pleasure than I have for some time experienced. If you feel thus, we shall assuredly be happy, however present events may cast a gloom over us. But it is this gloom which appears to have taken so strong a hold of your mind that I wish to dissipate. Tell me, therefore, whether you object to an immediate solemnization of the marriage. We have been unfortunate, and recent events have drawn us from that everyday tranquillity befitting my years and infirmities. You are younger; yet I do not suppose, possessed as you are of a competent fortune, that an early marriage would at all interfere with any future plans of honour and utility that you may have formed. Do not suppose, however, that I wish to dictate happiness to you or that a delay on your part would cause me any serious uneasiness. Interpret my words with candour and answer me, I conjure you, with confidence and sincerity."

I listened to my father in silence and remained for some time incapable of offering any reply. I revolved rapidly in my mind a multitude of thoughts and endeavoured to arrive at some conclusion. Alas! **To me the idea of an immediate union with my Elizabeth was one of horror and dismay.** I was bound by a solemn promise which I had not yet fulfilled and dared not break, or if I did, what manifold miseries might not impend over me and my devoted family! **Could I enter into a festival with this deadly weight yet hanging round my neck and bowing me to the ground? I must perform my engagement and let the monster depart with his mate before I allowed myself to enjoy the delight of a union from which I expected peace.**

I remembered also the necessity imposed upon me of either journeying to England or entering into a long correspondence with those philosophers of that country whose knowledge and discoveries were of indispensable use to me in my present undertaking. The latter method of obtaining the desired intelligence was dilatory and unsatisfactory; besides, I had an insurmountable aversion to the idea of engaging myself in my loathsome task in my father's house while in habits of familiar intercourse with those I loved. I knew that a thousand fearful accidents might occur, the slightest of which would disclose a tale to thrill all connected with me with horror. I was aware also that I should often lose all self-command, all capacity of hiding the harrowing sensations that would possess me during the progress of my unearthly occupation. I must absent myself from all I loved while thus employed. Once commenced, it would quickly be achieved, and I might be restored to my family in peace and happiness. My promise fulfilled, the monster would depart forever. Or (so my fond fancy imaged) some accident might meanwhile occur to destroy him and put an end to my slavery forever.

These feelings dictated my answer to my father. I expressed a wish to visit England, but concealing the true reasons of this request, I clothed my desires under a guise which excited no suspicion, while I urged my desire with an earnestness that easily induced my father to comply. After so long a period of an absorbing melancholy that resembled madness in its intensity and effects, he was glad to find that I was capable of taking pleasure in the idea of such a journey, and he hoped that change of scene and varied amusement would, before my return, have restored me entirely to myself.

The duration of my absence was left to my own choice; a few months, or at most a year, was the period contemplated. One paternal kind precaution he had taken to ensure my having a companion. Without previously communicating with me, he had, in concert with Elizabeth, arranged that Clerval should join me at Strasbourg. This interfered with the solitude I coveted for the prosecution of my task; yet at the commencement of my journey the presence of my friend could in no way be an impediment, and truly I rejoiced that thus I should be saved many hours of lonely, maddening reflection. Nay, Henry might stand between me and the intrusion of my foe. If I were alone, would he not at times force his abhorred presence on me to remind me of my task or to contemplate its progress?

To England, therefore, I was bound, and it was understood that my union with Elizabeth should take place immediately on my return. My father's age rendered him extremely averse to delay. **For myself, there was one reward I promised myself from my detested toils—one consolation for my unparalleled sufferings; it was the prospect of that day when, enfranchised from my miserable slavery, I might claim Elizabeth and forget the past in my union with her.**

I now made arrangements for my journey, but one feeling haunted me which filled me with fear and agitation. During my absence I should leave my friends unconscious of the existence of their enemy and unprotected from his attacks, exasperated as he might be by my departure. But he had promised to follow me wherever I might go, and would he not accompany me to England? This imagination was dreadful in itself, but soothing inasmuch as it supposed the safety of my friends. I was agonized with the idea of the possibility that the reverse of this might happen. But through the whole period during which I was the slave of my creature I allowed myself to be governed by the impulses of the moment; and **my present sensations strongly intimated that the fiend would follow me and exempt my family from the danger of his machinations.**

• ANALYZING THE SCENE •
CHAPTER 18 – SCENE 36

A Story Event is an active change of universal human value for one or more characters as a result of conflict (one character's desires clash with another's or an environmental shift changes the universal human value).

A Working Scene contains at least one Story Event. To determine a scene's Story Event, answer these four questions:

1. What are the characters literally doing—that is, what are their micro on-the-ground actions?

Frankenstein remains in Geneva, not doing anything in particular. His father discusses Elizabeth with him.

2. What is the essential tactic of the characters—that is, what macro behaviors are they employing that are linked to a universal human value?

Frankenstein is procrastinating. He knows he needs to go to England in order to do the research needed to build the female creature, but he can't seem to get started. His father asks him to consider marrying his foster sister Elizabeth immediately, and he dreads this prospect so much, he decides to leave for England immediately rather than marry her so soon.

3. What universal human values have changed for one or more characters in the scene? Which one of those value changes is most important and should be included in the Story Grid Spreadsheet?

Frankenstein knows he needs to get started on his new project, but he doesn't want to. However, when his father suggests he marry Elizabeth immediately, he knows he cannot possibly celebrate a marriage with this dreaded task hanging over his head. This inspires him to stop procrastinating and head out to England in order to do the research necessary to create his female creature.

Inactive to Active

4. What is the Story Event that sums up the scene's on-the-ground actions, essential tactics, and value change? We will enter that event in the Story Grid Spreadsheet.

Frankenstein returns to Geneva, where his father asks him to marry Elizabeth immediately. He knows he cannot marry her while he is building another monster, so he makes plans to go to England to work on this new creature.

HOW THE SCENE ABIDES BY THE FIVE COMMANDMENTS OF STORYTELLING

Inciting Incident: Frankenstein's father asks him to marry Elizabeth immediately.

Turning Point Progressive Complication: Frankenstein knows he cannot marry Elizabeth while still trying to create the female creature he has promised. He needs to be alone.

Crisis: How should Frankenstein react to his father's request? Best bad choice.

Climax: It's time to fulfill his promise to the creature. Frankenstein persuades his father to let him travel to England since he knows he needs to do research there in order to complete his project.

Resolution: His father agrees, hoping a trip to England will make him happy.

NOTES

- Frankenstein has calmed down since his encounter with the creature. He tries to put thoughts of his promise out of his mind, and when he is able to forget about the creature, he is actually quite happy.
- Shelley has an unerring instinct for the perfect Horror setup. Here, she introduces a calm vibe at the beginning of the scene. Frankenstein is procrastinating, spending days on the lake in a little boat, "watching the clouds and listening to the rippling of the waves." The reader knows something terrible has to happen in order to interrupt this tranquil phase of Frankenstein's life.
- The inciting incident that will disrupt Frankenstein's life is his father's request that he marry Elizabeth as soon as possible. This is a terrific setup; after all, a wedding is a happy occasion, and Frankenstein's father is getting older. After the tragedy of losing little William, Frankenstein's father wants Victor to be happy again. It's a great twist to have this source of happiness be a source of misery for Victor! The reader expects something bad to happen because Frankenstein has been refusing to engage, but a wedding is a surprising twist.
- However, Frankenstein declines the wedding because he knows he can't relax until he's dealt with the creature. So the inciting incident does indeed serve to push him out of his tranquil Geneva life and into the unknown, albeit in an unexpected way. It's good to remember that a progressive complication doesn't necessarily have to be bad news. It might be good news with bad implications.

CHAPTER 18 – SCENE 37

It was in the latter end of September that I again quitted my native country. My journey had been my own suggestion, and Elizabeth therefore acquiesced, but she was filled with disquiet at the idea of my suffering, away from her, the inroads of misery and grief. It had been her care which provided me a companion in Clerval—and yet a man is blind to a thousand minute circumstances which call forth a woman's sedulous attention. She longed to bid me hasten my return; a thousand conflicting emotions rendered her mute as she bade me a tearful, silent farewell.

I threw myself into the carriage that was to convey me away, hardly knowing whither I was going, and careless of what was passing around. I remembered only, and it was with a bitter anguish that I reflected on it, to order that my chemical instruments should be packed to go with me. Filled with dreary imaginations, I passed through many beautiful and majestic scenes, but my eyes were fixed and unobserving. I could only think of the bourne of my travels and the work which was to occupy me whilst they endured.

After some days spent in listless indolence, during which I traversed many leagues, I arrived at Strasbourg, where I waited two days for Clerval. He came. **Alas, how great was the contrast between us! He was alive to every new scene, joyful when he saw the beauties**

of the setting sun, and more happy when he beheld it rise and recommence a new day. He pointed out to me the shifting colours of the landscape and the appearances of the sky. "This is what it is to live," he cried; "how I enjoy existence! But you, my dear Frankenstein, wherefore are you desponding and sorrowful!" In truth, I was occupied by gloomy thoughts and neither saw the descent of the evening star nor the golden sunrise reflected in the Rhine. And you, my friend, would be far more amused with the journal of Clerval, who observed the scenery with an eye of feeling and delight, than in listening to my reflections. I, a miserable wretch, haunted by a curse that shut up every avenue to enjoyment.

We had agreed to descend the Rhine in a boat from Strasbourg to Rotterdam, whence we might take shipping for London. During this voyage we passed many willowy islands and saw several beautiful towns. We stayed a day at Mannheim, and on the fifth from our departure from Strasbourg, arrived at Mainz. The course of the Rhine below Mainz becomes much more picturesque. The river descends rapidly and winds between hills, not high, but steep, and of beautiful forms. We saw many ruined castles standing on the edges of precipices, surrounded by black woods, high and inaccessible. This part of the Rhine, indeed, presents a singularly variegated landscape. In one spot you view rugged hills, ruined castles overlooking tremendous precipices, with the dark Rhine rushing beneath; and on the sudden turn of a promontory, flourishing vineyards with green sloping banks and a meandering river and populous towns occupy the scene. *[More glorious description of the natural landscape!]*

We travelled at the time of the vintage and heard the song of the labourers as we glided down the stream. Even I, depressed in mind, and my spirits continually agitated by gloomy feelings, even I was pleased. I lay at the bottom of the boat, and as I gazed on the cloudless blue sky, I seemed to drink in a tranquillity to which I had long been a stranger. And if these were my sensations, who can describe those of Henry? He felt as if he had been transported to fairy-land and enjoyed a happiness seldom tasted by man. "I have seen," he said, "the most beautiful scenes of my own country; I have visited the lakes of Lucerne and Uri, where the snowy mountains descend almost perpendicularly to the water, casting black and impenetrable shades, which would cause a gloomy and mournful appearance were it not for the most verdant islands that believe the eye by their gay appearance; I have seen this lake agitated by a tempest, when the wind tore up whirlwinds of water and gave you an idea of what the water-spout must be on the great ocean; and the waves dash with fury the base of the mountain, where the priest and his mistress were overwhelmed by an avalanche and where their dying voices are still said to be heard amid the pauses of the nightly wind; I have seen the mountains of La Valais, and the Pays de Vaud; but this country, Victor, pleases me more than all those wonders. The mountains of Switzerland are more majestic and strange, but there is a charm in the banks of this divine river that I never before saw equalled. Look at that castle which overhangs yon precipice; and that also on the island, almost concealed amongst the foliage of those lovely trees; and now that group of labourers coming from among their vines; and that village half hid in the recess of the mountain. Oh, surely the spirit that inhabits and guards this place has a soul more in harmony with man than those who pile the glacier or retire to the inaccessible peaks of the mountains of our own country." Clerval! Beloved friend! **Even now it delights me to record your words and to dwell on the praise of which you are so eminently deserving. He was a being formed in the "very poetry of nature." His wild and enthusiastic imagination was chastened by the sensibility of his heart. His soul overflowed with ardent affections, and his friendship was of that devoted and wondrous nature that the world-minded teach us to look for only in the imagination. But even human sympathies were not sufficient to satisfy his eager mind. The scenery of external nature, which others regard only with admiration, he loved with ardour:—**

——The sounding cataract
Haunted him like a passion: the tall rock,
The mountain, and the deep and gloomy wood,
Their colours and their forms, were then to him
An appetite; a feeling, and a love,
That had no need of a remoter charm,
By thought supplied, or any interest

Unborrow'd from the eye.

[Wordsworth's "Tintern Abbey"]

And where does he now exist? **Is this gentle and lovely being lost forever**? Has this mind, so replete with ideas, imaginations fanciful and magnificent, which formed a world, whose existence depended on the life of its creator;—has this mind perished? Does it now only exist in my memory? No, it is not thus; your form so divinely wrought, and beaming with beauty, has decayed, but your spirit still visits and consoles your unhappy friend.

Pardon this gush of sorrow; these ineffectual words are but a slight tribute to the unexampled worth of Henry, but they soothe my heart, overflowing with the anguish which his remembrance creates. I will proceed with my tale.

Beyond Cologne we descended to the plains of Holland; and we resolved to post the remainder of our way, for the wind was contrary and the stream of the river was too gentle to aid us. Our journey here lost the interest arising from beautiful scenery, but we arrived in a few days at Rotterdam, whence we proceeded by sea to England. It was on a clear morning, in the latter days of December, that I first saw the white cliffs of Britain. The banks of the Thames presented a new scene; they were flat but fertile, and almost every town was marked by the remembrance of some story. We saw Tilbury Fort and remembered the Spanish Armada, Gravesend, Woolwich, and Greenwich—places which I had heard of even in my country.

At length we saw the numerous steeples of London, St. Paul's towering above all, and the Tower famed in English history.

• ANALYZING THE SCENE •
CHAPTER 18 – SCENE 37

A Story Event is an active change of universal human value for one or more characters as a result of conflict (one character's desires clash with

another's or an environmental shift changes the universal human value).

A Working Scene contains at least one Story Event. To determine a scene's Story Event, answer these four questions:

1. What are the characters literally doing—that is, what are their micro on-the-ground actions?

Frankenstein has left Geneva en route to England.

2. What is the essential tactic of the characters—that is, what macro behaviors are they employing that are linked to a universal human value?

Victor is traveling with his best friend, Clerval, who never fails to make him happy. He describes the beautiful scenery they pass through and Clerval's delicate sensibilities, with ample foreshadowing that Clerval is also destined to die.

3. What universal human values have changed for one or more characters in the scene? Which one of those value changes is most important and should be included in the Story Grid Spreadsheet?

Victor starts out the scene in "bitter anguish" as he leaves Geneva. He is upset as he considers the work he must do in England. He meets Clerval in Strasbourg, and as they start their journey toward England together, his mood improves. Clerval's mood remains optimistic and energetic as usual. Frankenstein's state moves from Depressed to Uplifted.

Depressed to Uplifted

4. What is the Story Event that sums up the scene's on-the-ground actions, essential tactics, and value change? We will enter that event in the Story Grid Spreadsheet.

Frankenstein leaves Geneva for England and meets Clerval on the way.

HOW THE SCENE ABIDES BY THE FIVE COMMANDMENTS OF STORYTELLING

Inciting Incident: Frankenstein leaves Geneva for England.

Turning Point Progressive Complication: Frankenstein has to meet Clerval in Strasbourg.

Crisis: "Is this gentle and lovely being lost forever?" Where is Clerval now? Best bad choice.

Climax: Frankenstein denies that Clerval only exists in his mind; his spirit "still visits and consoles" him. Frankenstein is obviously in denial and Clerval is obviously dead.

Resolution: Frankenstein gets back to his story; he and Clerval continued their journey and arrived in London.

NOTES

- This is a challenging scene to evaluate because Victor steps out of the story momentarily to explain to Walton the extent of his attachment to Clerval. In order to track the movement of the scene properly, we have to include the flashback and the momentary return to the present on the same timeline; in other words, instead of using a temporal timeline, we'll use the emotional timeline as experienced by the reader since we as writers are most concerned about the reader's emotional journey.
- We also have to go back to the previous scene to remind ourselves that the complication in this scene is Clerval himself. Frankenstein needs to go to England in order to create the female creature the monster desires. The last thing he wants is company because he is leaving Geneva in order to escape Elizabeth and the upcoming nuptials. He knows he will be under pressure and therefore emotionally

volatile while he works on his project, and he doesn't want to be around his family. When Elizabeth and his father conspire to send Clerval to England with him, this is a problem.

- So this scene starts with Frankenstein's departure for England; he is in a bad emotional place, as he knows that he has this wretched project ahead of him. He meets Clerval in Strasbourg, and tells Walton, "Alas, how great was the contrast between us!" Clerval is joyful, thrilled with every bit of beautiful landscape, and aware of every subtle change in the sky. Namely, he is Frankenstein's opposite in every way. Eventually, even Frankenstein begins to enjoy the journey, but Clerval enjoys it to an even greater degree than he does.
- At that point, Frankenstein steps out of the story and the POV of the passage switches. Frankenstein begins to quote Clerval, whose passionate description of the journey raises the emotional temperature of the passage. Frankenstein has begun to enjoy the journey in spite of himself, but Clerval is in ecstasy.
- Then, Frankenstein begins to speak directly to Walton, describing the wonderful, passionate man Clerval is (or was?). "His soul overflowed with ardent affections," he says, and ends up quoting Wordsworth's "Tintern Abbey" in tribute.
- At this height of emotion, one can imagine Walton listening in growing delight to this description of this amazing man, but then Frankenstein says, "And where does he now exist? Is this gentle and lovely being lost forever?" This is the climactic question. Where is Clerval? Is he dead? The reader experiences a sense of dread at this point.
- No! Clerval is not lost forever, Frankenstein claims. He refuses to accept that his friend is gone. His friend's "spirit still visits."
- But for the reader, this is a creepy and uncomfortable answer. Clerval must be dead. And we have to suspect that the monster has killed him.

- Frankenstein goes back to his description of the sights and sounds of the journey, ending in England. Meanwhile, the reader is distracted, trying to pay attention—our minds are back at Clerval. What is about to happen to Clerval?
- It is tempting to blame the structure of this scene on clunky Victorian literature, but if one frees one's mind from the constraints of modern writing and allows for a bit of slow reading—it's brilliant. Well done, Shelley. She has infused us with just the right amount of confusion and dread.

CHAPTER 19 – SCENE 38

London was our present point of rest; we determined to remain several months in this wonderful and celebrated city. Clerval desired the intercourse of the men of genius and talent who flourished at this time, but this was with me a secondary object; I was principally occupied with the means of obtaining the information necessary for the completion of my promise and quickly availed myself of the letters of introduction that I had brought with me, addressed to the most distinguished natural philosophers.

If this journey had taken place during my days of study and happiness, it would have afforded me inexpressible pleasure. But a blight had come over my existence, and I only visited these people for the sake of the information they might give me on the subject in which my interest was so terribly profound. Company was irksome to me; when alone, I could fill my mind with the sights of heaven and earth; the voice of Henry soothed me, and I could thus cheat myself into a transitory peace. But busy, uninteresting, joyous faces brought back despair to my heart. *[This is very poetic; haven't we all been disturbed at the sight of people who don't know we are suffering?]* **I saw an insurmountable barrier placed between me and my fellow men; this barrier was sealed with the blood of William and Justine, and to reflect on the events connected with those names filled my soul with anguish.**

But in Clerval I saw the image of my former self; he was inquisitive and anxious to gain experience and instruction. The difference of manners which he observed was to him an inexhaustible source of instruction and amusement. He was also pursuing an object he had long had in view. **His design was to visit India, in the belief that he had in his knowledge of its various languages, and in the views he had taken of its society, the means of materially assisting the progress of European colonization and trade. In Britain only could he further the execution of his plan**. He was forever busy, and the only check to his enjoyments was my sorrowful and dejected mind. I tried to conceal this as much as possible, that I might not debar him from the pleasures natural to one who was entering on a new scene of life, undisturbed by any care or bitter recollection. I often refused to accompany him, alleging another engagement, that I might remain alone. I now also began to collect the materials necessary for my new creation, and this was to me like **the torture of single drops of water continually falling on the head.** Every thought that was devoted to it was an extreme anguish, and every word that I spoke in allusion to it caused my lips to quiver, and my heart to palpitate.

After passing some months in London, we received a letter from a person in Scotland who had formerly been our visitor at Geneva. He mentioned the beauties of his native country and asked us if those were not sufficient allurements to induce us to prolong our journey as far north as Perth, where he resided. Clerval eagerly desired to accept this invitation, and I, although I abhorred society, wished to view again mountains and streams and all the wondrous works with which Nature adorns her chosen dwelling-places. We had arrived in England at the beginning of October, and it was now February. We accordingly determined to commence our journey towards the north at the expiration of another month. In this expedition we did not intend to follow the great road to Edinburgh, but to visit Windsor, Oxford, Matlock, and the Cumberland lakes, resolving to arrive at the completion of this tour about the end of July. I packed up my chemical instruments and the materials I had collected, resolving to finish my labours in some obscure nook in the northern highlands of Scotland.

We quitted London on the 27th of March and remained a few days at Windsor, rambling in its beautiful forest. This was a new scene to us mountaineers; the majestic oaks, the quantity of game, and the herds of stately deer were all novelties to us.

From thence we proceeded to Oxford. As we entered this city our minds were filled with the remembrance of the events that had been transacted there more than a century and a half before. It was here that Charles I. had collected his forces. This city had remained faithful to him, after the whole nation had forsaken his cause to join the standard of Parliament and liberty. The memory of that unfortunate king and his companions, the amiable Falkland, the insolent Goring, his queen, and son, gave a peculiar interest to every part of the city which they might be supposed to have inhabited. The spirit of elder days found a dwelling here, and we delighted to trace its footsteps. If these feelings had not found an imaginary gratification, the appearance of the city had yet in itself sufficient beauty to obtain our admiration. The colleges are ancient and picturesque; the streets are almost magnificent; and the lovely Isis, which flows beside it through meadows of exquisite verdure, is spread forth into a placid expanse of waters, which reflects its majestic assemblage of towers, and spires, and domes, embosomed among aged trees. *[More detailed travelogue courtesy of Shelley.]*

I enjoyed this scene, and yet **my enjoyment was embittered both by the memory of the past and the anticipation of the future.** I was formed for peaceful happiness. During my youthful days discontent never visited my mind, and if I was ever overcome by ennui, the sight of what is beautiful in nature or the study of what is excellent and sublime in the productions of man could always interest my heart and communicate elasticity to my spirits. **But I am a blasted tree; the bolt has entered my soul; and I felt then that I should survive to exhibit what I shall soon cease to be—a miserable spectacle of wrecked humanity, pitiable to others and intolerable to myself.** *[This is a fascinating metaphor. Shelley is obviously referring back to the tree struck by lightning during Frankenstein's teen years. Readers have long assumed that the lightning strike was an allusion to the power of electricity, but perhaps there is another meaning. Perhaps Frankenstein's dreamy soul was pierced by the practical bolt of science, wrecking him as a human being.]*

We passed a considerable period at Oxford, rambling among its environs and endeavouring to identify every spot which might relate to the most animating epoch of English history. Our little voyages of discovery were often prolonged by the successive objects that presented themselves. We visited the tomb of the illustrious Hampden and the field on which that patriot fell. For a moment my soul was elevated from its debasing and miserable fears to contemplate the divine ideas of liberty and self sacrifice of which these sights were the monuments and the remembrancers. For an instant I dared to shake off my chains and look around me with a free and lofty spirit, but the iron had eaten into my flesh, and I sank again, trembling and hopeless, into my miserable self.

We left Oxford with regret and proceeded to Matlock, which was our next place of rest. The country in the neighbourhood of this village resembled, to a greater degree, the scenery of Switzerland; but everything is on a lower scale, and the green hills want the crown of distant white Alps which always attend on the piny mountains of my native country. We visited the wondrous cave and the little cabinets of natural history, where the curiosities are disposed in the same manner as in the collections at Servox and Chamounix. The latter name made me tremble when pronounced by Henry, and I hastened to quit Matlock, with which that terrible scene was thus associated.

From Derby, still journeying northwards, we passed two months in Cumberland and Westmorland. I could now almost fancy myself among the Swiss mountains. The little patches of snow which yet lingered on the northern sides of the mountains, the lakes, and the dashing of the rocky streams were all familiar and dear sights to me. Here also we made some acquaintances, who almost contrived to cheat me into happiness. The delight of Clerval was proportionably greater than mine; his mind expanded in the company of men of talent, and he found in his own nature greater capacities and resources than he could have imagined himself to have possessed while he associated with his inferiors. "I could pass my life here," said he to me; "and among these mountains I should scarcely regret Switzerland and the Rhine."

But he found that a traveller's life is one that includes much pain amidst its enjoyments. His feelings are forever on the stretch; and when he begins to sink into repose, he finds himself obliged to quit that on which he rests in pleasure for something new, which again engages his attention, and which also he forsakes for other novelties.

We had scarcely visited the various lakes of Cumberland and Westmorland and conceived an affection for some of the inhabitants when the period of our appointment with our Scotch friend approached, and we left them to travel on. For my own part I was not sorry. **I had now neglected my promise for some time, and I feared the effects of the daemon's disappointment. He might remain in Switzerland and wreak his vengeance on my relatives. This idea pursued me and tormented me at every moment from which I might otherwise have snatched repose and peace.** I waited for my letters with feverish impatience; if they were delayed I was miserable and overcome by a thousand fears; *[foreshadowing!]* and when they arrived and I saw the superscription of Elizabeth or my father, I hardly dared to read and ascertain my fate. Sometimes I thought that the fiend followed me and might expedite my remissness by murdering my companion. When these thoughts possessed me, I would not quit Henry for a moment, but followed him as his shadow, to protect him from the fancied rage of his destroyer. I felt as if I had committed some great crime, the consciousness of which haunted me. I was guiltless, but I had indeed drawn down a horrible curse upon my head, as mortal as that of crime.

I visited Edinburgh with languid eyes and mind; and yet that city might have interested the most unfortunate being. Clerval did not like it so well as Oxford, for the antiquity of the latter city was more pleasing to him. But the beauty and regularity of the new town of Edinburgh, its romantic castle and its environs, the most delightful in the world, Arthur's Seat, St. Bernard's Well, and the Pentland Hills compensated him for the change and filled him with cheerfulness and admiration. But I was impatient to arrive at the termination of my journey.

We left Edinburgh in a week, passing through Coupar, St. Andrew's, and along the banks of the Tay, to Perth, where our friend expected us. But **I was in no mood to laugh and talk with strangers or enter into their feelings or plans with the good humour expected from a guest; and accordingly I told Clerval that I wished to make the tour of**

Scotland alone. "Do you," said I, "enjoy yourself, and let this be our rendezvous. I may be absent a month or two; but do not interfere with my motions, I entreat you; leave me to peace and solitude for a short time; and when I return, I hope it will be with a lighter heart, more congenial to your own temper."

Henry wished to dissuade me, but seeing me bent on this plan, ceased to remonstrate. He entreated me to write often. "I had rather be with you," he said, "in your solitary rambles, than with these Scotch people, whom I do not know; hasten, then, my dear friend, to return, that I may again feel myself somewhat at home, which I cannot do in your absence."

Having parted from my friend, I determined to visit some remote spot of Scotland and finish my work in solitude. I did not doubt but that the monster followed me and would discover himself to me when I should have finished, that he might receive his companion. **With this resolution I traversed the northern highlands and fixed on one of the remotest of the Orkneys as the scene of my labours. It was a place fitted for such a work, being hardly more than a rock whose high sides were continually beaten upon by the waves.** The soil was barren, scarcely affording pasture for a few miserable cows, and oatmeal for its inhabitants, which consisted of five persons, whose gaunt and scraggy limbs gave tokens of their miserable fare. Vegetables and bread, when they indulged in such luxuries, and even fresh water, was to be procured from the mainland, which was about five miles distant.

On the whole island there were but three miserable huts, and one of these was vacant when I arrived. This I hired. It contained but two rooms, and these exhibited all the squalidness of the most miserable penury. The thatch had fallen in, the walls were unplastered, and the door was off its hinges. I ordered it to be repaired, bought some furniture, and took possession, an incident which would doubtless have occasioned some surprise had not all the senses of the cottagers been benumbed by want and squalid poverty. As it was, I lived ungazed at and unmolested, hardly thanked for the pittance of food and clothes which I gave, so much does suffering blunt even the coarsest sensations of men.

In this retreat I devoted the morning to labour; but in the evening, when the weather permitted, I walked on the stony beach of the sea to listen to the waves as they roared and dashed at my feet. It was a monotonous yet ever-changing scene. I thought of Switzerland; it was far different from this desolate and appalling landscape. Its hills are covered with vines, and its cottages are scattered thickly in the plains. Its fair lakes reflect a blue and gentle sky, and when troubled by the winds, their tumult is but as the play of a lively infant when compared to the roarings of the giant ocean.

In this manner I distributed my occupations when I first arrived, but as I proceeded in my labour, it became every day more horrible and irksome to me. Sometimes I could not prevail on myself to enter my laboratory for several days, and at other times I toiled day and night in order to complete my work. **It was, indeed, a filthy process in which I was engaged. During my first experiment, a kind of enthusiastic frenzy had blinded me to the horror of my employment; my mind was intently fixed on the consummation of my labour, and my eyes were shut to the horror of my proceedings. But now I went to it in cold blood, and my heart often sickened at the work of my hands.**

Thus situated, employed in the most detestable occupation, immersed in a solitude where nothing could for an instant call my attention from the actual scene in which I was engaged, my spirits became unequal; I grew restless and nervous. Every moment I feared to meet my persecutor. Sometimes I sat with my eyes fixed on the ground, fearing to raise them lest they should encounter the object which I so much dreaded to behold. I feared to wander from the sight of my fellow creatures lest when alone he should come to claim his companion.

In the mean time I worked on, and my labour was already considerably advanced. I looked towards its completion with a tremulous and eager hope, which I dared not trust myself to question but which was intermixed with **obscure forebodings of evil that made my heart sicken in my bosom.**

CHAPTER 19 – SCENE 38

A Story Event is an active change of universal human value for one or more characters as a result of conflict (one character's desires clash with another's or an environmental shift changes the universal human value).

A Working Scene contains at least one Story Event. To determine a scene's Story Event, answer these four questions:

1. What are the characters literally doing—that is, what are their micro on-the-ground actions?

Clerval and Frankenstein are journeying through England on their way to Scotland, where Frankenstein is planning to set up his project.

2. What is the essential tactic of the characters—that is, what macro behaviors are they employing that are linked to a universal human value?

Frankenstein is in agony because he is surrounded by beautiful scenery and Clerval's enthusiasm but mentally focused on planning his creation. He is tormented by the contrast.

3. What universal human values have changed for one or more characters in the scene? Which one of those value changes is most important and should be included in the Story Grid Spreadsheet?

Frankenstein journeys through England, unhappy because he sees joyful people around him and because Clerval is so happy. He dreads the task that lies ahead. But eventually, he leaves Clerval and goes to the remotest part of the Orkney Islands in order to be alone; he needs to start constructing another creature.

The emotional temperature of this scene seems to change only slightly as Frankenstein starts out feeling dread and ends up actually actively experiencing the horror of the task he has been dreading. Given the global value of Life to Death, it is probably a starker change in value to highlight the fact that he must be alone in order to fulfill his task. He starts the scene with Clerval and the many cheerful people around him; he ends the task alone in a hut at one of the remotest Orkneys.

Companionship to Isolated

4. What is the Story Event that sums up the scene's on-the-ground actions, essential tactics, and value change? We will enter that event in the Story Grid Spreadsheet.

Frankenstein and Clerval journey through England; Victor heads up to Scotland alone and starts his project.

HOW THE SCENE ABIDES BY THE FIVE COMMANDMENTS OF STORYTELLING

Inciting Incident: Clerval and Frankenstein journey through England.

Turning Point Progressive Complication: Frankenstein needs to start the dreaded construction of the female creature, but he needs to do this alone. When they arrive in Perth, he insists on heading to Scotland without Clerval.

Crisis: Frankenstein knows he needs to do this alone. He dreads the task and cannot stop thinking about it. When will he do it? How will he do it when he is traveling with Clerval?

Climax: Clerval argues briefly. He doesn't want Frankenstein to go off on his own, but Frankenstein parts from Clerval in order to begin the dreaded task.

Resolution: Frankenstein begins his project alone in a hut on a remote Orkney island.

NOTES

- It is always difficult to know where to break a chapter into separate scenes. One rule of thumb is to look at the average length of the scene for a particular writer. They tend to be of a similar length. In Shelley's case, her scenes are normally in the 1,300–1,800-word range.
- Another helpful gauge is to look at what has changed. Chapter 19 could probably have been broken up into two scenes. The first one would have encompassed the travels of Frankenstein and Clerval until Edinburgh while the second would have started with their separation as Frankenstein journeys to the remote Orkneys in order to set up his project while Clerval continues to tour Scotland with fellow travelers. In terms of an inciting incident, this makes sense because the inciting incident of the latter scene would be Frankenstein separating himself in order to finally stop procrastinating and begin his work. While that seems reasonable, not much happens between starting his work and the end of that scene.
- However, looking at the emotional journey of Frankenstein, there isn't much change between the beginning of his travels until his separation from Clerval, or between Frankenstein's in the Orkneys and the initiation of his project. The larger emotional change occurs as he leaves behind his dread and actually starts working, which only happens after he has purposefully set up his project in the Orkneys. At this point, he is not only alone, but very alone, both in terms of his psyche and being on this extremely remote island.
- It's probably a better option to measure change over a longer scene rather than to focus on word length or geography.

CHAPTER 20 – SCENE 39

I sat one evening in my laboratory; the sun had set, and the moon was just rising from the sea; I had not sufficient light for my employment, and I remained idle, in a pause of consideration of whether I should leave my labour for the night or hasten its conclusion by an unremitting attention to it. As I sat, a train of reflection occurred to me which led me to consider the effects of what I was now doing. Three years before, I was engaged in the same manner and had created a fiend whose unparalleled barbarity had desolated my heart and filled it forever with the bitterest remorse. I was now about to form another being of whose dispositions I was alike ignorant; she might become ten thousand times more malignant than her mate and delight, for its own sake, in murder and wretchedness. He had sworn to quit the neighbourhood of man and hide himself in deserts, but she had not; and **she, who in all probability was to become a thinking and reasoning animal, might refuse to comply with a compact made before her creation**. They might even hate each other; the creature who already lived loathed his own deformity, and might he not conceive a greater abhorrence for it when it came before his eyes in the female form? She also might turn with disgust from him to the superior beauty of man; she might quit him, and he be again alone, exasperated by the fresh provocation of being deserted by one of his own species. Even if they were to leave Europe and inhabit the deserts of the new world, yet one of the first results of those sympathies for which the daemon thirsted would be children, and a race of devils would be propagated upon the earth who might make the very existence of the species of man a condition precarious and full of terror. Had I right, for my own benefit, to inflict this curse upon everlasting generations? **I had before been moved by the sophisms of the being I had created; I had been struck senseless by his fiendish threats; but now, for the first time, the wickedness of my promise burst upon me; I shuddered to think that future ages might curse me as their pest, whose selfishness had not hesitated to buy its own peace at the price, perhaps, of the existence of the whole human race.**

I trembled and my heart failed within me, when, on looking up, **I saw by the light of the moon the daemon at the casement. A ghastly grin wrinkled his lips as he gazed on me, where I sat fulfilling the task which he had allotted to me.** Yes, he had followed me in my travels; he had loitered in forests, hid himself in caves, or taken refuge in wide and desert heaths; and he now came to mark my progress and claim the fulfilment of my promise.

As I looked on him, his countenance expressed the utmost extent of malice and treachery. **I thought with a sensation of madness on my promise of creating another like to him, and trembling with passion, tore to pieces the thing on which I was engaged. The wretch saw me destroy the creature on whose future existence he depended for happiness, and with a howl of devilish despair and revenge, withdrew.** *[The monster shows up at exactly the wrong moment, just when Frankenstein is worrying about the possibility that he will not be able to convince the female creature to obey her male counterpart and leave peacefully. Here is the "Victim at the Mercy of the Monster" scene, if you feel Frankenstein is the Monster in this story. He is the only person who can give the Monster what he wants, and the Monster will now unleash his revenge.]*

I left the room, and locking the door, made a solemn vow in my own heart never to resume my labours; and then, with trembling steps, I sought my own apartment. I was alone; none were near me to dissipate the gloom and relieve me from the sickening oppression of the most terrible reveries.

Several hours passed, and I remained near my window gazing on the sea; it was almost motionless, for the winds were hushed, and all nature reposed under the eye of the quiet moon. A few fishing vessels alone specked the water, and now and then the gentle breeze wafted the sound of voices as the fishermen called to one another. I felt the silence, although I was hardly conscious of its extreme profundity, until my ear was suddenly arrested by the paddling of oars near the shore, and a person landed close to my house.

In a few minutes after, I heard the creaking of my door, as if some one endeavoured to open it softly. I trembled from head to foot; I felt a presentiment of who it was and wished to rouse one of the peasants who dwelt in a cottage not far from mine; but I was overcome by the sensation of helplessness, so often felt in frightful dreams, when you in vain endeavour to fly from an impending danger, and was rooted to the spot. Presently I heard the sound of footsteps along the passage; the door opened, and the wretch whom I dreaded appeared.

Shutting the door, he approached me and said in a smothered voice, "You have destroyed the work which you began; what is it that you intend? Do you dare to break your promise? I have endured toil and misery; I left Switzerland with you; I crept along the shores of the Rhine, among its willow islands and over the summits of its hills. I have dwelt many months in the heaths of England and among the deserts of Scotland. I have endured incalculable fatigue, and cold, and hunger; do you dare destroy my hopes?"

"Begone! I do break my promise; never will I create another like yourself, equal in deformity and wickedness."

"Slave, I before reasoned with you, but you have proved yourself unworthy of my condescension. Remember that I have power; you believe yourself miserable, but I can make you so wretched that the light of day will be hateful to you. **You are my creator, but I am your master; obey!**" *[Here is the "Speech in Praise of the Monster" at last!]*

"The hour of my irresolution is past, and the period of your power is arrived. Your threats cannot move me to do an act of wickedness; but they confirm me in a determination of not creating you a companion in vice. Shall I, in cool blood, set loose upon the earth a daemon whose delight is in death and wretchedness? Begone! I am firm, and your words will only exasperate my rage."

The monster saw my determination in my face and gnashed his teeth in the impotence of anger. "Shall each man," cried he, "find a wife for his bosom, and each beast have his mate, and I be alone? I had feelings of affection, and they were requited by detestation and scorn. Man! You may hate, but beware! Your hours will pass in dread and misery, and soon the bolt will fall which must ravish from you your happiness forever. Are you to be happy while I grovel in the intensity of my wretchedness? You can blast my other passions, but revenge remains—revenge, henceforth dearer than light or food! I may die, but first you, my tyrant and tormentor, shall curse the sun that gazes on your misery. Beware, for I am fearless and therefore powerful. I will watch with the wiliness of a snake, that I may sting with its venom. Man, you shall repent of the injuries you inflict."

"Devil, cease; and do not poison the air with these sounds of malice. I have declared my resolution to you, and I am no coward to bend beneath words. Leave me; I am inexorable."

"It is well. I go; but **remember, I shall be with you on your wedding-night**."

I started forward and exclaimed, "Villain! Before you sign my death-warrant, be sure that you are yourself safe."

I would have seized him, but he eluded me and quitted the house with precipitation. In a few moments I saw him in his boat, which shot across the waters with an arrowy swiftness and was soon lost amidst the waves.

All was again silent, but his words rang in my ears. I burned with rage to pursue the murderer of my peace and precipitate him into the ocean. I walked up and down my room hastily and perturbed, while my imagination conjured up a thousand images to torment and sting me. Why had I not followed him and closed with him in mortal strife? But I had suffered him to depart, and he had directed his course towards the mainland. I shuddered to think who might be the next victim sacrificed to his insatiate revenge. And then I thought again of his words—**"I WILL BE WITH YOU ON YOUR WEDDING-NIGHT." That, then, was the period fixed for the fulfilment of my**

destiny. In that hour I should die and at once satisfy and extinguish his malice. The prospect did not move me to fear; yet when I thought of my beloved Elizabeth, of her tears and endless sorrow, when she should find her lover so barbarously snatched from her, tears, the first I had shed for many months, streamed from my eyes, and I resolved not to fall before my enemy without a bitter struggle.

• ANALYZING THE SCENE •
CHAPTER 20 – SCENE 39

A Story Event is an active change of universal human value for one or more characters as a result of conflict (one character's desires clash with another's or an environmental shift changes the universal human value).

A Working Scene contains at least one Story Event. To determine a scene's Story Event, answer these four questions:

1. What are the characters literally doing—that is, what are their micro on-the-ground actions?

Frankenstein decides that he regrets promising to create this new creature and destroys it; his original creature appears and threatens him.

2. What is the essential tactic of the characters—that is, what macro behaviors are they employing that are linked to a universal human value?

This is the final battle between Frankenstein and his creature. Frankenstein finally realizes he cannot control the new creature he is building, and his first creature swears revenge.

3. What universal human values have changed for one or more

characters in the scene? Which one of those value changes is most important and should be included in the Story Grid Spreadsheet?

Both Frankenstein and the creature experience emotional turmoil in this scene. Frankenstein suddenly decides that setting yet another creature loose upon the world is wrong. When he sees the first creature spying on him and grinning, he tears the new creature to pieces. His trajectory is from Indecision to Decisiveness. He has been uncertain all along that he should be doing what he's doing, but in this scene, he decides once and for all to take the consequences and die if necessary —he will not create another monster. The creature starts out grinning with pleasure but ends enraged.

It is probably better to highlight the emotional change in Frankenstein because it is the peak of an emotional trajectory that has been a long time coming.

Indecision to Decisiveness

4. What is the Story Event that sums up the scene's on-the-ground actions, essential tactics, and value change? We will enter that event in the Story Grid Spreadsheet.

Frankenstein has built much of the new creature, but he suddenly realizes she may be dangerous. When he sees the creature spying on him, he destroys the new creature. His first creature threatens him.

HOW THE SCENE ABIDES BY THE FIVE COMMANDMENTS OF STORYTELLING

Inciting Incident: Frankenstein suddenly comes to the realization that he can't control what this new creature will think or feel, and she may end up refusing to comply with his wishes.

Turning Point Progressive Complication: Frankenstein sees the monster spying on him, reminding him that he is holding him hostage to their agreement.

Crisis: What if the new creature refuses to do as he wants? What if she loathes her male counterpart? What if she deserts her mate and he is enraged at being deserted? Frankenstein is tormented over whether he should keep doing this work or not. Best bad choice.

Climax: Frankenstein destroys the new creature and swears not to create another.

Resolution: The creature swears he will be with Frankenstein on his wedding night, which Frankenstein interprets as a "death warrant." Frankenstein resolves that he will fight back.

NOTES

- Ever since the deaths of William and Justine, we have been hearing about the creature's sad experience as he tries to figure out what it means to be human. We've been tempted to sympathize with his pain, and when he tells Frankenstein his story, Frankenstein likewise feels sympathy and also responsibility. But after making the promise to create a female being for the creature in exchange for him leaving Europe and settling somewhere far away from human habitation, Frankenstein realizes no one can guarantee the new creature's quiescence.
- All of the dithering stops right at the moment when he comes to this conclusion. It's a little bit precipitous, as we wonder why he never realized this before! But just as he realizes that he isn't in control of what his creations think, feel, or do, he sees the creature, who has followed him to this remote corner of Scotland and is grinning in what he characterizes as a malicious fashion. This triggers his response, and he destroys the new creature.
- Frankenstein has almost become a new person himself at this moment. The creature threatens him, and he resolves to fight back; in fact, he is angry with himself that he didn't take the opportunity to fight him right then and there. He

takes the creature's threat about his wedding night as a death sentence, and says, "The prospect did not move me to fear." However, out of consideration for Elizabeth's sadness, he resolves not to die without a struggle. Hurray for Frankenstein—he sounds like a hero! This is the climax and resolution of the Middle Build. He has decided to act. We are about to enter an exciting Ending Payoff.

CHAPTER 20 – SCENE 40

The night passed away, and the sun rose from the ocean; my feelings became calmer, if it may be called calmness when the violence of rage sinks into the depths of despair. I left the house, the horrid scene of the last night's contention, and walked on the beach of the sea, which I almost regarded as an insuperable barrier between me and my fellow creatures; nay, a wish that such should prove the fact stole across me.

I desired that I might pass my life on that barren rock, wearily, it is true, but uninterrupted by any sudden shock of misery. If I returned, it was to be sacrificed or to see those whom I most loved die under the grasp of a daemon whom I had myself created.

I walked about the isle like a restless spectre, separated from all it loved and miserable in the separation. When it became noon, and the sun rose higher, I lay down on the grass and was overpowered by a deep sleep. *[There are several occasions during the book where people are asleep; this fits in with the Life-Death trajectory where "unconsciousness" is the stage between Life and Death.]* I had been awake the whole of the preceding night, my nerves were agitated, and my eyes inflamed by watching and misery. The sleep into which I now sank refreshed me; and when I awoke, I again felt as if I belonged to a race of human beings like myself, and I began to reflect upon what had passed with greater composure; yet still the words of the fiend rang in my ears like a death-knell; they appeared like a dream, yet distinct and oppressive as a reality.

The sun had far descended, and I still sat on the shore, satisfying my appetite, which had become ravenous, with an oaten cake, when I saw a fishing-boat land close to me, and one of the men brought me a packet; it contained letters from Geneva, and one from Clerval entreating me to join him. *[A wonderful distraction from the horror that just happened and that which is about to happen.]* He said that he was wearing away his time fruitlessly where he was, that letters from the friends he had formed in London desired his return to complete the negotiation they had entered into for his Indian enterprise. He could not any longer delay his departure; but as his journey to London might be followed, even sooner than he now conjectured, by his longer voyage, he entreated me to bestow as much of my society on him as I could spare. He besought me, therefore, to leave my solitary isle and to meet him at Perth, that we might proceed southwards together. This letter in a degree recalled me to life, and I determined to quit my island at the expiration of two days. Yet, before I departed, there was a task to perform, on which I shuddered to reflect; I must pack up my chemical instruments, and for that purpose I must enter the room which had been the scene of my odious work, and I must handle those utensils the sight of which was sickening to me. The next morning, at daybreak, I summoned sufficient courage and unlocked the door of my laboratory. The remains of the half-finished creature, whom I had destroyed, lay scattered on the floor, and I almost felt as if I had mangled the living flesh of a human being. *[Strange that this is the first time he has considered the sanctity of human flesh?]* I paused to collect myself and then entered the chamber. With trembling hand I conveyed the instruments out of the room, but I reflected that I ought not to leave the relics of my work to excite the horror and suspicion of the peasants; and I accordingly put them into a basket, with a great quantity of stones, and laying them up, determined to throw them into the sea that very night; and in the meantime I sat upon the beach, employed in cleaning and arranging my chemical apparatus.

Nothing could be more complete than the alteration that had taken place in my feelings since the night of the appearance of the daemon. I had before regarded my promise with a gloomy despair as a thing that, with whatever consequences, must be fulfilled; but I now felt as if a film had been taken from before my eyes and that I for the first time saw clearly. The idea of renewing my labours did not for one instant occur to me; the threat I had heard weighed on my thoughts, but I did not reflect that a voluntary act of mine could avert it. **I had resolved in my own mind that to create another like the fiend I had first made would be an act of the basest and most atrocious selfishness**, and I banished from my mind every thought that could lead to a different conclusion.

Between two and three in the morning the moon rose; and I then, putting my basket aboard a little skiff, sailed out about four miles from the shore. The scene was perfectly solitary; a few boats were returning towards land, but I sailed away from them. I felt as if I was about the commission of a dreadful crime and avoided with shuddering anxiety any encounter with my fellow creatures. At one time the moon, which had before been clear, was suddenly overspread by a thick cloud, and I took advantage of the moment of darkness and cast my basket into the sea; I listened to the gurgling sound as it sank and then sailed away from the spot. The sky became clouded, but the air was pure, although chilled by the northeast breeze that was then rising. But it refreshed me and filled me with such agreeable sensations that I resolved to prolong my stay on the water, and fixing the rudder in a direct position, stretched myself at the bottom of the boat. Clouds hid the moon, everything was obscure, and I heard only the sound of the boat as its keel cut through the waves; the murmur lulled me, and in a short time I slept soundly. I do not know how long I remained in this situation, but when I awoke I found that the sun had already mounted considerably. The wind was high, and the waves continually threatened the safety of my little skiff. I found that the wind was northeast and must have driven me far from the coast from which I had embarked. I endeavoured to change my course but quickly found that if I again made the attempt the boat would be instantly filled with water. Thus situated, my only resource was to drive before the wind. I confess that I felt a few sensations of terror. I had no compass with me and was so slenderly acquainted with the geography of this part of the world that the sun was of little benefit to me. I might be driven into the wide Atlantic and feel all the tortures of starvation or be swallowed up in the immeasurable waters that roared and buffeted around me. I had already been out many hours and felt the torment of a burning thirst, a prelude to my other sufferings. I looked on the heavens, which were covered by clouds that flew before the wind, only to be replaced by others; I looked upon the sea; it was to be my grave. *[There are several boat-based scenes in the book; Frankenstein has considered suicide while in a boat. Boats and death seem to go together.]*

"Fiend," I exclaimed, "your task is already fulfilled!" I thought of Elizabeth, of my father, and of Clerval—all left behind, on whom the monster might satisfy his sanguinary and merciless passions. This idea plunged me into a reverie so despairing and frightful that even now, when the scene is on the point of closing before me forever, I shudder to reflect on it.

Some hours passed thus; but by degrees, as the sun declined towards the horizon, the wind died away into a gentle breeze and the sea became free from breakers. But these gave place to a heavy swell; I felt sick and hardly able to hold the rudder, when suddenly I saw a line of high land towards the south.

Almost spent, as I was, by fatigue and the dreadful suspense I endured for several hours, this sudden certainty of life rushed like a flood of warm joy to my heart, and tears gushed from my eyes.

How mutable are our feelings, and how strange is that clinging love we have of life even in the excess of misery! I constructed another sail with a part of my dress and eagerly steered my course towards the land.

It had a wild and rocky appearance, but as I approached nearer I easily perceived the traces of cultivation. I saw vessels near the shore and found myself suddenly transported back to the neighbourhood of civilized man. I carefully traced the windings of the land and hailed a steeple which I at length saw issuing from behind a small promontory. As I was in a state of extreme debility, I resolved to sail directly towards the town, as a place where I could most easily procure nourishment. Fortunately I had money with me.

As I turned the promontory I perceived a small neat town and a good harbour, which I entered, my heart bounding with joy at my unexpected escape.

As I was occupied in fixing the boat and arranging the sails, several people crowded towards the spot. They seemed much surprised at my appearance, but instead of offering me any assistance, whispered together with gestures that at any other time might have produced in me a slight sensation of alarm. As it was, I merely remarked that they spoke English, and I therefore addressed them in that language. "My good friends," said I, "will you be so kind as to tell me the name of this town and inform me where I am?"

"You will know that soon enough," replied a man with a hoarse voice. "Maybe you are come to a place that will not prove much to your taste, but you will not be consulted as to your quarters, I promise you."

I was exceedingly surprised on receiving so rude an answer from a stranger, and I was also disconcerted on perceiving the frowning and angry countenances of his companions. "Why do you answer me so roughly?" I replied. "Surely it is not the custom of Englishmen to receive strangers so inhospitably."

"I do not know," said the man, "what the custom of the English may be, but it is the custom of the Irish to hate villains." While this strange dialogue continued, I perceived the crowd rapidly increase. Their faces expressed a mixture of curiosity and anger, which annoyed and in some degree alarmed me.

I inquired the way to the inn, but no one replied. I then moved forward, and a murmuring sound arose from the crowd as they followed and surrounded me, when an ill-looking man approaching tapped me on the shoulder and said, "Come, sir, you must follow me to Mr. Kirwin's to give an account of yourself."

"Who is Mr. Kirwin? Why am I to give an account of myself? Is not this a free country?"

"Ay, sir, free enough for honest folks. Mr. Kirwin is a magistrate, and you are to give an account of the death of a gentleman who was found murdered here last night."

This answer startled me, but I presently recovered myself. I was innocent; that could easily be proved; accordingly I followed my conductor in silence and was led to one of the best houses in the town. I was ready to sink from fatigue and hunger, but being surrounded by a crowd, I thought it politic to rouse all my strength, that no physical debility might be construed into apprehension or conscious guilt.

Little did I then expect the calamity that was in a few moments to overwhelm me and extinguish in horror and despair all fear of ignominy or death. I must pause here, for it requires all my fortitude to recall the memory of the frightful events which I am about to relate, in proper detail, to my recollection.

• ANALYZING THE SCENE •
CHAPTER 20 – SCENE 40

A Story Event is an active change of universal human value for one or more characters as a result of conflict (one character's desires clash with another's or an environmental shift changes the universal human value).

A Working Scene contains at least one Story Event. To determine a scene's Story Event, answer these four questions:

1. What are the characters literally doing—that is, what are their micro on-the-ground actions?

Frankenstein dumps the remains of his project in the sea, and his boat is carried away by the wind. He finally lands on a shore and is safe.

2. What is the essential tactic of the characters—that is, what macro behaviors are they employing that are linked to a universal human value?

Frankenstein has a near-death experience. For someone who has spent many months reflecting on his miserable life, he fights to save himself when his boat is swept away by wind and waves.

3. What universal human values have changed for one or more

characters in the scene? Which one of those value changes is most important and should be included in the Story Grid Spreadsheet?

Frankenstein starts out by cleaning up his disastrous project and ends up in a boat in the wee hours of the morning, disposing of the remains of his creature at sea. He falls asleep, and when he awakens, he finds that he is being swept out into the Atlantic. Despite all of his sadness at the state of his life, he tries desperately to save himself. Fortunately, the wind dies away and he drifts toward land.

Unsafe to Safe

4. What is the Story Event that sums up the scene's on-the-ground actions, essential tactics, and value change? We will enter that event in the Story Grid Spreadsheet.

Frankenstein has a near-death experience as he dumps his project into the sea.

HOW THE SCENE ABIDES BY THE FIVE COMMANDMENTS OF STORYTELLING

Inciting Incident: Frankenstein decides that he wants to leave the island in order to meet Clerval and takes a boat out to dispose of the remains of his new creature.

Turning Point Progressive Complication: He falls asleep in the boat, and when he awakens, he discovers that a wind has picked up and he has been taken way beyond his island.

Crisis: He tries to change course but cannot; he will either drown or be taken out to sea. Should he try to survive or give up?

Climax: At first he gives up, but when the wind dies down he finds himself suddenly eager to live. He constructs a sail and steers toward shore.

Resolution: He lands on shore.

NOTES

- This is another scene that is challenging to evaluate, as it seems to encompass several scenes within the larger container. In fact, there are three distinct parts to this scene, and they are geographically separate, so it is tempting to split the single scene into three. However, just because a protagonist travels from one locale to another doesn't mean the major action or emotional journey is taking place within each separate locale. For example, in his original location, Frankenstein receives a letter from Clerval urging him to join him, so he decides to leave the island. The next location is where Frankenstein is in the boat, disposing of the remains of the new creature and then fighting the wind and thinking he will die at sea. The last location is the new beach where he lands and hears that he is suspected of murder. There really isn't enough happening in each separate location to justify looking at each of them for an emotional arc. The most distinctive arc takes place between the beginning (where he decides to take the boat to sea so he can finish closing down his misguided project) and the safe arrival on the beach. Everything else is the expression of a single emotion rather than a series.
- It's interesting that Shelley comments on Frankenstein's desperate attempt to save his life. She says, "How mutable are our feelings, and how strange is that clinging love we have of life even in the excess of misery!" and Frankenstein says, "my heart bounding with joy at my unexpected escape." Frankenstein was actually afraid to die.

CHAPTER 21 – SCENE 41

I was soon introduced into the presence of the magistrate, an old benevolent man with calm and mild manners. He looked upon me, however, with some degree of severity, and then, turning towards my conductors, he asked who appeared as witnesses on this occasion.

About half a dozen men came forward; and, one being selected by the magistrate, he deposed that he had been out fishing the night before with his son and brother-in-law, Daniel Nugent, when, about ten o'clock, they observed a strong northerly blast rising, and they accordingly put in for port. It was a very dark night, as the moon had not yet risen; they did not land at the harbour, but, as they had been accustomed, at a creek about two miles below. He walked on first, carrying a part of the fishing tackle, and his companions followed him at some distance.

As he was proceeding along the sands, he struck his foot against something and fell at his length on the ground. His companions came up to assist him, and by the light of their lantern they found that he had fallen on the body of a man, who was to all appearance dead. Their first supposition was that it was the corpse of some person who had been drowned and was thrown on shore by the waves, but on examination they found that the clothes were not wet and even that the body was not then cold. They instantly carried it to the cottage of an old woman near the spot and endeavoured, but in vain, to restore it to life. It appeared to be a handsome young man, about five and twenty years of age. He had apparently been strangled, for there was no sign of any violence except the black mark of fingers on his neck.

The first part of this deposition did not in the least interest me, but when the mark of the fingers was mentioned I remembered the murder of my brother and felt myself extremely agitated; my limbs trembled, and a mist came over my eyes, which obliged me to lean on a chair for support. The magistrate observed me with a keen eye and of course drew an unfavourable augury from my manner.

The son confirmed his father's account, but when Daniel Nugent was called he swore positively that just before the fall of his companion, he saw a boat, with a single man in it, at a short distance from the shore; and as far as he could judge by the light of a few stars, it was the same boat in which I had just landed. A woman deposed that she lived near the beach and was standing at the door of her cottage, waiting for the return of the fishermen, about an hour before she heard of the discovery of the body, when she saw a boat with only one man in it push off from that part of the shore where the corpse was afterwards found.

Another woman confirmed the account of the fishermen having brought the body into her house; it was not cold. They put it into a bed and rubbed it, and Daniel went to the town for an apothecary, but life was quite gone.

Several other men were examined concerning my landing, and they agreed that, with the strong north wind that had arisen during the night, it was very probable that I had beaten about for many hours and had been obliged to return nearly to the same spot from which I had departed. Besides, they observed that it appeared that I had brought the body from another place, and it was likely that as I did not appear to know the shore, I might have put into the harbour ignorant of the distance of the town of — from the place where I had deposited the corpse.

Mr. Kirwin, on hearing this evidence, desired that I should be taken into the room where the body lay for interment, that it might be observed what effect the sight of it would produce upon me. This idea was probably suggested by the extreme agitation I had exhibited when the mode of the murder had been described. I was accordingly conducted, by the magistrate and several other persons, to the inn. I could not help being struck by the strange coincidences that had taken place during this eventful night; but, **knowing that I had been conversing with several persons in the island I had inhabited about the time that the body had been found, I was perfectly tranquil as to the consequences of the affair.** I entered the room where the corpse lay and was led up to the coffin. How can I describe my sensations on beholding it? I feel yet parched with horror, nor can I reflect on that terrible moment without shuddering and agony. The examination, the presence of the magistrate and witnesses, passed like a dream from my memory when I saw the lifeless form of Henry Clerval stretched before me. I gasped for breath, and throwing myself on the body, I exclaimed, **"Have my murderous machinations deprived you also, my dearest Henry, of life? Two I have already destroyed; other victims await their destiny; but you, Clerval, my friend, my benefactor—"**

The human frame could no longer support the agonies that I endured, and I was carried out of the room in strong convulsions. A fever succeeded to this. I lay for two months on the point of death; my ravings, as I afterwards heard, were frightful; I called myself the murderer of William, of Justine, and of Clerval. Sometimes I entreated my attendants to assist me in the destruction of the fiend by whom I was tormented; and at others I felt the fingers of the monster already grasping my neck, and screamed aloud with agony and terror. Fortunately, as I spoke my native language, Mr. Kirwin alone understood me; but my gestures and bitter cries were sufficient to affright the other witnesses. Why did I not die? More miserable than man ever was before, why did I not sink into forgetfulness and rest? Death snatches away many blooming children, the only hopes of their doting parents; how many brides and youthful lovers have been one day in the bloom of health and hope, and the next a prey for worms and the decay of the tomb! Of what materials was I made that I could thus resist so many shocks, which, like the turning of the wheel, continually renewed the torture?

But I was doomed to live and in two months found myself as

awaking from a dream, in a prison, stretched on a wretched bed, surrounded by jailers, turnkeys, bolts, and all the miserable apparatus of a dungeon. It was morning, I remember, when I thus awoke to understanding; I had forgotten the particulars of what had happened and only felt as if some great misfortune had suddenly overwhelmed me; but when I looked around and saw the barred windows and the squalidness of the room in which I was, all flashed across my memory and I groaned bitterly.

This sound disturbed an old woman who was sleeping in a chair beside me. She was a hired nurse, the wife of one of the turnkeys, and her countenance expressed all those bad qualities which often characterize that class. The lines of her face were hard and rude, like that of persons accustomed to see without sympathizing in sights of misery. Her tone expressed her entire indifference; she addressed me in English, and the voice struck me as one that I had heard during my sufferings. "Are you better now, sir?" said she.

I replied in the same language, with a feeble voice, "I believe I am; but if it be all true, if indeed I did not dream, I am sorry that I am still alive to feel this misery and horror."

"For that matter," replied the old woman, "if you mean about the gentleman you murdered, I believe that it were better for you if you were dead, for I fancy it will go hard with you! However, that's none of my business; I am sent to nurse you and get you well; I do my duty with a safe conscience; it were well if everybody did the same."

I turned with loathing from the woman who could utter so unfeeling a speech to a person just saved, on the very edge of death; but I felt languid and unable to reflect on all that had passed. The whole series of my life appeared to me as a dream; I sometimes doubted if indeed it were all true, for it never presented itself to my mind with the force of reality.

As the images that floated before me became more distinct, I grew feverish; a darkness pressed around me; no one was near me who soothed me with the gentle voice of love; no dear hand supported me. The physician came and prescribed medicines, and the old woman prepared them for me; but utter carelessness was visible in the first, and the expression of brutality was strongly marked in the visage of the second. Who could be interested in the fate of a murderer but the hangman who would gain his fee?

• ANALYZING THE SCENE •
CHAPTER 21 – SCENE 41

A Story Event is an active change of universal human value for one or more characters as a result of conflict (one character's desires clash with another's or an environmental shift changes the universal human value).

A Working Scene contains at least one Story Event. To determine a scene's Story Event, answer these four questions:

1. What are the characters literally doing—that is, what are their micro on-the-ground actions?

Frankenstein is accused of murder, and the magistrate and several witnesses are making their case; when he sees the deceased, he is horrified to realize it is Clerval.

2. What is the essential tactic of the characters—that is, what macro behaviors are they employing that are linked to a universal human value?

Frankenstein discovers that Clerval has been murdered, and he rants about his own culpability in the crime, as well as in the deaths of William and Justine. He falls into convulsions and is near death; when he awakens he is in prison.

3. What universal human values have changed for one or more characters in the scene? Which one of those value changes is most important and should be included in the Story Grid Spreadsheet?

Frankenstein starts out the scene accused and ends the scene in prison. The major difference is that he originally was not concerned about the accusation, as he knows that he can prove he was elsewhere at the time of the murder. However, when he sees Clerval's body, he begins to rant about William and Justine as well. He ends the scene in prison.

Innocent to Accused

4. What is the Story Event that sums up the scene's on-the-ground actions, essential tactics, and value change? We will enter that event in the Story Grid Spreadsheet.

When Frankenstein comes ashore, he finds himself in Ireland; he is accused of murder, and discovers the victim is Clerval.

HOW THE SCENE ABIDES BY THE FIVE COMMANDMENTS OF STORYTELLING

Inciting Incident: Frankenstein is taken to the local magistrate because he is under suspicion for a murder.

Turning Point Progressive Complication: The magistrate has Frankenstein view the body—it is Clerval.

Crisis: He can focus on not appearing to be guilty or he can allow himself to experience his grief. Best bad choice.

Climax: Frankenstein raves that he is responsible now for three murders, those of William, Justine, and now Clerval.

Resolution: He falls into convulsions, and when he awakens, two months have gone by and he is in prison.

NOTES

- The discovery that Clerval would be another of the creature's fatalities was probably long expected by most readers, but Shelley does a beautiful job of setting it up. Recall that Frankenstein receives a letter from Clerval as the impetus for him to clean up his project and leave the remote island in order to meet him. Shelley has thrown out a red herring here. Clerval is dead, or at least, about to die. The letter must have been posted quite a while ago.

- Frankenstein is not even worried about the accusation of murder, because he thinks he has alibis back on the island. This is another great red herring. We're assured that this strange misunderstanding can't possibly affect him. As a writer, if you know you're going to do something dramatic in the scene and end the character's emotional journey in a bad, stressful place, it helps to start with a calm, steady state of mind.
- "The black mark of fingers on his neck" is a great nod toward the reader—yes, we suspected it all along! Bonus points are accrued here for having Frankenstein grow agitated and thus invite suspicion upon himself.

CHAPTER 21 – SCENE 42

These were my first reflections, but I soon learned that **Mr. Kirwin had shown me extreme kindness.** He had caused the best room in the prison to be prepared for me (wretched indeed was the best); and it was he who had provided a physician and a nurse. It is true, he seldom came to see me, for although he ardently desired to relieve the sufferings of every human creature, he did not wish to be present at the agonies and miserable ravings of a murderer. He came, therefore, sometimes to see that I was not neglected, but his visits were short and with long intervals. One day, while I was gradually recovering, I was seated in a chair, my eyes half open and my cheeks livid like those in death. I was overcome by gloom and misery and often reflected I had better seek death than desire to remain in a world which to me was replete with wretchedness. At one time I considered whether I should not declare myself guilty and suffer the penalty of the law, less innocent than poor Justine had been. Such were my thoughts when the door of my apartment was opened and Mr. Kirwin entered. His countenance expressed sympathy and compassion; he drew a chair close to mine and addressed me in French, "I fear that this place is very shocking to you; can I do anything to make you more comfortable?"

"I thank you, but all that you mention is nothing to me; on the whole earth there is no comfort which I am capable of receiving."

"I know that the sympathy of a stranger can be but of little relief to one borne down as you are by so strange a misfortune. But you will, I hope, soon quit this melancholy abode, for doubtless evidence can easily be brought to free you from the criminal charge."

"That is my least concern; I am, by a course of strange events, become the most miserable of mortals. Persecuted and tortured as I am and have been, can death be any evil to me?"

"Nothing indeed could be more unfortunate and agonizing than the strange chances that have lately occurred. You were thrown, by some surprising accident, on this shore, renowned for its hospitality, seized immediately, and charged with murder. The first sight that was presented to your eyes was the body of your friend, murdered in so unaccountable a manner and placed, as it were, by some fiend across your path."

As Mr. Kirwin said this, notwithstanding the agitation I endured on this retrospect of my sufferings, I also felt considerable surprise at the knowledge he seemed to possess concerning me. I suppose some astonishment was exhibited in my countenance, for Mr. Kirwin hastened to say, "Immediately upon your being taken ill, all the papers that were on your person were brought me, and I examined them that I might discover some trace by which I could send to your relations an account of your misfortune and illness. I found several letters, and, among others, one which I discovered from its commencement to be from your father. I instantly wrote to Geneva; nearly two months have elapsed since the departure of my letter. But you are ill; even now you tremble; you are unfit for agitation of any kind."

"This suspense is a thousand times worse than the most horrible event; tell me what new scene of death has been acted, and whose murder I am now to lament?"

"Your family is perfectly well," said Mr. Kirwin with gentleness; "and someone, a friend, is come to visit you."

I know not by what chain of thought the idea presented itself, but it instantly darted into my mind that the murderer had come to mock at my misery and taunt me with the death of Clerval, as a new incitement for me to comply with his hellish desires. I put my hand before my eyes, and cried out in agony, "Oh! Take him away! I cannot see him; for God's sake, do not let him enter!"

Mr. Kirwin regarded me with a troubled countenance. He could not help regarding my exclamation as a presumption of my guilt and said in rather a severe tone, "I should have thought, young man, that the presence of your father would have been welcome instead of inspiring such violent repugnance."

"My father!" cried I, while every feature and every muscle was relaxed from anguish to pleasure. "Is my father indeed come? How kind, how very kind! But where is he, why does he not hasten to me?"

My change of manner surprised and pleased the magistrate; perhaps he thought that my former exclamation was a momentary return of delirium, and now he instantly resumed his former benevolence. He rose and quitted the room with my nurse, and in a moment my father entered it.

Nothing, at this moment, could have given me greater pleasure than the arrival of my father. I stretched out my hand to him and cried, "Are you, then, safe—and Elizabeth—and Ernest?" My father calmed me with assurances of their welfare and endeavoured, by dwelling on these subjects so interesting to my heart, to raise my desponding spirits; but he soon felt that a prison cannot be the abode of cheerfulness.

"What a place is this that you inhabit, my son!" said he, looking mournfully at the barred windows and wretched appearance of the room. "You travelled to seek happiness, but a fatality seems to pursue you. And poor Clerval—"

The name of my unfortunate and murdered friend was an agitation too great to be endured in my weak state; I shed tears. "Alas! Yes, my father," replied I; "some destiny of the most horrible kind hangs over me, and I must live to fulfil it, or surely I should have died on the coffin of Henry."

We were not allowed to converse for any length of time, for the precarious state of my health rendered every precaution necessary that could ensure tranquillity. Mr. Kirwin came in and insisted that my strength should not be exhausted by too much exertion. But the appearance of my father was to me like that of my good angel, and I gradually recovered my health.

As my sickness quitted me, I was absorbed by a gloomy and black melancholy that nothing could dissipate. The image of Clerval was forever before me, ghastly and murdered. More than once the agitation into which these reflections threw me made my friends dread a dangerous relapse. Alas! Why did they preserve so miserable and detested a life? It was surely that I might fulfil my destiny, which is now drawing to a close. Soon, oh, very soon, will death extinguish these throbbings and relieve me from the mighty weight of anguish that bears me to the dust; and, in executing the award of justice, I shall also sink to rest. Then the appearance of death was distant, although the wish was ever present to my thoughts; and I often sat for hours motionless and speechless, wishing for some mighty revolution that might bury me and my destroyer in its ruins.

• ANALYZING THE SCENE •
CHAPTER 21 – SCENE 42

A Story Event is an active change of universal human value for one or more characters as a result of conflict (one character's desires clash with another's or an environmental shift changes the universal human value).

A Working Scene contains at least one Story Event. To determine a scene's Story Event, answer these four questions:

1. What are the characters literally doing—that is, what are their micro on-the-ground actions?

Frankenstein is in prison, and Mr. Kirwin, the magistrate, has come to visit. He has summoned Frankenstein's father, who arrives.

2. What is the essential tactic of the characters—that is, what macro behaviors are they employing that are linked to a universal human value?

Mr. Kirwin shows that he thinks Frankenstein is innocent. He has gone through Frankenstein's papers and has sent for his father, which turns around Frankenstein's health. Frankenstein, on the other hand, is passively awaiting his fate.

3. What universal human values have changed for one or more characters in the scene? Which one of those value changes is most important and should be included in the Story Grid Spreadsheet?

Frankenstein is deeply depressed at awakening and finding himself a prisoner. However, he discovers that the magistrate has been very kind. He has procured medical treatment and sent for his father, and Frankenstein eventually recovers his health.

Ill to Convalescent

4. What is the Story Event that sums up the scene's on-the-ground actions, essential tactics, and value change? We will enter that event in the Story Grid Spreadsheet.

The Irish magistrate arranges for Victor's father to come to be with him. After being ill for a long time, his health improves.

HOW THE SCENE ABIDES BY THE FIVE COMMANDMENTS OF STORYTELLING

Inciting Incident: Mr. Kirwin, the magistrate, visits Frankenstein and seems to believe he is innocent of the charges.

Turning Point Progressive Complication: He tells Frankenstein he has a visitor.

Crisis: Frankenstein thinks the visitor is the creature. Does he beg Mr. Kirwin to not let him enter? Best bad choice.

Climax: He cries out that he doesn't want to see the visitor, that he should be sent away.

Resolution: The visitor is his father, and he is overjoyed. His health improves.

NOTES

- Mr. Kirwin is introduced as a sympathetic character.
- In addition, Clerval has been replaced by Frankenstein's father as a traveling companion. Frankenstein always has someone with him who must be lied to.

CHAPTER 21 – SCENE 43

The season of the assizes approached. I had already been three months in prison, and although I was still weak and in continual danger of a relapse, I was obliged to travel nearly a hundred miles to the country town where the court was held. Mr. Kirwin charged himself with every care of collecting witnesses and arranging my defence. I was spared the disgrace of appearing publicly as a criminal, as the case was not brought before the court that decides on life and death. **The grand jury rejected the bill, on its being proved that I was on the Orkney Islands at the hour the body of my friend was found; and a fortnight after my removal I was liberated from prison.** *[This was a little too easy!]*

My father was enraptured on finding me freed from the vexations of a criminal charge, that I was again allowed to breathe the fresh atmosphere and permitted to return to my native country. I did not participate in these feelings, for to me the walls of a dungeon or a palace were alike hateful. The cup of life was poisoned forever, and although the sun shone upon me, as upon the happy and gay of heart, I saw around me nothing but a dense and frightful darkness, penetrated by no light but the glimmer of two eyes that glared upon me. Sometimes they were the expressive eyes of Henry, languishing in death, the dark orbs nearly covered by the lids and the long black lashes that fringed them; sometimes it was the watery, clouded eyes of the monster, as I first saw them in my chamber at Ingolstadt.

My father tried to awaken in me the feelings of affection. He talked of Geneva, which I should soon visit, of Elizabeth and Ernest; but these words only drew deep groans from me. Sometimes, indeed, I felt a wish for happiness and thought with melancholy delight of my beloved cousin or longed, with a devouring maladie du pays, to see once more the blue lake and rapid Rhone, that had been so dear to me in early childhood; but my general state of feeling was a torpor in which a prison was as welcome a residence as the divinest scene in nature; and these fits were seldom interrupted but by paroxysms of anguish and despair. **At these moments I often endeavoured to put an end to the existence I loathed, and it required unceasing attendance and vigilance to restrain me from committing some dreadful act of violence.** *[Frankenstein is suicidal.]*

Yet one duty remained to me, the recollection of which finally triumphed over my selfish despair. It was necessary that I should return without delay to Geneva, there to watch over the lives of those I so fondly loved and to lie in wait for the murderer, that if any chance led me to the place of his concealment, or if he dared again to blast me by his presence, I might, with unfailing aim, put an end to the existence of the monstrous image which I had endued with the mockery of a soul still more monstrous. My father still desired to delay our departure, fearful that I could not sustain the fatigues of a journey, for I was a shattered wreck—the shadow of a human being. My strength was gone. I was a mere skeleton, and fever night and day preyed upon my wasted frame. Still, as I urged our leaving Ireland with such inquietude and impatience, my father thought it best to yield. We took our passage on board a vessel bound for Havre-de-Grace and sailed with a fair wind from the Irish shores. It was midnight. **I lay on the deck looking at the stars and listening to the dashing of the waves.** I hailed the darkness that shut Ireland from my sight, and my pulse beat with a feverish joy when I reflected that I should soon see Geneva. The past appeared to me in the light of a frightful dream; yet the vessel in which I was, the wind that blew me from the detested shore of Ireland, and the sea which surrounded me told me too forcibly that I was deceived by no vision and that Clerval, my friend and dearest companion, had fallen a victim to me and the monster of my creation. I repassed, in my memory, my whole life—my quiet happiness while residing with my family in Geneva, the death of my mother, and my departure for Ingolstadt. I remembered, shuddering, the mad enthusiasm that hurried me on to the creation of my hideous enemy, and I called to mind the night in which he first lived. I was unable to pursue the train of thought; a thousand feelings pressed upon me, and I wept bitterly. Ever since my recovery from the fever I had been in the custom of taking every night a small quantity of laudanum, for it was by means of this drug only that I was enabled to gain the rest necessary for the preservation of life. Oppressed by the recollection of my various misfortunes, I now swallowed double my usual quantity and soon slept profoundly. But sleep did not afford me respite from thought and misery; my dreams presented a thousand objects that scared me. Towards morning I was possessed by a kind of nightmare; I felt the fiend's grasp in my neck and could not free myself from it; groans and cries rang in my ears. My father, who was watching over me, perceiving my restlessness, awoke me; the dashing waves were around, the cloudy sky above, the fiend was not here: a sense of security, a feeling that a truce was established between the present hour and the irresistible, disastrous future imparted to me a kind of calm forgetfulness, of which the human mind is by its structure peculiarly susceptible.

• ANALYZING THE SCENE •
CHAPTER 21 – SCENE 43

A Story Event is an active change of universal human value for one or more characters as a result of conflict (one character's desires clash with another's or an environmental shift changes the universal human value).

A Working Scene contains at least one Story Event. To determine a scene's Story Event, answer these four questions:

1. What are the characters literally doing—that is, what are their micro on-the-ground actions?

Frankenstein has been cleared of the murder charges and rushes back to Geneva to protect his family from the creature and to try to find and possibly kill him.

2. What is the essential tactic of the characters—that is, what macro behaviors are they employing that are linked to a universal human value?

Frankenstein is reflecting on all of the events that have gotten him to this point as he journeys back to Geneva for what it seems will be a final reckoning of some kind. He is trying to make sense of everything that has happened.

3. What universal human values have changed for one or more characters in the scene? Which one of those value changes is most important and should be included in the Story Grid Spreadsheet?

Frankenstein is so distraught and distracted, he requires laudanum to sleep. After taking a double dose of laudanum, he finally sleeps. Although he is asleep, he still has nightmares, so it is not a restful sleep but a form of torture beyond the numbness of death—perhaps even a form of damnation on the global value spectrum.

Insomnia to Sleep

4. What is the Story Event that sums up the scene's on-the-ground actions, essential tactics, and value change? We will enter that event in the Story Grid Spreadsheet.

Victor is released after being acquitted; he urgently wants to return to Geneva because he fears the creature will murder again.

HOW THE SCENE ABIDES BY THE FIVE COMMANDMENTS OF STORYTELLING

Inciting Incident: Frankenstein is acquitted of Clerval's murder and released.

Turning Point Progressive Complication: Frankenstein wants to hurry back to Geneva because he worries the creature will attack his family, but his father wants to delay.

Crisis: Frankenstein is still thin and wasted after his illness. Does he delay? Best bad choice.

Climax: No, Frankenstein argues that they need to leave immediately, so his father yields.

Resolution: Frankenstein boards a ship for Europe and sees visions and dreams in his sleep.

NOTES

- This is almost a placeholder type of scene; nothing specific seems to happen although the scene does have all the components for a scene. Looking at it from Shelley's point of view, it almost seems as if the purpose of the scene is to present for the reader a complete reckoning of the events of Frankenstein's life. We have a sense that the big climax is coming, and this is a lull before the storm.
- In addition, this scene may be a further resolution of the previous scene's convenient and speedy trial that results in Frankenstein's release.
- Accordingly, Shelley writes that Frankenstein has been having trouble sleeping. He takes a sleep aid called laudanum, and on the boat back to Europe, he takes a double dose because he cannot sleep any other way. Unfortunately, he is rewarded with disturbing visions and dreams. In his dreams, the creature is choking him to death. It is an interesting parallel; he is afraid he cannot sleep because of all the thoughts tumbling about in his mind, but

when he does finally sleep, the creature is there. Awake to Asleep seem to parallel the trajectory of Life to Death.

CHAPTER 22 – SCENE 44

The voyage came to an end. We landed, and proceeded to Paris. I soon found that I had overtaxed my strength and that I must repose before I could continue my journey. My father's care and attentions were indefatigable, but he did not know the origin of my sufferings and sought erroneous methods to remedy the incurable ill. He wished me to seek amusement in society. I abhorred the face of man. Oh, not abhorred! They were my brethren, my fellow beings, and I felt attracted even to the most repulsive among them, as to creatures of an angelic nature and celestial mechanism. But I felt that I had no right to share their intercourse. I had unchained an enemy among them whose joy it was to shed their blood and to revel in their groans. How they would, each and all, abhor me and hunt me from the world did they know my unhallowed acts and the crimes which had their source in me!

My father yielded at length to my desire to avoid society and strove by various arguments to banish my despair. Sometimes he thought that I felt deeply the degradation of being obliged to answer a charge of murder, and he endeavoured to prove to me the futility of pride.

"Alas! My father," said I, "how little do you know me. Human beings, their feelings and passions, would indeed be degraded if such a wretch as I felt pride. Justine, poor unhappy Justine, was as innocent as I, and she suffered the same charge; she died for it; and I am the cause of this—I murdered her. William, Justine, and Henry—they all died by my hands."

My father had often, during my imprisonment, heard me make the same assertion; when I thus accused myself, he sometimes seemed to desire an explanation, and at others he appeared to consider it as the offspring of delirium, and that, during my illness, some idea of this kind had presented itself to my imagination, the remembrance of which I preserved in my convalescence.

I avoided explanation and maintained a continual silence concerning the wretch I had created. I had a persuasion that I should be supposed mad, and this in itself would forever have chained my tongue. But, besides, I could not bring myself to disclose a secret which would fill my hearer with consternation and make fear and unnatural horror the inmates of his breast. I checked, therefore, my impatient thirst for sympathy and was silent when I would have given the world to have confided the fatal secret. Yet, still, words like those I have recorded would burst uncontrollably from me. I could offer no explanation of them, but their truth in part relieved the burden of my mysterious woe. Upon this occasion my father said, with an expression of unbounded wonder, "My dearest Victor, what infatuation is this? My dear son, I entreat you never to make such an assertion again."

"I am not mad," I cried energetically; "the sun and the heavens, who have viewed my operations, can bear witness of my truth. I am the assassin of those most innocent victims; they died by my machinations. A thousand times would I have shed my own blood, drop by drop, to have saved their lives; but I could not, my father, indeed I could not sacrifice the whole human race."

The conclusion of this speech convinced my father that my ideas were deranged, and he instantly changed the subject of our conversation and endeavoured to alter the course of my thoughts. He wished as much as possible to obliterate the memory of the scenes that had taken place in Ireland and never alluded to them or suffered me to speak of my misfortunes.

As time passed away I became more calm; misery had her dwelling in my heart, but I no longer talked in the same incoherent manner of my own crimes; sufficient for me was the consciousness of them. By the utmost self-violence I curbed the imperious voice of wretchedness, which sometimes desired to declare itself to the whole world, and my manners were calmer and more composed than they had ever been since my journey to the sea of ice. A few days before we left Paris on our way to Switzerland, I received the following letter from Elizabeth:

"My dear Friend,

"It gave me the greatest pleasure to receive a letter from my uncle dated at Paris; you are no longer at a formidable distance, and I may hope to see you in less than a fortnight. My poor cousin, how much you must have suffered! I expect to see you looking even more ill than when you quitted Geneva. This winter has been passed most miserably, tortured as I have been by anxious suspense; yet I hope to see peace in your countenance and to find that your heart is not totally void of comfort and tranquillity.

"Yet I fear that the same feelings now exist that made you so miserable a year ago, even perhaps augmented by time. I would not disturb you at this period, when so many misfortunes weigh upon you, but a conversation that I had with my uncle previous to his departure renders some explanation necessary before we meet. Explanation! You may possibly say, What can Elizabeth have to explain? If you really say this, my questions are answered and all my doubts satisfied. But you are distant from me, and it is possible that you may dread and yet be pleased with this explanation; and in a probability of this being the case, I dare not any longer postpone writing what, during your absence, I have often wished to express to you but have never had the courage to begin.

"You well know, Victor, that our union had been the favourite plan of your parents ever since our infancy. We were told this when young, and taught to look forward to it as an event that would certainly take place. We were affectionate playfellows during childhood, and, I believe, dear and valued friends to one another as we grew older. But as brother and sister often entertain a lively affection towards each other without desiring a more intimate union, may not such also be our case? Tell me, dearest Victor. Answer me, I conjure you by our mutual happiness, with simple truth—Do you not love another?

"You have travelled; you have spent several years of your life at Ingolstadt; and I confess to you, my friend, that when I saw you last autumn so unhappy, flying to solitude from the society of every creature, I could not help supposing that you might regret our connection and believe yourself bound in honour to fulfil the wishes of your parents, although they opposed themselves to your inclinations. But this is false reasoning. I confess to you, my friend, that I love you and that in my airy dreams of futurity you have been my constant friend and companion. But it is your happiness I desire as well as my own when I declare to you that our marriage would render me eternally miserable unless it were the dictate of your own free choice. Even now I weep to think that, borne down as you are by the cruellest misfortunes, you may stifle, by the word 'honour,' all hope of that love and happiness which would alone restore you to yourself. I, who have so disinterested an affection for you, may increase your miseries tenfold by being an obstacle to your wishes. Ah! Victor, be assured that your cousin and playmate has too sincere a love for you not to be made miserable by this supposition. Be happy, my friend; and if you obey me in this one request, remain satisfied that nothing on earth will have the power to interrupt my tranquillity.

"Do not let this letter disturb you; do not answer tomorrow, or the next day, or even until you come, if it will give you pain. My uncle will send me news of your health, and if I see but one smile on your lips when we meet, occasioned by this or any other exertion of mine, I shall need no other happiness.

"Elizabeth Lavenza

"Geneva, May 18th, 17—"

This letter revived in my memory what I had before forgotten, the threat of the fiend—"I WILL BE WITH YOU ON YOUR WEDDING-NIGHT!" Such was my sentence, and on that night would the daemon employ every art to destroy me and tear me from the glimpse of happiness which promised partly to console my sufferings. On that night he had determined to consummate his crimes by my death. Well, be it so; a deadly struggle would then assuredly take place, in which if he were victorious I should be at peace and his power over me be at an end. If he were vanquished, I should be a free man. Alas! What freedom? Such as the peasant enjoys when his family have been massacred before his eyes, his cottage burnt, his lands laid waste, and he is turned adrift, homeless, penniless, and alone, but free. Such would be my liberty except that in my Elizabeth I possessed a treasure, alas, balanced by those horrors of remorse and guilt which would pursue me until death.

Sweet and beloved Elizabeth! I read and reread her letter, and some softened feelings stole into my heart and dared to whisper paradisiacal dreams of love and joy; but the apple was already eaten, and the angel's arm bared to drive me from all hope. Yet I would die to make her happy. If the monster executed his threat, death was inevitable; yet, again, I considered whether my marriage would hasten my fate. My destruction might indeed arrive a few months sooner, but if my torturer should suspect that I postponed it, influenced by his menaces, he would surely find other and perhaps more dreadful means of revenge.

He had vowed TO BE WITH ME ON MY WEDDING-NIGHT, yet he did not consider that threat as binding him to peace in the meantime, for as if to show me that he was not yet satiated with blood, he had murdered Clerval immediately after the enunciation of his threats. **I resolved, therefore, that if my immediate union with my cousin would conduce either to hers or my father's happiness, my adversary's designs against my life should not retard it a single hour.** *[Frankenstein decides his goal is to make his father and Elizabeth happy, and he doesn't care if his life is shorter as a result.]*

In this state of mind I wrote to Elizabeth. My letter was calm and affectionate. "I fear, my beloved girl," I said, "little happiness remains for us on earth; yet all that I may one day enjoy is centred in you. Chase away your idle fears; to you alone do I consecrate my life and my endeavours for contentment. I have one secret, Elizabeth, a dreadful one; when revealed to you, it will chill your frame with horror, and then, far from being surprised at my misery, you will only wonder that I survive what I have endured. **I will confide this tale of misery and**

terror to you the day after our marriage shall take place, for, my sweet cousin, there must be perfect confidence between us. But until then, I conjure you, do not mention or allude to it. This I most earnestly entreat, and I know you will comply." *[Frankenstein decides to tell Elizabeth everything, even after seeing the effect his words had on his father.]*

• ANALYZING THE SCENE •
CHAPTER 22 – SCENE 44

A Story Event is an active change of universal human value for one or more characters as a result of conflict (one character's desires clash with another's or an environmental shift changes the universal human value).

A Working Scene contains at least one Story Event. To determine a scene's Story Event, answer these four questions:

1. What are the characters literally doing—that is, what are their micro on-the-ground actions?

Frankenstein and his father are in Europe on their way home. Victor receives a letter from Elizabeth, who wonders if he still wants to marry her. He writes back and says yes.

2. What is the essential tactic of the characters—that is, what macro behaviors are they employing that are linked to a universal human value?

Frankenstein is thinking about the creature's threat to be with him on his wedding night and trying to figure out the best way to address it. He decides there is no guarantee that the creature will restrict his threat to his wedding night, so he will indeed marry Elizabeth. He also decides to tell Elizabeth about the creature after their marriage.

3. What universal human values have changed for one or more characters in the scene? Which one of those value changes is most important and should be included in the Story Grid Spreadsheet?

Frankenstein starts the scene in the depths of self-blame for the deaths of William, Justine, and Clerval. When Elizabeth's letter arrives, he decides to create as much happiness for Elizabeth and his father as possible by marrying her immediately. He changes from Victim to Fighter because he decides there is no guarantee that being cautious or waiting guarantees the monster will not kill in the meantime.

Also, we need to highlight Frankenstein's movement from Victim to Fighter in this scene, as we know we're coming up on the big climax of the ending payoff.

Victim to Fighter

4. What is the Story Event that sums up the scene's on-the-ground actions, essential tactics, and value change? We will enter that event in the Story Grid Spreadsheet.

A letter from Elizabeth arrives, asking if Victor still wants to marry her; he replies and says that he does and will tell her a "terrible secret" after they are married.

HOW THE SCENE ABIDES BY THE FIVE COMMANDMENTS OF STORYTELLING

Inciting Incident: Victor and his father complete their sea voyage and proceed to Paris.

Turning Point Progressive Complication: A letter from Elizabeth arrives, asking questions about Victor's proposed marriage.

Crisis: Should Victor procrastinate on his marriage to Elizabeth since the creature has threatened to ruin his wedding night, presumably by killing him? Will he avoid or delay his eventual death (or anyone else's) by waiting? Best bad choice.

Climax: Frankenstein decides he cannot guarantee the creature's good behavior no matter when he marries Elizabeth, and he might as well make Elizabeth and his father happy as soon as possible.

Resolution: Frankenstein writes the letter to Elizabeth saying he wants to marry her, and he will share a terrible secret with her the day after their wedding.

NOTES

- This is a slightly longer scene than usual for Shelley. It could be broken into two scenes, but it's probably better to keep it as one. Frankenstein tells his father he is responsible for the deaths of William, Justine, and Clerval, and his father finally protests. This leads Frankenstein to make the assertion again, and his father concludes that he is "deranged." After this, Frankenstein does not talk about the subject. This little mini-scene does have all Five Commandments of Storytelling, but it doesn't stand alone in a terribly interesting fashion and could even be cut without doing any harm to the narrative. Therefore we can leave it as an introduction to the meat of the overall scene, which is the exchange of letters between Elizabeth and Victor.
- This letter exchange is also rather curious, as it must be difficult to receive mail while traveling through Europe. Victor receives her letter in Paris, a few days before they leave for Switzerland. Shelley is using this scene to have Victor decide that he will marry Elizabeth as soon as possible when he returns. This is actually somewhat of a repeat of both his and her intentions (recall that Victor's father already asked him if he had another love interest or some other reason why he seemed to be showing no inclination to marry Elizabeth, and his response was to request a trip to England), and the utility here is merely to show that Victor is going to marry Elizabeth sooner rather than later. It's not clear why Shelley chose to get the action

moving in quite this way. It seems there might have been other, more original choices.

- The one piece of information that is shared here which is original is that Victor plans to tell Elizabeth, and only Elizabeth, about his creature. In the initial mini-scene, where he is in conflict with his father over his seemingly irrational claim of responsibility for the deaths of William, Justine, and Clerval, he explains that he could not bring himself to tell his father the truth about giving life to the creature. Apparently, he has had a mental shift between that moment and the moment he writes his reply to Elizabeth because she is the first person he has decided to reveal the truth to.

CHAPTER 22 – SCENE 45

In about a week after the arrival of Elizabeth's letter we returned to Geneva. The sweet girl welcomed me with warm affection, yet tears were in her eyes as she beheld my emaciated frame and feverish cheeks. I saw a change in her also. She was thinner and had lost much of that heavenly vivacity that had before charmed me; but her gentleness and soft looks of compassion made her a more fit companion for one blasted and miserable as I was. The tranquility which I now enjoyed did not endure. Memory brought madness with it, and when I thought of what had passed, a real insanity possessed me; sometimes I was furious and burnt with rage, sometimes low and despondent. I neither spoke nor looked at anyone, but sat motionless, bewildered by the multitude of miseries that overcame me.

Elizabeth alone had the power to draw me from these fits; her gentle voice would soothe me when transported by passion and inspire me with human feelings when sunk in torpor. She wept with me and for me. When reason returned, she would remonstrate and endeavour to inspire me with resignation. Ah! It is well for the unfortunate to be resigned, but for the guilty there is no peace. The agonies of remorse poison the luxury there is otherwise sometimes found in indulging the excess of grief. Soon after my arrival my father spoke of my immediate marriage with Elizabeth. I remained silent.

"Have you, then, some other attachment?"

"None on earth. I love Elizabeth and look forward to our union with delight. Let the day therefore be fixed; and on it I will consecrate myself, in life or death, to the happiness of my cousin."

"My dear Victor, do not speak thus. Heavy misfortunes have befallen us, but let us only cling closer to what remains and transfer our love for those whom we have lost to those who yet live. Our circle will be small but bound close by the ties of affection and mutual misfortune. And when time shall have softened your despair, new and dear objects of care will be born to replace those of whom we have been so cruelly deprived."

Such were the lessons of my father. But to me the remembrance of the threat returned; nor can you wonder that, omnipotent as the fiend had yet been in his deeds of blood, I should almost regard him as invincible, and that when he had pronounced the words "I SHALL BE WITH YOU ON YOUR WEDDING-NIGHT," I should regard the threatened fate as unavoidable. But death was no evil to me if the loss of Elizabeth were balanced with it, and I therefore, **with a contented and even cheerful countenance**, agreed with my father that if my cousin would consent, the ceremony should take place in ten days, and thus put, as I imagined, the seal to my fate.

Great God! If for one instant I had thought what might be the hellish intention of my fiendish adversary, I would rather have banished myself forever from my native country and wandered a friendless outcast over the earth than have consented to this miserable marriage. **But, as if possessed of magic powers, the monster had blinded me to his real intentions; and when I thought that I had prepared only my own death, I hastened that of a far dearer victim.** *[So now we know what's going to happen!]*

As the period fixed for our marriage drew nearer, whether from cowardice or a prophetic feeling, I felt my heart sink within me. But I concealed my feelings by an appearance of hilarity that brought smiles and joy to the countenance of my father, but hardly deceived the ever-watchful and nicer eye of Elizabeth. She looked forward to our union with placid contentment, not unmingled with a little fear, which past misfortunes had impressed, that what now appeared certain and tangible happiness might soon dissipate into an airy dream and leave no trace but deep and everlasting regret. Preparations were made for the event, congratulatory visits were received, and all wore a smiling appearance. I shut up, as well as I could, in my own heart the anxiety that preyed there and entered with seeming earnestness into the plans of my father, although they might only serve as the decorations of my tragedy. Through my father's exertions a part of the inheritance of Elizabeth had been restored to her by the Austrian government. A small possession on the shores of Como belonged to her. It was agreed that, immediately after our union, we should proceed to Villa Lavenza and spend our first days of happiness beside the beautiful lake near which it stood.

In the meantime I took every precaution to defend my person in case the fiend should openly attack me. I carried pistols and a dagger constantly about me and was ever on the watch to prevent artifice, and by these means gained a greater degree of tranquillity. Indeed, as the period approached, the threat appeared more as a delusion, not to be regarded as worthy to disturb my peace, while the happiness I hoped for in my marriage wore a greater appearance of certainty as the day fixed for its solemnization drew nearer and I heard it continually spoken of as an occurrence which no accident could possibly prevent.

Elizabeth seemed happy; my tranquil demeanour contributed greatly to calm her mind. But on the day that was to fulfil my wishes and my destiny, she was melancholy, and a presentiment of evil pervaded her; and perhaps also she thought of the dreadful secret which I had promised to reveal to her on the following day. My father was in the meantime overjoyed and in the bustle of preparation only recognized in the melancholy of his niece the diffidence of a bride.

After the ceremony was performed a large party assembled at my father's, but it was agreed that Elizabeth and I should commence our journey by water *[another boat!]*, sleeping that night at Evian and continuing our voyage on the following day. The day was fair, the wind favourable; all smiled on our nuptial embarkation.

Those were the last moments of my life during which I enjoyed the feeling of happiness. We passed rapidly along; the sun was hot, but we were sheltered from its rays by a kind of canopy while we enjoyed the beauty of the scene, sometimes on one side of the lake, where we saw Mont Saleve, the pleasant banks of Montalegre, and at a distance, surmounting all, the beautiful Mont Blanc and the assemblage of snowy mountains that in vain endeavour to emulate her; sometimes coasting the opposite banks, we saw the mighty Jura opposing its dark side to the ambition that would quit its native country, and an almost insurmountable barrier to the invader who should wish to enslave it.

I took the hand of Elizabeth. "You are sorrowful, my love. Ah! If you knew what I have suffered and what I may yet endure, you would endeavour to let me taste the quiet and freedom from despair that this one day at least permits me to enjoy."

"Be happy, my dear Victor," replied Elizabeth; "there is, I hope, nothing to distress you; and be assured that if a lively joy is not painted in my face, my heart is contented. **Something whispers to me not to depend too much on the prospect that is opened before us, but I will not listen to such a sinister voice.** Observe how fast we move along and how the clouds, which sometimes obscure and sometimes rise above the dome of Mont Blanc, render this scene of beauty still more interesting. Look also at the innumerable fish that are swimming in the clear waters, where we can distinguish every pebble that lies at the bottom. What a divine day! How happy and serene all nature appears!"

Thus Elizabeth endeavoured to divert her thoughts and mine from all reflection upon melancholy subjects. But her temper was fluctuating; joy for a few instants shone in her eyes, but it continually gave place to distraction and reverie.

The sun sank lower in the heavens; we passed the river Drance and observed its path through the chasms of the higher and the glens of the lower hills. The Alps here come closer to the lake, and we approached the amphitheatre of mountains which forms its eastern boundary. The spire of Evian shone under the woods that surrounded it and the range of mountain above mountain by which it was overhung.

The wind, which had hitherto carried us along with amazing rapidity, sank at sunset to a light breeze; the soft air just ruffled the water and caused a pleasant motion among the trees as we approached the shore, from which it wafted the most delightful scent of flowers and

hay. The sun sank beneath the horizon as we landed, and as I touched the shore I felt those cares and fears revive which soon were to clasp me and cling to me forever.

• ANALYZING THE SCENE •
CHAPTER 22 – SCENE 45

A Story Event is an active change of universal human value for one or more characters as a result of conflict (one character's desires clash with another's or an environmental shift changes the universal human value).

A Working Scene contains at least one Story Event. To determine a scene's Story Event, answer these four questions:

1. What are the characters literally doing—that is, what are their micro on-the-ground actions?

Victor and Elizabeth get married and travel to their honeymoon destination, a villa on the shores of Lake Como.

2. What is the essential tactic of the characters—that is, what macro behaviors are they employing that are linked to a universal human value?

Frankenstein is moving forward on his decision to finally confront the creature.

3. What universal human values have changed for one or more characters in the scene? Which one of those value changes is most important and should be included in the Story Grid Spreadsheet?

Both Elizabeth and Frankenstein go from Alone to Married. Frankenstein also believes himself to be a step closer to death, and he cannot help but be anxious. His state changes from resolved to anxious, and interestingly, so does Elizabeth's.

In a Horror story, the global value at stake is Life to Death. As Shelley turns up the temperature, we would track both Elizabeth's and Frankenstein's feelings, from Resolved to Anxious.

Resolved to Anxious

4. What is the Story Event that sums up the scene's on-the-ground actions, essential tactics, and value change? We will enter that event in the Story Grid Spreadsheet.

Frankenstein decides to marry Elizabeth immediately even though the creature has threatened to kill him on their wedding night. He arms himself in preparation, and they get married.

HOW THE SCENE ABIDES BY THE FIVE COMMANDMENTS OF STORYTELLING

Inciting Incident: Victor's father wants him to marry Elizabeth immediately.

Turning Point Progressive Complication: Frankenstein knows the creature is going to try to make good on his threat.

Crisis: How should Frankenstein deal with the creature's vow to disrupt his wedding night? Best bad choice.

Climax: Frankenstein decides to fight and arms himself in preparation.

Resolution: The wedding takes place and the couple leaves for their honeymoon.

NOTES

- Very little energy is spent on the wedding in this scene, so the climax is probably not the wedding itself, which is a little unusual. In a love story, the wedding would have been the point of the scene. In Horror, we are preoccupied with the rising tension that will lead us inevitably to a battle of life and death, so Shelley spends her emotional capital on having both Victor and Elizabeth growing more and more anxious as preparations for the wedding move forward. The wedding itself barely takes up a line.

- So why is Elizabeth anxious? Good question. And if we were writing this scene, would we want her to be anxious? Or would we want her to be bubbling with excitement over the prospect of her wedding? It's interesting to consider the characterization choices that Shelley makes while writing *Frankenstein*. In some ways, Elizabeth is Frankenstein's moral compass. She is the stand-in for both his mother and father, two moral examples who came before her. He has promised to tell her his big, troubling secret, and she has guessed that something is not normal about his constant state of depression. She tries to be happy about her wedding but can't shake the feeling of oppression and dread that is growing. She's experiencing the same feelings the reader experiences—both she and the reader are intelligent, interested bystanders.
- What's more, Frankenstein drops a bomb in the middle of this scene. What do we do with his statement that the creature is going to kill Elizabeth? When the speaker drops in and out of the present time at will, the writer can do some crazy things with the level of tension in the story. But there isn't any way to account for it in the scene, because the scene holds together even if you remove that one comment! Perhaps Shelley just drops that sentence in there for fun.

CHAPTER 23 – SCENE 46

It was eight o'clock when we landed; we walked for a short time on the shore, enjoying the transitory light, and then retired to the inn and contemplated the lovely scene of waters, woods, and mountains, obscured in darkness, yet still displaying their black outlines.

The wind, which had fallen in the south, now rose with great violence in the west. The moon had reached her summit in the heavens and was beginning to descend; the clouds swept across it swifter than the flight of the vulture and dimmed her rays, while the lake reflected the scene of the busy heavens, rendered still busier by the restless waves that were beginning to rise. **Suddenly a heavy storm of rain descended.** *[More beautiful, cinematic backdrop to the horror that is about to occur.]*

I had been calm during the day, but so soon as night obscured the shapes of objects, a thousand fears arose in my mind. **I was anxious and watchful**, while my right hand grasped a pistol which was hidden in my bosom; every sound terrified me, but I resolved that I would sell my life dearly and not shrink from the conflict until my own life or that of my adversary was extinguished. Elizabeth observed my agitation for some time in timid and fearful silence, but there was something in my glance which communicated terror to her, and trembling, she asked, "What is it that agitates you, my dear Victor? What is it you fear?"

"Oh! Peace, peace, my love," replied I; "this night, and all will be safe; but this night is dreadful, very dreadful."

I passed an hour in this state of mind, when **suddenly I reflected how fearful the combat which I momentarily expected would be to my wife, and I earnestly entreated her to retire, resolving not to join her until I had obtained some knowledge as to the situation of my enemy.**

She left me, and I continued some time walking up and down the passages of the house and inspecting every corner that might afford a retreat to my adversary. But I discovered no trace of him and was beginning to conjecture that some fortunate chance had intervened to prevent the execution of his menaces when suddenly I heard a shrill and dreadful scream. It came from the room into which Elizabeth had retired. As I heard it, the whole truth rushed into my mind, my arms dropped, the motion of every muscle and fibre was suspended; I could feel the blood trickling in my veins and tingling in the extremities of my limbs. This state lasted but for an instant; the scream was repeated, and I rushed into the room. Great God! Why did I not then expire! Why am I here to relate the destruction of the best hope and the purest creature on earth? She was there, lifeless and inanimate, thrown across the bed, her head hanging down and her pale and distorted features half covered by her hair. Everywhere I turn I see the same figure—her bloodless arms and relaxed form flung by the murderer on its bridal bier. Could I behold this and live? Alas! **Life is obstinate and clings closest where it is most hated.** For a moment only did I lose recollection; I fell senseless on the ground.

When I recovered I found myself surrounded by the people of the inn; their countenances expressed a breathless terror, but the horror of others appeared only as a mockery, a shadow of the feelings that oppressed me. I escaped from them to the room where lay the body of Elizabeth, my love, my wife, so lately living, so dear, so worthy. She had been moved from the posture in which I had first beheld her, and now, as she lay, her head upon her arm and a handkerchief thrown across her face and neck, I might have supposed her asleep. I rushed towards her and embraced her with ardour, but the deadly languor and coldness of the limbs told me that what I now held in my arms had ceased to be the Elizabeth whom I had loved and cherished. The murderous mark of the fiend's grasp was on her neck, and the breath had ceased to issue from her lips. While I still hung over her in the agony of despair, I happened to look up. The windows of the room had before been darkened, and I felt a kind of panic on seeing the pale yellow light of the moon illuminate the chamber. **The shutters had been thrown back, and with a sensation of horror not to be described, I saw at the open window a figure the most hideous and abhorred. A grin was on the face of the monster; he seemed to jeer, as with his fiendish finger he pointed towards the corpse of my wife. I rushed towards the window, and drawing a pistol from my bosom, fired; but he eluded me, leaped from his station, and running with the swiftness of lightning, plunged into the lake.** *[Quite a dramatic description.]*

The report of the pistol brought a crowd into the room. I pointed to the spot where he had disappeared, and we followed the track with boats; nets were cast, but in vain. After passing several hours, we returned hopeless, most of my companions believing it to have been a form conjured up by my fancy. After having landed, they proceeded to search the country, parties going in different directions among the woods and vines.

I attempted to accompany them and proceeded a short distance from the house, but my head whirled round, my steps were like those of a drunken man, I fell at last in a state of utter exhaustion; a film covered my eyes, and my skin was parched with the heat of fever. In this state I was carried back and placed on a bed, hardly conscious of what had happened; my eyes wandered round the room as if to seek something that I had lost.

After an interval I arose, and as if by instinct, crawled into the room where the corpse of my beloved lay. There were women weeping around; I hung over it and joined my sad tears to theirs; all this time no distinct idea presented itself to my mind, but my thoughts rambled to various subjects, reflecting confusedly on my misfortunes and their cause. I was bewildered, in a cloud of wonder and horror. The death of William, the execution of Justine, the murder of Clerval, and lastly of my wife; even at that moment I knew not that my only remaining friends were safe from the malignity of the fiend; my father even now might be writhing under his grasp, and Ernest might be dead at his feet. This idea made me shudder and recalled me to action. I started up and resolved to return to Geneva with all possible speed.

There were no horses to be procured, and I must return by the lake; but the wind was unfavourable, and the rain fell in torrents. However, it was hardly morning, and I might reasonably hope to arrive by night. I hired men to row and took an oar myself, for I had always experienced relief from mental torment in bodily exercise. *[Torrents of rain, rowing in a boat on a lake during a storm, tears ... almost a visual definition for the word "gothic."]* But the overflowing misery I now felt, and the excess of agitation that I endured rendered me incapable of any exertion. I threw down the oar, and leaning my head upon my hands, gave way to every gloomy idea that arose. If I looked up, I saw scenes which were familiar to me in my happier time and which I had contemplated but the day before in the company of her who was now but a shadow and a recollection. Tears streamed from my eyes. The rain had ceased for a moment, and I saw the fish play in the waters as they had done a few hours before; they had then been observed by Elizabeth. **Nothing is so painful to the human mind as a great and sudden change.** The sun might shine or the clouds might lower, but nothing could appear to me as it had done the day before. A fiend had snatched from me every hope of future happiness; no creature had ever been so miserable as I was; so frightful an event is single in the history of man. But why should I dwell upon the incidents that followed this last overwhelming event? Mine has been a tale of horrors; I have reached their acme, and what I must now relate can but be tedious to you. Know that, one by one, my friends were snatched away; I was left desolate. My own strength is exhausted, and I must tell, in a few words, what remains of my hideous narration. I arrived at Geneva. My father and Ernest yet lived, but the former sunk under the tidings that I bore. I see him now, excellent and venerable old man! His eyes wandered in vacancy, for they had lost their charm and their delight—his Elizabeth, his more than daughter, whom he doted on with all that affection which a man feels, who in the decline of life, having few affections, clings more earnestly to those that remain. Cursed, cursed be the fiend that brought misery on his grey hairs and doomed him to waste in wretchedness! He could not live under the horrors that were accumulated around him; the springs of existence suddenly gave way; he was unable to rise from his bed, and in a few days he died in my arms.

• ANALYZING THE SCENE •
CHAPTER 23 – SCENE 46

A Story Event is an active change of universal human value for one or more characters as a result of conflict (one character's desires clash with another's or an environmental shift changes the universal human value).

A Working Scene contains at least one Story Event. To determine a scene's Story Event, answer these four questions:

1. What are the characters literally doing—that is, what are their micro on-the-ground actions?

Victor is nervously awaiting the creature. He sends Elizabeth to bed while he keeps watch, only to hear her scream. The creature has killed her, and Victor sees him jeering in the window, pointing at her. Victor rushes back to Geneva. His family is safe, but his father dies of a broken heart shortly thereafter.

2. What is the essential tactic of the characters—that is, what macro behaviors are they employing that are linked to a universal human value?

The creature is carrying through on his threat. Victor seeks to confront the creature but has misunderstood the threat to be against him personally, as the creature murdered Elizabeth instead.

3. What universal human values have changed for one or more

characters in the scene? Which one of those value changes is most important and should be included in the Story Grid Spreadsheet?

Elizabeth has gone from Alive to Dead. Victor has gone from Married to Widowed, or Together to Alone.

In a Horror story, the global value at stake is Life to Death, but this scene goes beyond Death. Victor was starting a new life with his bride one moment and then widowed the next. In this case, it is more reflective of the story's themes to choose Together to Alone.

Together to Alone

4. What is the Story Event that sums up the scene's on-the-ground actions, essential tactics, and value change? We will enter that event in the Story Grid Spreadsheet.

The creature murders Elizabeth and not Frankenstein as expected; the creature escapes and Frankenstein rushes back to Geneva.

HOW THE SCENE ABIDES BY THE FIVE COMMANDMENTS OF STORYTELLING

Inciting Incident: Night falls and Victor grows nervous about what he anticipates will be a tremendous battle between himself and the creature.

Turning Point Progressive Complication: Victor suddenly realizes how much the confrontation will terrify Elizabeth.

Crisis: How does Frankenstein handle the confrontation he knows will come? Best bad choice.

Climax: He urges Elizabeth to go to bed ahead of him because he plans to search for the creature. He hears a scream. He rushes into the bedroom and finds Elizabeth dead.

Resolution: Frankenstein sees the creature at the window and fires at him but misses; he leads a search but they find nothing. He rushes back to Geneva in fear for his family, and while he finds them safe, his father dies shortly thereafter.

NOTES

- Once more, Shelley delights in using the weather and nature as a character itself, to show the rising level of anxiety and dread. The scene opens with a wind rising with "great violence" and a "heavy storm of rain."
- Note that Frankenstein doesn't himself murder anyone, but bears "responsibility" for all the murders. In the case of Elizabeth's murder, he is the one who sends her away to rest because he is under the misconception the creature wants his death.
- Also note that the creature is interested in punishing Frankenstein with the same hand he was dealt, so he does not actually try to murder Frankenstein—he is taking away the family that he himself does not have. This was Frankenstein's grave miscalculation and cost him Elizabeth.
- What a pity that Shelley did not have motion picture technology back in the early 1800s! The paragraph where she describes the creature in the window—backlit by the moon, as he points a finger at Elizabeth's dead body and jeers—is cinematic, to say the least.
- When Frankenstein realizes that Ernest and his father are at risk, he knows he needs to rush back to Geneva, but of course there are no horses and he must travel via the lake. Once again, this is both dramatic and an amazing mental picture as he attempts to help the men row his boat. Add to this the awful experience of leaving the same way he arrived; he is forced to contrast the current journey to the last journey he took on the lake with Elizabeth.
- As the resolution of this horrible climax, Victor's elderly father dies. You can't get more final than that.

CHAPTER 23 – SCENE 47

What then became of me? I know not; I lost sensation, and chains and darkness were the only objects that pressed upon me. **Sometimes, indeed, I dreamt that I wandered in flowery meadows and pleasant vales with the friends of my youth, but I awoke and found myself in a dungeon.** Melancholy followed, but by degrees I gained a clear conception of my miseries and situation and was then released from my prison. For they had called me mad, and during many months, as I understood, a solitary cell had been my habitation.

Liberty, however, had been a useless gift to me, had I not, as I awakened to reason, at the same time awakened to revenge. As the memory of past misfortunes pressed upon me, I began to reflect on their cause—the monster whom I had created, the miserable daemon whom I had sent abroad into the world for my destruction. I was possessed by a maddening rage when I thought of him, and desired and ardently prayed that I might have him within my grasp to wreak a great and signal revenge on his cursed head.

Nor did my hate long confine itself to useless wishes; I began to reflect on the best means of securing him; and for this purpose, about a month after my release, I repaired to a criminal judge in the town and told him that I had an accusation to make, that I knew the destroyer of my family, and that I required him to exert his whole authority for the apprehension of the murderer. *[Frankenstein decides to ask for help from the law; he goes to the magistrate to make a clean breast of his tale.]* The magistrate listened to me with attention and kindness.

"Be assured, sir," said he, "no pains or exertions on my part shall be spared to discover the villain."

"I thank you," replied I; "listen, therefore, to the deposition that I have to make. It is indeed a tale so strange that I should fear you would not credit it were there not something in truth which, however wonderful, forces conviction. The story is too connected to be mistaken for a dream, and I have no motive for falsehood." My manner as I thus addressed him was impressive but calm; I had formed in my own heart a resolution to pursue my destroyer to death, and this purpose quieted my agony and for an interval reconciled me to life. I now related my history briefly but with firmness and precision, marking the dates with accuracy and never deviating into invective or exclamation. The magistrate appeared at first perfectly incredulous, but as I continued he became more attentive and interested; I saw him sometimes shudder with horror; at others a lively surprise, unmingled with disbelief, was painted on his countenance. When I had concluded my narration I said, "**This is the being whom I accuse and for whose seizure and punishment I call upon you to exert your whole power**. It is your duty as a magistrate, and I believe and hope that your feelings as a man will not revolt from the execution of those functions on this occasion." This address caused a considerable change in the physiognomy of my own auditor. He had heard my story with that half kind of belief that is given to a tale of spirits and supernatural events; but when he was called upon to act officially in consequence, the whole tide of his incredulity returned. He, however, answered mildly, "I would willingly afford you every aid in your pursuit, but the creature of whom you speak appears to have powers which would put all my exertions to defiance. Who can follow an animal which can traverse the sea of ice and inhabit caves and dens where no man would venture to intrude? Besides, some months have elapsed since the commission of his crimes, and no one can conjecture to what place he has wandered or what region he may now inhabit."

"I do not doubt that he hovers near the spot which I inhabit, and if he has indeed taken refuge in the Alps, he may be hunted like the chamois and destroyed as a beast of prey. But I perceive your thoughts; you do not credit my narrative and do not intend to pursue my enemy with the punishment which is his desert." As I spoke, rage sparkled in my eyes; the magistrate was intimidated. "You are mistaken," said he. "I will exert myself, and if it is in my power to seize the monster, be assured that he shall suffer punishment proportionate to his crimes. But I fear, from what you have yourself described to be his properties, that this will prove impracticable; and thus, while every proper measure is pursued, you should make up your mind to disappointment."

"That cannot be; but all that I can say will be of little avail. My revenge is of no moment to you; yet, while I allow it to be a vice, I confess that it is the devouring and only passion of my soul. My rage is unspeakable when I reflect that the murderer, whom I have turned loose upon society, still exists. **You refuse my just demand; I have but one resource, and I devote myself, either in my life or death, to his destruction.**"

I trembled with excess of agitation as I said this; there was a frenzy in my manner, and something, I doubt not, of that haughty fierceness which the martyrs of old are said to have possessed. But to a Genevan magistrate, whose mind was occupied by far other ideas than those of devotion and heroism, this elevation of mind had much the appearance of madness. He endeavoured to soothe me as a nurse does a child and reverted to my tale as the effects of delirium.

"Man," I cried, "how ignorant art thou in thy pride of wisdom! Cease; you know not what it is you say."

I broke from the house angry and disturbed and retired to meditate on some other mode of action.

• ANALYZING THE SCENE •
CHAPTER 23 – SCENE 47

A Story Event is an active change of universal human value for one or more characters as a result of conflict (one character's desires clash with another's or an environmental shift changes the universal human value).

A Working Scene contains at least one Story Event. To determine a scene's Story Event, answer these four questions:

1. What are the characters literally doing—that is, what are their micro on-the-ground actions?

Frankenstein goes to a criminal judge in town and tells him the whole story; he appeals to him to pursue the creature.

2. What is the essential tactic of the characters—that is, what macro behaviors are they employing that are linked to a universal human value?

It has taken until now for Frankenstein to tell anyone what he has done; he is owning up to his role and responsibility publicly, but to no avail. He is alone in his battle.

3. What universal human values have changed for one or more characters in the scene? Which one of those value changes is most important and should be included in the Story Grid Spreadsheet?

Frankenstein starts out this scene attempting to do the right thing. He appeals to justice but is denied and is angry and frustrated. His state changes from calm to angry as he tries to put his outrageous tale into words for the legal system.

We are tracking Frankenstein's emotions in this scene as his outrage at the law's refusal to believe his story results in his determination to exact revenge on the creature himself.

Calm to Angry

4. What is the Story Event that sums up the scene's on-the-ground

actions, essential tactics, and value change? We will enter that event in the Story Grid Spreadsheet.

Victor tells the local magistrate the whole story, but he doesn't believe him. Victor swears to devote his life to destroying the creature himself.

HOW THE SCENE ABIDES BY THE FIVE COMMANDMENTS OF STORYTELLING

Inciting Incident: Victor tells the town judge about the creature.

Turning Point Progressive Complication: The judge doesn't believe him.

Crisis: Victor sees that the judge thinks he is crazy and won't organize a chase after the creature or otherwise help destroy him. Best bad choice.

Climax: Victor declares that he must devote his life to destroying the creature himself.

Resolution: The judge tries to soothe him but only succeeds at making Frankenstein angrier.

NOTES

- How fascinating that both in the case of Justine and in this case, Frankenstein thinks "justice" is the answer.
- The very beginning of this scene is beautifully written. Frankenstein, who was so recently released from a prison in Ireland, dreams of wandering through flower meadows but then awakens and finds himself in a dungeon. He has been locked up in yet another kind of prison because people thought he had gone mad. Shelley then writes, "Liberty, however, had been a useless gift to me, had I not, as I awakened to reason, at the same time awakened to revenge." The metaphor of being

trapped and being free is presented in terms of whether Frankenstein appreciates or can use the liberty he has, and he realizes that his freedom is his weapon against the monster.

- Then, Shelley reminds us that the arbiter of freedom and imprisonment is none other than the magistrate. Remember the Irish magistrate? He was instrumental in terms of securing Frankenstein's release from prison in Ireland. Magistrates were the power behind Justine's death sentence. Safia's father, the Turk, was falsely imprisoned. Felix and his family were imprisoned after trying to help the Turk. Frankenstein goes to the town criminal judge for justice.
- What is the answer of the magistrate who hears Frankenstein's plea? He is pleasant and offers no help. He denies that he does not believe the tale. Rather, he declines to become involved because it sounds like too much trouble to go after a creature with such incredible properties. The justice system fails again, and Frankenstein announces that he has no choice but to take the law into his own hands.

CHAPTER 24 – SCENE 48

My present situation was one in which all voluntary thought was swallowed up and lost. I was hurried away by fury; revenge alone endowed me with strength and composure; it moulded my feelings and allowed me to be calculating and calm at periods when otherwise delirium or death would have been my portion.

My first resolution was to quit Geneva forever; my country, which, when I was happy and beloved, was dear to me, now, in my adversity, became hateful. I provided myself with a sum of money, together with a few jewels which had belonged to my mother, and departed. And now my wanderings began which are to cease but with life. I have traversed a vast portion of the earth and have endured all the hardships which travellers in deserts and barbarous countries are wont to meet. How I have lived I hardly know; many times have I stretched my failing limbs upon the sandy plain and prayed for death. But revenge kept me alive; I dared not die and leave my adversary in being.

When I quitted Geneva my first labour was to gain some clue by which I might trace the steps of my fiendish enemy. But my plan was unsettled, and I wandered many hours round the confines of the town, uncertain what path I should pursue. **As night approached I found myself at the entrance of the cemetery where William, Elizabeth, and my father reposed.** I entered it and approached the tomb which marked their graves. Everything was silent except the leaves of the trees, which were gently agitated by the wind; the night was nearly dark, and the scene would have been solemn and affecting even to an uninterested observer. The spirits of the departed seemed to flit around and to cast a shadow, which was felt but not seen, around the head of the mourner.

The deep grief which this scene had at first excited quickly gave way to rage and despair. They were dead, and I lived; their murderer also lived, and to destroy him I must drag out my weary existence. I knelt on the grass and kissed the earth and with quivering lips exclaimed, "**By the sacred earth on which I kneel, by the shades that wander near me, by the deep and eternal grief that I feel, I swear; and by thee, O Night, and the spirits that preside over thee, to pursue the daemon who caused this misery, until he or I shall perish in mortal conflict.** For this purpose I will preserve my life; to execute this dear revenge will I again behold the sun and tread the green herbage of earth, which otherwise should vanish from my eyes forever. And **I call on you, spirits of the dead, and on you, wandering ministers of vengeance, to aid and conduct me in my work. Let the cursed and hellish monster drink deep of agony; let him feel the despair that now torments me.**" *[Here is the "Victim at the Mercy of the Monster" scene —it is also the Core Event, where Frankenstein reckons with the fact that "All is Lost."]* I had begun my adjuration with solemnity and an awe which almost assured me that the shades of my murdered friends heard and approved my devotion, but the furies possessed me as I concluded, and rage choked my utterance.

I was answered through the stillness of night by a loud and fiendish laugh. It rang on my ears long and heavily; the mountains re-echoed it, and I felt as if all hell surrounded me with mockery and laughter. Surely in that moment I should have been possessed by frenzy and have destroyed my miserable existence but that my vow was heard and that I was reserved for vengeance. The laughter died away, when a well-known and abhorred voice, apparently close to my ear, addressed me in an audible whisper, "I am satisfied, miserable wretch! You have determined to live, and I am satisfied."

I darted towards the spot from which the sound proceeded, but the devil eluded my grasp. Suddenly the broad disk of the moon arose and shone full upon his ghastly and distorted shape as he fled with more than mortal speed. *[Another beautifully cinematic scene!]*

I pursued him, and for many months this has been my task. Guided by a slight clue, I followed the windings of the Rhone, but vainly. The blue Mediterranean appeared, and by a strange chance, I saw the fiend enter by night and hide himself in a vessel bound for the Black Sea. I took my passage in the same ship, but he escaped, I know not how.

Amidst the wilds of Tartary and Russia, although he still evaded me, I have ever followed in his track. Sometimes the peasants, scared by this horrid apparition, informed me of his path; **sometimes he himself, who feared that if I lost all trace of him I should despair and die, left some mark to guide me.** The snows descended on my head, and I saw the print of his huge step on the white plain. To you first entering on life, to whom care is new and agony unknown, how can you understand what I have felt and still feel? Cold, want, and fatigue were the least pains which I was destined to endure; **I was cursed by some devil and carried about with me my eternal hell; yet still a spirit of good followed and directed my steps and when I most murmured would suddenly extricate me from seemingly insurmountable difficulties. Sometimes, when nature, overcome by hunger, sank under the exhaustion, a repast was prepared for me in the desert that restored and inspirited me. The fare was, indeed, coarse, such as the peasants of the country ate, but I will not doubt that it was set there by the spirits that I had invoked to aid me. Often, when all was dry, the heavens cloudless, and I was parched by thirst, a slight cloud would bedim the sky, shed the few drops that revived me, and vanish.**

I followed, when I could, the courses of the rivers; but the daemon generally avoided these, as it was here that the population of the country chiefly collected. In other places human beings were seldom seen, and I generally subsisted on the wild animals that crossed my path. I had money with me and gained the friendship of the villagers by distributing it; or I brought with me some food that I had killed, which, after taking a small part, I always presented to those who had provided me with fire and utensils for cooking.

My life, as it passed thus, was indeed hateful to me, and it was during sleep alone that I could taste joy. O blessed sleep! Often, when most miserable, I sank to repose, and my dreams lulled me even to rapture. The spirits that guarded me had provided these moments, or rather hours, of happiness that I might retain strength to fulfil my pilgrimage. Deprived of this respite, I should have sunk under my hardships. During the day I was sustained and inspirited by the hope of night, for in sleep I saw my friends, my wife, and my beloved country; again I saw the benevolent countenance of my father, heard the silver tones of my Elizabeth's voice, and beheld Clerval enjoying health and youth. Often, when wearied by a toilsome march, I persuaded myself that I was dreaming until night should come and that I should then enjoy reality in the arms of my dearest friends. What agonizing fondness did I feel for them! How did I cling to their dear forms, as sometimes they haunted even my waking hours, and persuade myself that they still lived! At such moments vengeance, that burned within me, died in my heart, and I pursued my path towards the destruction of the daemon more as a task enjoined by heaven, as the mechanical impulse of some power of which I was unconscious, than as the ardent desire of my soul. What his feelings were whom I pursued I cannot know. **Sometimes, indeed, he left marks in writing on the barks of the trees or cut in stone that guided me and instigated my fury. "My reign is not yet over"—these words were legible in one of these inscriptions—"you live, and my power is complete.** Follow me; I seek the everlasting ices of the north, where you will feel the misery of cold and frost, to which I am impassive. You will find near this place, if you follow not too tardily, a dead hare; eat and be refreshed. Come on, my enemy; we have yet to wrestle for our lives, but many hard and miserable hours must you endure until that period shall arrive."

Scoffing devil! Again do I vow vengeance; again do I devote thee, miserable fiend, to torture and death. Never will I give up my search until he or I perish; and then with what ecstasy shall I join my Elizabeth and my departed friends, who even now prepare for me the reward of my tedious toil and horrible pilgrimage!

• ANALYZING THE SCENE •
CHAPTER 24 – SCENE 48

A Story Event is an active change of universal human value for one or more characters as a result of conflict (one character's desires clash with another's or an environmental shift changes the universal human value).

A Working Scene contains at least one Story Event. To determine a scene's Story Event, answer these four questions:

1. What are the characters literally doing—that is, what are their micro on-the-ground actions?

Frankenstein leaves Geneva and chases after the creature.

2. What is the essential tactic of the characters—that is, what macro behaviors are they employing that are linked to a universal human value?

The creature flees, and Frankenstein chases, but Frankenstein is kept alive by some mysterious combination of good luck, spirits, and the creature himself.

3. What universal human values have changed for one or more characters in the scene? Which one of those value changes is most important and should be included in the Story Grid Spreadsheet?

Frankenstein craves revenge, and the energy from his fury drives him to search long and hard for the creature. He starts out the scene in Geneva but then leaves after paying a visit to the tombs of William, Elizabeth, and his father. His condition goes from resident to wanderer.

We are tracking the major movements in this scene, which involve Frankenstein's need to leave Geneva in order to follow the creature all over the world.

Resident to Wanderer

4. What is the Story Event that sums up the scene's on-the-ground actions, essential tactics, and value change? We will enter that event in the Story Grid Spreadsheet.

Victor decides to leave Geneva. He visits the family graves and swears he will avenge them. The creature's voice comes out of the dark to say he is "satisfied," and Victor pursues him.

HOW THE SCENE ABIDES BY THE FIVE COMMANDMENTS OF STORYTELLING

Inciting Incident: Victor decides he needs to leave Geneva.

Turning Point Progressive Complication: Victor pays a visit to the family tomb and swears aloud to pursue the creature until death. The voice of the creature addresses Victor and tells him, "You have determined to live, and I am satisfied."

Crisis: How should Victor deal with his thirst for revenge, given that the creature claims to be "satisfied"? Does he pursue him or not? Best bad choice.

Climax: Victor determines to pursue him.

Resolution: Victor sees the creature fleeing; he pursues him all over the world.

NOTES

- Again, it's too bad that Shelley was not alive in the era of cinema. It's hard to do better than a scene where Frankenstein kisses the earth by the graves of his dead family members and swears to destroy the creature, surrounded by darkness and a sense of doom and flitting spirits.
- When the creature's voice comes out of the dark and says,

"You have determined to live, and I am satisfied," we are left with questions. Was the creature afraid that Frankenstein would end his life? What would happen to the creature if Frankenstein died? He would have no connection to anyone on earth then—did he realize this?

- Accordingly, as Frankenstein sets out to chase down the creature and endures privation and discomfort beyond what he has ever imagined, he mentions that the creature himself occasionally left marks to guide him. He would also find meals and food available when he needed it. He credits "spirits," but the creature is a more logical explanation, just as the creature was the reason for the De Lacey family's mysterious firewood deliveries. The creature, it seems, cannot bear to think of losing the only connection he has to humanity.

CHAPTER 24 – SCENE 49

As I still pursued my journey to the northward, the snows thickened and the cold increased in a degree almost too severe to support. The peasants were shut up in their hovels, and only a few of the most hardy ventured forth to seize the animals whom starvation had forced from their hiding-places to seek for prey. The rivers were covered with ice, and no fish could be procured; and thus I was cut off from my chief article of maintenance. **The triumph of my enemy increased with the difficulty of my labours. One inscription that he left was in these words: "Prepare! Your toils only begin; wrap yourself in furs and provide food, for we shall soon enter upon a journey where your sufferings will satisfy my everlasting hatred."**

My courage and perseverance were invigorated by these scoffing words; I resolved not to fail in my purpose, and calling on heaven to support me, I continued with unabated fervour to traverse immense deserts, until the ocean appeared at a distance and formed the utmost boundary of the horizon. Oh! How unlike it was to the blue seasons of the south! Covered with ice, it was only to be distinguished from land by its superior wildness and ruggedness. The Greeks wept for joy when they beheld the Mediterranean from the hills of Asia, and hailed with rapture the boundary of their toils. I did not weep, but I knelt down and with a full heart thanked my guiding spirit for conducting me in safety to the place where I hoped, notwithstanding my adversary's gibe, to meet and grapple with him.

Some weeks before this period I had procured a sledge and dogs and thus traversed the snows with inconceivable speed. I know not whether the fiend possessed the same advantages, but I found that, as before I had daily lost ground in the pursuit, I now gained on him, so much so that when I first saw the ocean he was but one day's journey in advance, and I hoped to intercept him before he should reach the beach. With new courage, therefore, I pressed on, and in two days arrived at a wretched hamlet on the seashore. I inquired of the inhabitants concerning the fiend and gained accurate information. **A gigantic monster, they said, had arrived the night before, armed with a gun and many pistols, putting to flight the inhabitants of a solitary cottage through fear of his terrific appearance. He had carried off their store of winter food, and placing it in a sledge, to draw which he had seized on a numerous drove of trained dogs, he had harnessed them, and the same night, to the joy of the horror-struck villagers, had pursued his journey across the sea in a direction that led to no land; and they conjectured that he must speedily be destroyed by the breaking of the ice or frozen by the eternal frosts.**

On hearing this information I suffered a temporary access of despair. He had escaped me, and I must commence a destructive and almost endless journey across the mountainous ices of the ocean, amidst cold that few of the inhabitants could long endure and which I, the native of a genial and sunny climate, could not hope to survive. Yet at the idea that the fiend should live and be triumphant, my rage and vengeance returned, and like a mighty tide, overwhelmed every other feeling. After a slight repose, during which the spirits of the dead hovered round and instigated me to toil and revenge, I prepared for my journey. I exchanged my land-sledge for one fashioned for the inequalities of the frozen ocean, and purchasing a plentiful stock of provisions, I departed from land.

I cannot guess how many days have passed since then, but I have endured misery which nothing but the eternal sentiment of a just retribution burning within my heart could have enabled me to support. Immense and rugged mountains of ice often barred up my passage, and

I often heard the thunder of the ground sea, which threatened my destruction. But again the frost came and made the paths of the sea secure.

By the quantity of provision which I had consumed, I should guess that I had passed three weeks in this journey; and the continual protraction of hope, returning back upon the heart, often wrung bitter drops of despondency and grief from my eyes. Despair had indeed almost secured her prey, and I should soon have sunk beneath this misery. Once, after the poor animals that conveyed me had with incredible toil gained the summit of a sloping ice mountain, and one, sinking under his fatigue, died, I viewed the expanse before me with anguish, when suddenly my eye caught a dark speck upon the dusky plain. I strained my sight to discover what it could be and uttered a wild cry of ecstasy when I distinguished a sledge and the distorted proportions of a well-known form within. Oh! With what a burning gush did hope revisit my heart! Warm tears filled my eyes, which I hastily wiped away, that they might not intercept the view I had of the daemon; but still my sight was dimmed by the burning drops, until, giving way to the emotions that oppressed me, I wept aloud.

But this was not the time for delay; I disencumbered the dogs of their dead companion, gave them a plentiful portion of food, and after an hour's rest, which was absolutely necessary, and yet which was bitterly irksome to me, I continued my route. The sledge was still visible, nor did I again lose sight of it except at the moments when for a short time some ice-rock concealed it with its intervening crags. I indeed perceptibly gained on it, and when, after nearly two days' journey, I beheld my enemy at no more than a mile distant, my heart bounded within me.

But now, when I appeared almost within grasp of my foe, my hopes were suddenly extinguished, and I lost all trace of him more utterly than I had ever done before. A ground sea was heard; the thunder of its progress, as the waters rolled and swelled beneath me, became every moment more ominous and terrific. I pressed on, but in vain. The wind arose; the sea roared; and, as with the mighty shock of an earthquake, it split and cracked with a tremendous and overwhelming sound. The work was soon finished; in a few minutes a tumultuous sea rolled between me and my enemy, and I was left drifting on a scattered piece of ice that was continually lessening and thus preparing for me a hideous death. In this manner many appalling hours passed; several of my dogs died, and I myself was about to sink under the accumulation of distress when I saw your vessel riding at anchor and holding forth to me hopes of succour and life. I had no conception that vessels ever came so far north and was astounded at the sight. I quickly destroyed part of my sledge to construct oars, and by these means was enabled, with infinite fatigue, to move my ice raft in the direction of your ship. **I had determined, if you were going southwards, still to trust myself to the mercy of the seas rather than abandon my purpose.** I hoped to induce you to grant me a boat with which I could pursue my enemy. But your direction was northwards. You took me on board when my vigour was exhausted, and I should soon have sunk under my multiplied hardships into a death which I still dread, for my task is unfulfilled.

Oh! When will my guiding spirit, in conducting me to the daemon, allow me the rest I so much desire; or must I die, and he yet live? If I do, swear to me, Walton, that he shall not escape, that you will seek him and satisfy my vengeance in his death. And do I dare to ask of you to undertake my pilgrimage, to endure the hardships that I have undergone? No; I am not so selfish. Yet, when I am dead, if he should appear, if the ministers of vengeance should conduct him to you, swear that he shall not live—swear that he shall not triumph over my accumulated woes and survive to add to the list of his dark crimes. He is eloquent and persuasive, and once his words had even power over my heart; but trust him not. His soul is as hellish as his form, full of treachery and fiend-like malice. Hear him not; call on the names of William, Justine, Clerval, Elizabeth, my father, and of the wretched Victor, and thrust your sword into his heart. I will hover near and direct the steel aright.

• ANALYZING THE SCENE •
CHAPTER 24 – SCENE 49

A Story Event is an active change of universal human value for one or more characters as a result of conflict (one character's desires clash with another's or an environmental shift changes the universal human value).

A Working Scene contains at least one Story Event. To determine a scene's Story Event, answer these four questions:

1. What are the characters literally doing—that is, what are their micro on-the-ground actions?

Frankenstein is chasing the monster through the frozen north.

2. What is the essential tactic of the characters—that is, what macro behaviors are they employing that are linked to a universal human value?

Frankenstein hears that the monster has headed out across the frozen sea, almost certainly to perish, and decides he must follow him anyway.

3. What universal human values have changed for one or more characters in the scene? Which one of those value changes is most important and should be included in the Story Grid Spreadsheet?

The ice begins to break and Frankenstein is adrift on a piece of ice. He almost dies but then Walton's boat appears.

Danger to Rescued

4. What is the Story Event that sums up the scene's on-the-ground actions, essential tactics, and value change? We will enter that event in the Story Grid Spreadsheet.

Victor chases the monster all over the world, including through the frozen north. The monster leaves him food, supplies, and directions as he flees. He eventually spies the monster in the distance but ends up adrift on floating ice to be rescued by Walton.

HOW THE SCENE ABIDES BY THE FIVE COMMANDMENTS OF STORYTELLING

Inciting Incident: Frankenstein is heading north, chasing the creature.

Turning Point Progressive Complication: He hears that the creature has gone across the sea in a direction that leads to no land and realizes will probably die.

Crisis: Frankenstein is devastated because he must risk his own life following the creature across the ice, or he will have to give up. Best bad choice.

Climax: He decides to follow him.

Resolution: He eventually spies the creature far in the distance, but he ends up adrift on a floating chunk of ice.

NOTES

- Once more, we are shown that while Frankenstein chases the creature because he wants to kill him, the creature actually looks after him with notes and supplies. The creature does not want him to perish.
- The creature heads off toward the sea, and the local villagers tell Frankenstein that he will either be destroyed by the breaking ice or be frozen to death. This news upsets Frankenstein, as he does not want to abandon his chase. He decides to continue to chase the creature and eventually catches sight of him. Soon afterward the ice begins to break and Frankenstein is adrift on a melting piece of ice. This is when Walton's ship appears and rescues him. This is the end of the story, and Frankenstein begs Walton to promise that if he dies, he will chase after him and kill him.

CHAPTER 24 – SCENE 50

Walton, in continuation.
August 26th, 17—

You have read this strange and terrific story, Margaret; and do you not feel your blood congeal with horror, like that which even now curdles mine? Sometimes, seized with sudden agony, he could not continue his tale; at others, his voice broken, yet piercing, uttered with difficulty the words so replete with anguish. His fine and lovely eyes were now lighted up with indignation, now subdued to downcast sorrow and quenched in infinite wretchedness. Sometimes he commanded his countenance and tones and related the most horrible incidents with a tranquil voice, suppressing every mark of agitation; then, like a volcano bursting forth, his face would suddenly change to an expression of the wildest rage as he shrieked out imprecations on his persecutor.

His tale is connected and told with an appearance of the simplest truth, yet I own to you that the letters of Felix and Safie, which he showed me, and the apparition of the monster seen from our ship, brought to me a greater conviction of the truth of his narrative than his asseverations, however earnest and connected. Such a monster has, then, really existence! I cannot doubt it, yet I am lost in surprise and admiration. **Sometimes I endeavoured to gain from Frankenstein the**

particulars of his creature's formation, but on this point he was impenetrable. "Are you mad, my friend?" said he. "Or whither does your senseless curiosity lead you? Would you also create for yourself and the world a demoniacal enemy? Peace, peace! Learn my miseries and do not seek to increase your own." Frankenstein discovered that I made notes concerning his history; he asked to see them and then himself corrected and augmented them in many places, but principally in giving the life and spirit to the conversations he held with his enemy. "Since you have preserved my narration," said he, "I would not that a mutilated one should go down to posterity."

Thus has a week passed away, while I have listened to the strangest tale that ever imagination formed. My thoughts and every feeling of my soul have been drunk up by the interest for my guest which this tale and his own elevated and gentle manners have created. **I wish to soothe him, yet can I counsel one so infinitely miserable, so destitute of every hope of consolation, to live? Oh, no! The only joy that he can now know will be when he composes his shattered spirit to peace and death.** Yet he enjoys one comfort, the offspring of solitude and delirium; he believes that when in dreams he holds converse with his friends and derives from that communion consolation for his miseries or excitements to his vengeance, that they are not the creations of his fancy, but the beings themselves who visit him from the regions of a remote world. This faith gives a solemnity to his reveries that render them to me almost as imposing and interesting as truth.

Our conversations are not always confined to his own history and misfortunes. On every point of general literature he displays unbounded knowledge and a quick and piercing apprehension. His eloquence is forcible and touching; nor can I hear him, when he relates a pathetic incident or endeavours to move the passions of pity or love, without tears. What a glorious creature must he have been in the days of his prosperity, when he is thus noble and godlike in ruin! He seems to feel his own worth and the greatness of his fall.

"When younger," said he, "I believed myself destined for some great enterprise. **My feelings are profound, but I possessed a coolness of judgment that fitted me for illustrious achievements.** This sentiment of the worth of my nature supported me when others would have been oppressed, for I deemed it criminal to throw away in useless grief those talents that might be useful to my fellow creatures. When I reflected on the work I had completed, no less a one than the creation of a sensitive and rational animal, I could not rank myself with the herd of common projectors. But this thought, which supported me in the commencement of my career, now serves only to plunge me lower in the dust. **All my speculations and hopes are as nothing, and like the archangel who aspired to omnipotence, I am chained in an eternal hell.** My imagination was vivid, yet my powers of analysis and application were intense; by the union of these qualities I conceived the idea and executed the creation of a man. Even now I cannot recollect without passion my reveries while the work was incomplete. I trod heaven in my thoughts, now exulting in my powers, now burning with the idea of their effects. From my infancy I was imbued with high hopes and a lofty ambition; but how am I sunk! Oh! My friend, if you had known me as I once was, you would not recognize me in this state of degradation. Despondency rarely visited my heart; a high destiny seemed to bear me on, until I fell, never, never again to rise." Must I then lose this admirable being? **I have longed for a friend; I have sought one who would sympathize with and love me. Behold, on these desert seas I have found such a one, but I fear I have gained him only to know his value and lose him. I would reconcile him to life, but he repulses the idea.**

"I thank you, Walton," he said, "for your kind intentions towards so miserable a wretch; but when you speak of new ties and fresh affections, think you that any can replace those who are gone? Can any man be to me as Clerval was, or any woman another Elizabeth? Even where the affections are not strongly moved by any superior excellence, **the companions of our childhood always possess a certain power over our minds which hardly any later friend can obtain.** They know our infantine dispositions, which, however they may be afterwards modified, are never eradicated; and they can judge of our actions with more certain conclusions as to the integrity of our motives. A sister or a brother can never, unless indeed such symptoms have been shown early, suspect the other of fraud or false dealing, when another friend, however strongly he may be attached, may, in spite of himself, be contemplated with suspicion. But I enjoyed friends, dear not only through habit and association, but from their own merits; and wherever I am, the soothing voice of my Elizabeth and the conversation of Clerval will be ever whispered in my ear. They are dead, and but one feeling in such a solitude can persuade me to preserve my life. If I were engaged in any high undertaking or design, fraught with extensive utility to my fellow creatures, then could I live to fulfil it. But such is not my destiny; I must pursue and destroy the being to whom I gave existence; then my lot on earth will be fulfilled and I may die."

• ANALYZING THE SCENE •
CHAPTER 24 – SCENE 50

A Story Event is an active change of universal human value for one or more characters as a result of conflict (one character's desires clash with another's or an environmental shift changes the universal human value).

A Working Scene contains at least one Story Event. To determine a scene's Story Event, answer these four questions:

1. What are the characters literally doing—that is, what are their micro on-the-ground actions?

We are back to Walton's letters. He tells Margaret that he believes Frankenstein's tale and has seen letters proving its veracity. Frankenstein himself has examined Walton's notes and made corrections.

2. What is the essential tactic of the characters—that is, what macro behaviors are they employing that are linked to a universal human value?

Walton tries to persuade Frankenstein to live.

3. What universal human values have changed for one or more characters in the scene? Which one of those value changes is most important and should be included in the Story Grid Spreadsheet?

Walton is not entirely convinced of the story by Frankenstein's word alone, but when he sees the letters from Safie and Felix, he accepts the story. He is saddened that he has found a friend and now must lose him again. His state changes from Shocked (at the tale he has heard) to Admiring (that Frankenstein is so impressive). Frankenstein's state does not change at all in this scene, as he is the source of the tale and the reason for Walton's sadness.

Shocked to Admiring

4. What is the Story Event that sums up the scene's on-the-ground actions, essential tactics, and value change? We will enter that event in the Story Grid Spreadsheet.

Frankenstein is done with his tale. Walton wants to persuade him to live, but Frankenstein says there is no reason to live.

HOW THE SCENE ABIDES BY THE FIVE COMMANDMENTS OF STORYTELLING

Inciting Incident: Frankenstein completes the telling of his story and provides proof of its veracity.

Turning Point Progressive Complication: Frankenstein is determined to die after killing the creature; Walton is unable to persuade Frankenstein to live.

Crisis: Can Walton persuade him to live?

Climax: Frankenstein refuses.

Resolution: He says no one can replace his childhood companions, and his one utility on earth is to destroy the monster.

NOTES

- It is fascinating that for only the second time in the book, Frankenstein makes a statement on refusing to say exactly how he created life in the monster. He refuses to tell Walton exactly how he did it because he does not want anyone to discover how to do it and perhaps create another monster. The famous movie version of Frankenstein attributes the life-giving force to electricity, but this is not stated anywhere in the book. The lightning motif is present, but not in a life-giving sense.
- Frankenstein continues to cling to the somewhat ghoulish notion that he actively converses with his dead friends.
- Frankenstein makes a moving speech in this scene: "All my speculations and hopes are as nothing, and like the archangel who aspired to omnipotence I am chained in an eternal hell." This is a reference to *Paradise Lost*. But what is particularly notable here is that he feels he is not useful to the human race, and therefore there is no point in continuing to live. The calm intellect that served him so well as a scientist seems to be no more.

CHAPTER 24 – SCENE 51

September 2nd
My beloved Sister,

I write to you, encompassed by peril and ignorant whether I am ever doomed to see again dear England and the dearer friends that inhabit it. I am surrounded by mountains of ice which admit of no escape and threaten every moment to crush my vessel. The brave fellows whom I have persuaded to be my companions look towards me for aid, but I have none to bestow. There is something terribly appalling in our situation, yet my courage and hopes do not desert me. Yet **it is terrible to reflect that the lives of all these men are endangered through me. If we are lost, my mad schemes are the cause.** *[Walton is responsible and conscientious.]*

And what, Margaret, will be the state of your mind? You will not hear of my destruction, and you will anxiously await my return. Years will pass, and you will have visitings of despair and yet be tortured by hope. Oh! My beloved sister, **the sickening failing of your heart-felt expectations is, in prospect, more terrible to me than my own death.**

But you have a husband and lovely children; you may be happy. Heaven bless you and make you so!

My unfortunate guest regards me with the tenderest compassion. He endeavours to fill me with hope and talks as if life were a possession which he valued. He reminds me how often the same accidents have happened to other navigators who have attempted this sea, and in spite of myself, he fills me with cheerful auguries. **Even the sailors feel the power of his eloquence; when he speaks, they no longer despair**; he rouses their energies, and while they hear his voice they believe these vast mountains of ice are mole-hills which will vanish before the resolutions of man. These feelings are transitory; each day of expectation delayed fills them with fear, and I almost dread a mutiny caused by this despair.

• ANALYZING THE SCENE •
CHAPTER 24 – SCENE 51

A Story Event is an active change of universal human value for one or more characters as a result of conflict (one character's desires clash with another's or an environmental shift changes the universal human value).

A Working Scene contains at least one Story Event. To determine a scene's Story Event, answer these four questions:

1. What are the characters literally doing—that is, what are their micro on-the-ground actions?

They are stuck, surrounded by "mountains of ice."

2. What is the essential tactic of the characters—that is, what macro behaviors are they employing that are linked to a universal human value?

Frankenstein, ironically, who holds his own life cheap, is keeping everyone's spirits raised.

3. What universal human values have changed for one or more

characters in the scene? Which one of those value changes is most important and should be included in the Story Grid Spreadsheet?

Everyone is terrified in this scene except for Frankenstein! He has taken it upon himself to be positive and to remind Walton and his men that they will be all right.

Despite Frankenstein's efforts to be positive, Walton is scared. His value goes from Anxious to Terrified.

Anxious to Terrified

4. What is the Story Event that sums up the scene's on-the-ground actions, essential tactics, and value change? We will enter that event in the Story Grid Spreadsheet.

Walton's ship is now stuck in sea ice, and his men are afraid; ironically, it is Frankenstein who is keeping everyone's spirits up by making cheerful speeches.

HOW THE SCENE ABIDES BY THE FIVE COMMANDMENTS OF STORYTELLING

Inciting Incident: Walton's ship is surrounded by ice that threatens to crush them.

Turning Point Progressive Complication: Walton is the one who has brought those sailors out to the Arctic, so if they die, it's his fault. Frankenstein keeps everyone's spirits up, making speeches reminding everyone that many sailors have gotten through ice.

Crisis: Will there be a mutiny? What should Walton do? Best bad choice.

Climax: Walton waits out the situation because there are no good options.

Resolution: Walton is not sure what will happen, but Frankenstein is keeping the situation stable.

NOTES

- Once again, we are dealing with the notion that one can be morally responsible without being directly responsible. Walton readily accepts that as the leader of the expedition, the men depend on him to make decisions. He is not obsessive the way Frankenstein is obsessive.

CHAPTER 24 – SCENE 52

September 5th

A scene has just passed of such uncommon interest that, although it is highly probable that these papers may never reach you, yet I cannot forbear recording it.

We are still surrounded by mountains of ice, still in imminent danger of being crushed in their conflict. The cold is excessive, and many of my unfortunate comrades have already found a grave amidst this scene of desolation. Frankenstein has daily declined in health; a feverish fire still glimmers in his eyes, but he is exhausted, and when suddenly roused to any exertion, he speedily sinks again into apparent lifelessness.

I mentioned in my last letter the fears I entertained of a mutiny. This morning, as I sat watching the wan countenance of my friend—his eyes half closed and his limbs hanging listlessly—I was roused by half a dozen of the sailors, who demanded admission into the cabin. They entered, and their leader addressed me. He told me that he and his companions had been chosen by the other sailors to come in deputation to me to make me a requisition which, in justice, I could not refuse. We were immured in ice and should probably never escape, but they feared that if, as was possible, the ice should dissipate and a free passage be opened, I should be rash enough to continue my voyage and lead them into fresh dangers, after they might happily have surmounted this. They insisted, therefore, that I should engage with a solemn promise that if the vessel should be freed I would instantly direct my course southwards.

This speech troubled me. I had not despaired, nor had I yet conceived the idea of returning if set free. Yet could I, in justice, or even in possibility, refuse this demand? *[Here is a parallel; the monster makes a just demand on Frankenstein, and the ship's crew makes a just demand on Walton.]* I hesitated before I answered, when **Frankenstein, who had at first been silent, and indeed appeared hardly to have force enough to attend, now roused himself; his eyes sparkled, and his cheeks flushed with momentary vigour. Turning towards the men, he said, "What do you mean? What do you demand of your captain? Are you, then, so easily turned from your design? Did you not call this a glorious expedition?**

"**And wherefore was it glorious? Not because the way was smooth and placid as a southern sea, but because it was full of dangers and terror, because at every new incident your fortitude was to be called forth and your courage exhibited, because danger and death surrounded it, and these you were to brave and overcome.** For this was it a glorious, for this was it an honourable undertaking. You were hereafter to be hailed as the benefactors of your species, your names adored as belonging to brave men who encountered death for honour and the benefit of mankind. And now, behold, with the first imagination of danger, or, if you will, the first mighty and terrific trial of your courage, you shrink away and are content to be handed down as men who had not strength enough to endure cold and peril; and so, poor souls, they were chilly and returned to their warm firesides. Why, that requires not this preparation; ye need not have come thus far and dragged your captain to the shame of a defeat merely to prove yourselves cowards. Oh! **Be men, or be more than men. Be steady to your purposes and firm as a rock.** This ice is not made of such stuff as your hearts may be; it is mutable and cannot withstand you if you say that it shall not. Do not return to your families with the stigma of disgrace marked on your brows. Return as heroes who have fought and conquered and who know not what it is to turn their backs on the foe." *[He is obsessed!]* He spoke this with a voice so modulated to the different feelings expressed in his speech, with an eye so full of lofty design and heroism, that can you wonder that these men were moved? They looked at one another and were unable to reply. I spoke; I told them to retire and consider of what had been said, that I would not lead them farther north if they strenuously desired the contrary, but that I hoped that, with reflection, their courage would return. They retired and I turned towards my friend, but he was sunk in languor and almost deprived of life. *[Walton is a very reasonable man.]*

How all this will terminate, I know not, but I had rather die than return shamefully, my purpose unfulfilled. Yet I fear such will be my fate; the men, unsupported by ideas of glory and honour, can never willingly continue to endure their present hardships. *[Walton understands what makes a person persist under impossible circumstances—the pursuit of glory.]*

• ANALYZING THE SCENE •
CHAPTER 24 – SCENE 52

A Story Event is an active change of universal human value for one or more characters as a result of conflict (one character's desires clash with another's or an environmental shift changes the universal human value).

A Working Scene contains at least one Story Event. To determine a scene's Story Event, answer these four questions:

1. What are the characters literally doing—that is, what are their micro on-the-ground actions?

The sailors tell Walton that if the ship gets clear of the ice, they insist on going back rather than continuing their voyage. Frankenstein scolds them and urges them to behave like heroes, not cowards, and to continue into the unknown.

2. What is the essential tactic of the characters—that is, what macro behaviors are they employing that are linked to a universal human value?

Frankenstein here is explaining his value system. He commends courage, creativity, and ambition, and decries cowardice. Walton quietly agrees, thinking he would "rather die than return shamefully," but also concedes that the men have a point.

3. What universal human values have changed for one or more characters in the scene? Which one of those value changes is most important and should be included in the Story Grid Spreadsheet?

Frankenstein's state remains the same; he believes what he believes. The men, who had entered intending to insist on their message, were moved, and became uncertain. And last, Walton also had not considered giving up his ambitions at first but became hesitant after hearing out his men. In this scene, we track the values of the men and Walton.

Certain to Uncertain

4. What is the Story Event that sums up the scene's on-the-ground actions, essential tactics, and value change? We will enter that event in the Story Grid Spreadsheet.

The ship is still surrounded by ice and the sailors are threatening a mutiny. They want Walton's guarantee that he will take them home if they get free of the ice. Frankenstein makes a speech, telling the men they should not act like cowards.

HOW THE SCENE ABIDES BY THE FIVE COMMANDMENTS OF STORYTELLING

Inciting Incident: The ship is still surrounded by mountains of ice. The sailors are threatening mutiny; they want Walton's guarantee that if the ice parts, he will take them home rather than to continue northward.

Turning Point Progressive Complication: Frankenstein makes a speech in which he tells the men to put aside their cowardice.

Crisis: How should Walton respond? Should he agree to return home or not? Best bad choice.

Climax: Walton tells the men to reflect on their course of action.

Resolution: The next entry, where Walton decides to return.

NOTES

- Walton fears a mutiny from his men. Surprisingly, Frankenstein suddenly rises in defense of Walton. He reminds them that the point of the expedition was that it was dangerous, and that if it had been easy, they wouldn't have wanted to do it.
- There is a parallel between Frankenstein's determination to never give up as he chases after the monster and his admonishment that the sailors should also never give up as they pursue their northern course.
- Walton, too, says he would "rather die than return shamefully." Yet he is responsible for these men, and if the journey is unsuccessful, they will die because of him. He is acutely aware of his responsibility. Frankenstein is also aware of his responsibility in the deaths of William, Justine, and Elizabeth, even though he did not actually kill them. This parallel is something Shelley may have considered a great deal. The monster wants Frankenstein to be responsible for what he did. He views this responsibility very differently from Frankenstein, however.

CHAPTER 24 – SCENE 53

September 7th

The die is cast; I have consented to return if we are not destroyed. Thus are my hopes blasted by cowardice and indecision; I come back ignorant and disappointed. It requires more philosophy than I possess to bear this injustice with patience.

• ANALYZING THE SCENE •
CHAPTER 24 – SCENE 53

A Story Event is an active change of universal human value for one or more characters as a result of conflict (one character's desires clash with another's or an environmental shift changes the universal human value).

A Working Scene contains at least one Story Event. To determine a scene's Story Event, answer these four questions:

1. What are the characters literally doing—that is, what are their micro on-the-ground actions?

Walton is finishing the thought process that began in the previous scene.

2. What is the essential tactic of the characters—that is, what macro behaviors are they employing that are linked to a universal human value?

Walton concludes that he must do as the sailors wish and head for home if they manage to survive the current crisis of being locked in the ice. He is reluctant and self-critical, labeling himself a coward, but he will do as his sailors wish.

3. What universal human values have changed for one or more characters in the scene? Which one of those value changes is most important and should be included in the Story Grid Spreadsheet?

Walton has made the decision that he was brooding over in the previous scene, even though Frankenstein made a case for continuing onward and Walton himself wishes to continue. Track "uncertain to reluctantly decided."

Uncertain to Reluctantly Decided

4. What is the Story Event that sums up the scene's on-the-ground actions, essential tactics, and value change? We will enter that event in the Story Grid Spreadsheet.

Walton decides he must follow the wishes of his men and return home if they manage to survive the ice. He is reluctant and dispirited, but he will do as they wish.

HOW THE SCENE ABIDES BY THE FIVE COMMANDMENTS OF STORYTELLING

This scene is the resolution to the previous scene and concludes the track that starts with the sailors demanding that they return home.

- Strictly speaking, this is not a "scene" in that it does not abide by the Five Commandments. In fact, it is more like an actor's beat—a moment that would require an actor to express a particular emotion before moving into the next. Beats are the components that make up scenes.
- Why, then, does this very short resolution to the previous scene get tracked independently on the spreadsheet? After all, it's part of the previous scene. This is a good question. The previous scene is a cliffhanger, where Mary Shelley hasn't told you what Walton's decision will be. Frankenstein makes a case for continuing the journey into the wild north, but Walton knows what Frankenstein's obsession has wrought. Will he bring that fate down on his men? The clear moral choice is to listen to his men and avoid further death and destruction. But at the end of Scene 52, we don't know what Walton will decide, because we know he idolizes Frankenstein.
- The answer to this question is in Scene 53, but Mary Shelley has given both Walton and the reader space as a way of paying respect to the mental and emotional journey that Walton must make privately in order to reach his decision. It is a wonderful literary choice, but the analytical tools that we are using to look at the structure of the story don't accommodate the silence that Shelley has introduced into the text. The reader is invited to make Walton's personal mental journey along with him. We know he didn't immediately jump from the indecision of Scene 52 into the reluctant certainty of Scene 53. If Shelley had put scene 53 right into scene 52, we would have lost the timespan during which Walton was thinking hard about what to do (as well as the corresponding journey in his emotional state). You would lose a lot of depth. For that reason, it's probably more faithful to the story to allow Scene 53 to stand alone on the spreadsheet and to give it

the emotional change on the graph that the text gives us with its silence.

- It's worth noting that this is an elegant way to handle a cliffhanger where the resolution to the scene's crisis moment is in the next chapter.

CHAPTER 24 – SCENE 54

September 12th

It is past; I am returning to England. I have lost my hopes of utility and glory; I have lost my friend. But I will endeavour to detail these bitter circumstances to you, my dear sister; and while I am wafted towards England and towards you, I will not despond.

September 9th, the ice began to move, and roarings like thunder were heard at a distance as the islands split and cracked in every direction. We were in the most imminent peril, but as we could only remain passive, my chief attention was occupied by my unfortunate guest whose illness increased in such a degree that he was entirely confined to his bed. The ice cracked behind us and was driven with force towards the north; a breeze sprang from the west, and on the 11th the passage towards the south became perfectly free. When the sailors saw this and that their return to their native country was apparently assured, a shout of tumultuous joy broke from them, loud and long-continued. Frankenstein, who was dozing, awoke and asked the cause of the tumult. "They shout," I said, "because they will soon return to England."

"Do you, then, really return?"

"Alas! Yes; I cannot withstand their demands. I cannot lead them unwillingly to danger, and I must return."

"Do so, if you will; but I will not. You may give up your purpose, but mine is assigned to me by heaven, and I dare not. I am weak, but surely the spirits who assist my vengeance will endow me with sufficient strength." Saying this, he endeavoured to spring from the bed, but the exertion was too great for him; he fell back and fainted.

It was long before he was restored, and I often thought that life was entirely extinct. At length he opened his eyes; he breathed with difficulty and was unable to speak. The surgeon gave him a composing draught and ordered us to leave him undisturbed. In the meantime he told me that my friend had certainly not many hours to live.

His sentence was pronounced, and I could only grieve and be patient. I sat by his bed, watching him; his eyes were closed, and I thought he slept; but presently he called to me in a feeble voice, and bidding me come near, said, "Alas! The strength I relied on is gone; I feel that I shall soon die, and he, my enemy and persecutor, may still be in being. Think not, Walton, that in the last moments of my existence I feel that burning hatred and ardent desire of revenge I once expressed; but I feel myself justified in desiring the death of my adversary. **During these last days I have been occupied in examining my past conduct; nor do I find it blamable. In a fit of enthusiastic madness I created a rational creature and was bound towards him to assure, as far as was in my power, his happiness and well-being.**

"This was my duty, but there was another still paramount to that. **My duties towards the beings of my own species had greater claims to my attention because they included a greater proportion of happiness or misery. Urged by this view, I refused, and I did right in refusing, to create a companion for the first creature.** He showed unparalleled malignity and selfishness in evil; he destroyed my friends; he devoted to destruction beings who possessed exquisite sensations, happiness, and wisdom; nor do I know where this thirst for vengeance may end. **Miserable himself that he may render no other wretched, he ought to die.** The task of his destruction was mine, but I have failed. When actuated by selfish and vicious motives, I asked you to undertake my unfinished work, and I renew this request now, when I am only induced by reason and virtue.

"Yet I cannot ask you to renounce your country and friends to fulfil this task; and now that you are returning to England, you will have little chance of meeting with him. But the consideration of these points, and the well balancing of what you may esteem your duties, I leave to you; my judgment and ideas are already disturbed by the near approach of death. I dare not ask you to do what I think right, for I may still be misled by passion.

"That he should live to be an instrument of mischief disturbs me; in other respects, this hour, when I momentarily expect my release, is the only happy one which I have enjoyed for several years. The forms of the beloved dead flit before me, and I hasten to their arms. Farewell, Walton! Seek happiness in tranquillity and avoid ambition, even if it be only the apparently innocent one of distinguishing yourself in science and discoveries. Yet why do I say this? I have myself been blasted in these hopes, yet another may succeed."

His voice became fainter as he spoke, and at length, exhausted by his effort, he sank into silence. About half an hour afterwards he attempted again to speak but was unable; he pressed my hand feebly, and his eyes closed forever, while the irradiation of a gentle smile passed away from his lips.

Margaret, what comment can I make on the untimely extinction of this glorious spirit? What can I say that will enable you to understand the depth of my sorrow? All that I should express would be inadequate and feeble. My tears flow; my mind is overshadowed by a cloud of disappointment. But I journey towards England, and I may there find consolation.

• ANALYZING THE SCENE •
CHAPTER 24 – SCENE 54

A Story Event is an active change of universal human value for one or more characters as a result of conflict (one character's desires clash with

another's or an environmental shift changes the universal human value).

A Working Scene contains at least one Story Event. To determine a scene's Story Event, answer these four questions:

1. What are the characters literally doing—that is, what are their micro on-the-ground actions?

Walton tells Frankenstein that he will return to England after all; Frankenstein repeats his request to Walton that he continue to hunt down the creature.

2. What is the essential tactic of the characters—that is, what macro behaviors are they employing that are linked to a universal human value?

Frankenstein is declaiming on the nature of responsibility. To whom is he ultimately responsible—the creature he has created or his fellow human beings? Walton here is not only acting responsibly (taking into account the earnest desires of his crew) but is repressing his own sense of what he wants in order to do something for the group.

3. What universal human values have changed for one or more characters in the scene? Which one of those value changes is most important and should be included in the Story Grid Spreadsheet?

At the end of this scene, Frankenstein dies.
Life to Death

4. What is the Story Event that sums up the scene's on-the-ground actions, essential tactics, and value change? We will enter that event in the Story Grid Spreadsheet.

The ship frees itself from the ice and Walton is going to take them home; Frankenstein objects because he is still searching for the creature, but he dies.

HOW THE SCENE ABIDES BY THE FIVE COMMANDMENTS OF STORYTELLING

Inciting Incident: The ship is freed from the ice.

Turning Point Progressive Complication: Walton tells Frankenstein of his intention to abandon the trip and return home.

Crisis: Should Frankenstein acquiesce or refuse to go along? Best bad choice.

Climax: Frankenstein tries to get out of bed because "surely the spirits who assist my vengeance will endow me with sufficient strength."

Resolution: Frankenstein finally gives up. He dies.

NOTES

- It certainly sounds as if Frankenstein's impassioned speech is about responsibility. He acknowledges his responsibility toward the creature, calling it his "duty" to be concerned about his happiness and well-being. However, he viewed his responsibility to his fellow man as being of paramount importance and continued to feel that it trumped the creature's claims on him. In a sense, it's an acceptance of reality. It's too late for him to do anything about the original creation of the monster now.
- Frankenstein still wants Walton to take on his project, but also says he cannot ask him to renounce his country and friends in order to do it.

CHAPTER 24 – SCENE 55

[September 12th continued]

I am interrupted. What do these sounds portend? It is midnight; the breeze blows fairly, and the watch on deck scarcely stir. Again there is a sound as of a human voice, but hoarser; it comes from the cabin where the remains of Frankenstein still lie. I must arise and examine. Good night, my sister.

Great God! what a scene has just taken place! I am yet dizzy with the remembrance of it. I hardly know whether I shall have the power to detail it; yet the tale which I have recorded would be incomplete without this final and wonderful catastrophe. I entered the cabin where lay the remains of my ill-fated and admirable friend. Over him hung a form which I cannot find words to describe—gigantic in stature, yet uncouth and distorted in its proportions. As he hung over the coffin, his face was concealed by long locks of ragged hair; but one vast hand was extended, in colour and apparent texture like that of a mummy. When he heard the sound of my approach, he ceased to utter exclamations of grief and horror and sprung towards the window. Never did I behold a vision so horrible as his face, of such loathsome yet appalling hideousness. I shut my eyes involuntarily and endeavoured to recollect what were my duties with regard to this destroyer. I called on him to stay.

He paused, looking on me with wonder, and again turning towards the lifeless form of his creator, he seemed to forget my presence, and every feature and gesture seemed instigated by the wildest rage of some uncontrollable passion.

"That is also my victim!" he exclaimed. "In his murder my crimes are consummated; the miserable series of my being is wound to its close! Oh, Frankenstein! Generous and self-devoted being! What does it avail that I now ask thee to pardon me? I, who irretrievably destroyed thee by destroying all thou lovedst. Alas! He is cold, he cannot answer me." His voice seemed suffocated, and my first impulses, which had suggested to me the duty of obeying the dying request of my friend in destroying his enemy, were now suspended by a mixture of curiosity and compassion. I approached this tremendous being; I dared not again raise my eyes to his face, there was something so scaring and unearthly in his ugliness. I attempted to speak, but the words died away on my lips. The monster continued to utter wild and incoherent self-reproaches. At length I gathered resolution to address him in a pause of the tempest of his passion.

"Your repentance," I said, "is now superfluous. If you had listened to the voice of conscience and heeded the stings of remorse before you had urged your diabolical vengeance to this extremity, Frankenstein would yet have lived."

"And do you dream?" said the daemon. "Do you think that I was then dead to agony and remorse? He," he continued, pointing to the corpse, "he suffered not in the consummation of the deed. Oh! Not the ten-thousandth portion of the anguish that was mine during the lingering detail of its execution. A frightful selfishness hurried me on, while my heart was poisoned with remorse. Think you that the groans of Clerval were music to my ears? My heart was fashioned to be susceptible of love and sympathy, and when wrenched by misery to vice and hatred, it did not endure the violence of the change without torture such as you cannot even imagine.

"After the murder of Clerval I returned to Switzerland, heart-broken and overcome. I pitied Frankenstein; my pity amounted to

horror; I abhorred myself. But when I discovered that he, the author at once of my existence and of its unspeakable torments, dared to hope for happiness, that while he accumulated wretchedness and despair upon me he sought his own enjoyment in feelings and passions from the indulgence of which I was forever barred, then impotent envy and bitter indignation filled me with an insatiable thirst for vengeance. I recollected my threat and resolved that it should be accomplished. I knew that I was preparing for myself a deadly torture, but I was the slave, not the master, of an impulse which I detested yet could not disobey. Yet when she died! Nay, then I was not miserable. I had cast off all feeling, subdued all anguish, to riot in the excess of my despair. Evil thenceforth became my good. Urged thus far, I had no choice but to adapt my nature to an element which I had willingly chosen. The completion of my demoniacal design became an insatiable passion. And now it is ended; there is my last victim!"

I was at first touched by the expressions of his misery; yet, when I called to mind what Frankenstein had said of his powers of eloquence and persuasion, and when I again cast my eyes on the lifeless form of my friend, indignation was rekindled within me. "Wretch!" I said. "It is well that you come here to whine over the desolation that you have made. You throw a torch into a pile of buildings, and when they are consumed, you sit among the ruins and lament the fall. Hypocritical fiend! If he whom you mourn still lived, still would he be the object, again would he become the prey, of your accursed vengeance. **It is not pity that you feel; you lament only because the victim of your malignity is withdrawn from your power.**"

"Oh, it is not thus—not thus," interrupted the being. "Yet such must be the impression conveyed to you by what appears to be the purport of my actions. Yet I seek not a fellow feeling in my misery. No sympathy may I ever find. When I first sought it, it was the love of virtue, the feelings of happiness and affection with which my whole being overflowed, that I wished to be participated. But now that virtue has become to me a shadow, and that happiness and affection are turned into bitter and loathing despair, in what should I seek for sympathy? I am content to suffer alone while my sufferings shall endure; when I die, I am well satisfied that abhorrence and opprobrium should load my memory. Once my fancy was soothed with dreams of virtue, of fame, and of enjoyment. Once I falsely hoped to meet with beings who, pardoning my outward form, would love me for the excellent qualities which I was capable of unfolding. I was nourished with high thoughts of honour and devotion. But now crime has degraded me beneath the meanest animal. No guilt, no mischief, no malignity, no misery, can be found comparable to mine. When I run over the frightful catalogue of my sins, I cannot believe that I am the same creature whose thoughts were once filled with sublime and transcendent visions of the beauty and the majesty of goodness. But it is even so; the fallen angel becomes a malignant devil. Yet even that enemy of God and man had friends and associates in his desolation; I am alone.

"You, who call Frankenstein your friend, seem to have a knowledge of my crimes and his misfortunes. But in the detail which he gave you of them he could not sum up the hours and months of misery which I endured wasting in impotent passions. For while I destroyed his hopes, I did not satisfy my own desires. They were forever ardent and craving; **still I desired love and fellowship, and I was still spurned. Was there no injustice in this? Am I to be thought the only criminal, when all humankind sinned against me**? Why do you not hate Felix, who drove his friend from his door with contumely? Why do you not execrate the rustic who sought to destroy the saviour of his child? Nay, these are virtuous and immaculate beings! I, the miserable and the abandoned, am an abortion, to be spurned at, and kicked, and trampled on. Even now my blood boils at the recollection of this injustice.

"But it is true that I am a wretch. I have murdered the lovely and the helpless; I have strangled the innocent as they slept and grasped to death his throat who never injured me or any other living thing. I have devoted my creator, the select specimen of all that is worthy of love and admiration among men, to misery; I have pursued him even to that irremediable ruin.

"There he lies, white and cold in death. You hate me, but your abhorrence cannot equal that with which I regard myself. I look on the hands which executed the deed; I think on the heart in which the imagination of it was conceived and long for the moment when these hands will meet my eyes, when that imagination will haunt my thoughts no more.

"Fear not that I shall be the instrument of future mischief. My work is nearly complete. **Neither yours nor any man's death is needed to consummate the series of my being and accomplish that which must be done, but it requires my own.** Do not think that I shall be slow to perform this sacrifice. **I shall quit your vessel on the ice raft which brought me thither and shall seek the most northern extremity of the globe; I shall collect my funeral pile and consume to ashes this miserable frame, that its remains may afford no light to any curious and unhallowed wretch who would create such another as I have been. I shall die. I shall no longer feel the agonies which now consume me or be the prey of feelings unsatisfied, yet unquenched.** He is dead who called me into being; and when I shall be no more, the very remembrance of us both will speedily vanish. I shall no longer see the sun or stars or feel the winds play on my cheeks.

"Light, feeling, and sense will pass away; and in this condition must I find my happiness. Some years ago, when the images which this world affords first opened upon me, when I felt the cheering warmth of summer and heard the rustling of the leaves and the warbling of the birds, and these were all to me, I should have wept to die; now it is my only consolation. Polluted by crimes and torn by the bitterest remorse, where can I find rest but in death?

"Farewell! I leave you, and in you the last of humankind whom these eyes will ever behold. Farewell, Frankenstein! If thou wert yet alive and yet cherished a desire of revenge against me, it would be better satiated in my life than in my destruction. But it was not so; thou didst seek my extinction, that I might not cause greater wretchedness; and if yet, in some mode unknown to me, thou hadst not ceased to think and feel, thou wouldst not desire against me a vengeance greater than that which I feel. Blasted as thou wert, my agony was still superior to thine, for the bitter sting of remorse will not cease to rankle in my wounds until death shall close them forever.

"But soon," he cried with sad and solemn enthusiasm, "I shall die, and what I now feel be no longer felt. Soon these burning miseries will be extinct. I shall ascend my funeral pile triumphantly and exult in the agony of the torturing flames. The light of that conflagration will fade away; my ashes will be swept into the sea by the winds. My spirit will sleep in peace, or if it thinks, it will not surely think thus.

Farewell."

He sprang from the cabin window as he said this, upon the ice raft which lay close to the vessel. He was soon borne away by the waves and lost in darkness and distance.

• ANALYZING THE SCENE •
CHAPTER 24 – SCENE 55

A Story Event is an active change of universal human value for one or more characters as a result of conflict (one character's desires clash with another's or an environmental shift changes the universal human value).

A Working Scene contains at least one Story Event. To determine a scene's Story Event, answer these four questions:

1. What are the characters literally doing—that is, what are their micro on-the-ground actions?

The creature has appeared and is mourning Frankenstein's death.

2. What is the essential tactic of the characters—that is, what macro behaviors are they employing that are linked to a universal human value?

The creature is also making a speech about responsibility; he acknowledges that he is effectively Frankenstein's murderer but explains his actions and why he did these things.

3. What universal human values have changed for one or more characters in the scene? Which one of those value changes is most important and should be included in the Story Grid Spreadsheet?

The monster is filled with remorse and wants to die; he wants to "consummate the series of my being" by dying. The monster's universal human value changes from Life to Death.

Life to Death

4. What is the Story Event that sums up the scene's on-the-ground actions, essential tactics, and value change? We will enter that event in the Story Grid Spreadsheet.

Walton sees the monster in the cabin where Frankenstein lies, grieving his death; the monster says he is responsible for his death, and he will now kill himself.

HOW THE SCENE ABIDES BY THE FIVE COMMANDMENTS OF STORYTELLING

Inciting Incident: Walton enters the cabin where Frankenstein lies and sees the creature grieving his death.

Turning Point Progressive Complication: The monster declares that his work is done; he will not harm anyone else.

Crisis: What will happen now? Will the creature attempt to go on living or not? Best bad choice.

Climax: The monster determines that his death is required to complete the "series of my being." He announces that he will die.

Resolution: The monster bids the dead Frankenstein good-bye and leaves.

NOTES

- The trajectory of the relationship between Frankenstein and the creature has gone from Parent-Child or perhaps Mentor-Student, to something quite different as the creature becomes the one to keep Frankenstein alive. He supplies directions, food, and hints as to his travels. Frankenstein seems to know that the monster is supplying this assistance, but he sometimes speaks about the spirits of his family and Clerval talking to him, so he might also be thinking that they are helping him.

- Frankenstein fails the creature in every capacity, in all of the ways the creature has learned through his short life—from the God/Adam relationship in *Paradise Lost* to the Father-Child relationships of the cottagers. He would not provide a female creature so the creature could have a Husband-Wife relationship or even a Friend, and when the creature tried to be a Savior (by rescuing the drowning girl) and a Brother (when he kidnapped William, thinking that he could raise a child), he was excluded and ostracized. Now, the creature has driven Frankenstein to the point of needing to rely on him to stay alive.
- So at the death of Frankenstein, the creature realizes his life is over. He has no one who hates him, let alone loves him—no relationships at all.

ABOUT THE AUTHOR

MAYA RUSHING WALKER writes slow-burn, often romantic literary fiction set in both historical and modern times, with a strong sense of place. She lives and writes in a 1780s farmhouse in northern New England, where she homeschooled four amazing young adults and was a dedicated swim and row mom. In a previous life, she was a US diplomat and a Wall Street banker, and holds a BS in international economics from Georgetown and an AM in East Asian Studies from Harvard. Her debut novel, *The Portrait*, was short-listed for the 2020 Eric Hoffer Book Award and won Honorable Mention in the Historical Fiction category. Her second novel, *Coming Home to Greenleigh*, was released in January 2020. Maya is a Story Grid Certified Editor and uses Story Grid to transform all of her work. You can find her online at mayarushingwalker.net.

ABOUT THE EDITORS

SHAWN COYNE created, developed, and expanded the story analysis and problem-solving methodology the Story Grid during his quarter-century-plus career in book publishing. A seasoned story editor, book publisher, and ghostwriter, Coyne has also co-authored *The Ones Who Hit the Hardest: The Steelers, the Cowboys, the '70s, and the Fight For America's Soul* with Chad Millman and *Cognitive Dominance: A Brain Surgeon's Quest to Out-Think Fear* with Mark McLaughlin, M.D. With his friend and editorial client Steven Pressfield, Coyne runs Black Irish Entertainment, LLC, publisher of the cult classic book *The War of Art.* Coyne oversees the Story Grid Universe, LLC, which includes Story Grid University and Story Grid Publishing, with his friend and editorial client Tim Grahl.

LESLIE WATTS is a Story Grid Certified Editor, writer, and podcaster based in Austin, Texas. She's been writing for as long as she can remember—from her sixth-grade magazine about cats to writing practice while drafting opinions for an appellate court judge. Leslie has co-authored *The Tipping Point by Malcolm Gladwell: A Story Grid Masterworks Analysis Guide* and *What's the Big Idea? Nonfiction Condensed*, both with Shelley Sperry, and *Conventions and Obligatory Moments: The Must-Haves to Meet Audience Expectations* with Kimberly Kessler. As an editor, Leslie helps fiction and nonfiction clients write epic stories that matter. She believes writers become better storytellers through study and practice and editors owe a duty of care to help writers with specific and supportive guidance. You can find her online at Writership.com.

NOTES

THE CONTROLLING IDEA

1. The story of Mary Shelley's life is easy to research, but a little complicated to lay out in an orderly fashion. The best online resource I have found if you are curious about the exact timeline of Mary Shelley's life is *A Biographical Sketch of Mary Wollstonecraft Shelley* (1797-1851), by Charlotte Pabst-Kastner, Associate Lecturer, Open University (UK), http://www.victorianweb.org/previctorian/mshelley/bio.html, accessed August 23, 2020.
2. Saul McLeod, "Maslow's Hierarchy of Needs," *Simply Psychology,* https://www.simplypsychology.org/maslow.html, updated 2017.

Made in the USA
Las Vegas, NV
15 May 2021

23112784R00262